FORGING THE FLEET

FORGING THE FLEET

NAVAL ARMOUR
AND THE ARMOUR MAKERS,
1860 TO 1916

DAVID BOURSNELL

**SHEFFIELD
INDUSTRIAL
MUSEUMS TRUST**

First published in Great Britain in 2016 by Sheffield Industrial Museums Trust

Copyright © David Boursnell 2016

A CIP catalogue record for this book is available from the British Library.

ISBN: 978-0-96321-271-0

Typeset in Gill Sans and Trade Gothic by D.R. ink

Printed and bound in Great Britain by CPI Anthony Rowe Ltd

Sheffield Industrial Museums Trust

Kelham Island Museum

Alma Street

Sheffield

S3 8RY

CONTENTS

PREFACE

I have been interested in history since school; when I was eleven, my history teacher wrote in my report, 'I call him my historian.' I have also always had a particular interest in naval history and over the years I have collected and read many books on the subject. Unfortunately, history did not turn out to be my career and the nearest I managed to get to the subject was to found and run a company that helped museums and other heritage organisations get funding for their projects. After I retired from the company, I spent a few years winding down in rural France growing my own vegetables, before my friends at Kelham Island Museum in Sheffield tempted me with a project I found irresistible.

Karen Middlemast, a curator at Kelham Island, had discovered a set of ledgers in the museum's collections. The ledgers showed a record of the orders received by the five British armour plate companies from 1903 to 1920. There was also a record of the invoices they had submitted and a mysterious additional column, which showed that 20 per cent of their income had been paid into a pool. Although the ledgers were important and the references to an armour plate 'pool' were intriguing, they clearly needed exploring further. After discussing the discovery with the head of the museum, John Hamshere, I recognised this as my ideal project, combining as it did historical research, naval history and the industrial heritage of Sheffield, a city I have enjoyed living in for thirty-five years.

Armour plate is undoubtedly more controversial that cutlery, Sheffield's other well-known product, and rightly so as it is incorporated into ships that are designed to sink other ships and kill their crews. So, while I feel we should be careful not to be uncritical of the armament industries, we should also recognise that in the sixty years between 1860 and 1920 the armour-plate industry was one of Sheffield's largest and that it provided highly skilled and relatively well-paid employment to a large number of workers.

I feel very lucky to have found a project that is so in line with my interests, and which has given me the opportunity to write this book about the history of armour plate and the ships it clad. There are many people who have helped me along the way. I would like to thank John and Karen at Kelham Island for firstly finding the ledgers and then giving me the opportunity to research them. I would also like to thank my family, particularly my daughter Hannah, who has found time from her busy life at the Little, Brown Book Group to guide me through the process of writing and publishing a book; her help has been invaluable and I am grateful to her that we have emerged from the process with our relationship intact. My wife, Shirley, has also been incredibly supportive throughout the research and writing and, as well as acting as a sounding board for ideas, has loyally proofread the early drafts of the text. I feel both grateful and immensely lucky to have had them around me. I would also like to thank my brother Mike, who helped me work out Tresidder's formula.

Catherine Hanley, who took on the task of copy-editing by text has been both thorough and sensitive and Sian Rance at the designers D.R.ink has integrated the text and pictures into what I think is a very pleasing whole. Thanks are also due to Chris Shaw for his eagle-eyed proofread. I am grateful to you all.

To all the people who helped me with the text along the way, I would like to say that I have learnt a lot from you and, if ever I do this again, I promise I will use more commas.

Lastly, I would like to thank the Sheffield Industrial Museums Trust for commissioning me to write this book and the Heritage Lottery Fund, who provided the grant that made it possible.

Supported by

 **The National Lottery** ®
through the Heritage Lottery Fund

 heritage lottery fund

INTRODUCTION: FORGING THE FLEET

The period between 1860 and 1916 was one of rapid technological and industrial change, coupled with a growth of social and political movements seeking to extend the rights of the burgeoning urban middle and working classes. The extent of the technological changes can be seen over the course of a single career in the navy. The future Admiral and First Sea Lord John Jellicoe, who joined the navy in 1872, started his service as an officer cadet in HMS *Newcastle*, an unarmoured wooden frigate whose main power was provided by sails, supported by a 2,000 horsepower steam engine. He would have learned to fire from smooth-bore muzzle-loaded guns at ranges of about 1,000 to 1,500 yards, which would have looked familiar to sailors at the Battle of Trafalgar nearly seventy years earlier. By the turn of the century, Jellicoe was captain of the second-class battleship HMS *Centurion* of 10,500 tons, built of steel, heavily armoured, powered entirely by triple expansion steam engines producing over 13,000 horsepower.[1] His new ship would have been capable of firing 500 lb shells from its 10-inch rifled breech loading guns at ranges of up to 10,000 yards. By 1916, Jellicoe commanded a fleet in which the fastest battleships carried 8,200 tons of armour and were powered by oil-fired boilers driving them at 24 knots. Their 15-inch guns fired 1,938 lb shells over a range of 19,000 yards and were centrally controlled by an early form of computer.

As a result of this rapid change, navies possessed a wide variety of types of battleship. Ships like the *Warrior*, with their guns laid out in a broadside along their length, were very rapidly replaced by ships with larger guns concentrated in a heavily fortified central battery. In turn by the 1870s turret ships with fewer heavier guns were making their appearance. It was a period when the gun was dominant and it was impossible to provide heavy enough armour to defend against modern weaponry. One of the responses was the emergence of the *Jeune École* (see Chapter 1) which played down the role of battleships and emphasised the role of the torpedo. The introduction of steel for shipbuilding enabled the development of light protected cruisers, which suited the role of commerce raiding that was central to the ideas of the *Jeune École*.

In the late 1870s the Sheffield firms of John Brown and Charles Cammell separately developed compound armour, which had a steel face and a wrought-iron back. This armour was significantly more effective than all-iron armour and it meant that armour on battleships did not need to be as heavy to protect them from enemy guns. This led to the development of a new type of battleship, known at the time as 'modern' battleships but later called the pre-Dreadnoughts. By the mid-1880s the new Director of Naval Construction, William White, had settled on a design concept that formed the basis of battleship design for the remainder of the pre-Dreadnought period. The *Royal Sovereign* class, designed as part of the Naval Defence Act of 1889, carried a main armament of four large guns mounted on armoured barbettes and a secondary armament in a central battery.

There were major developments in armour plate manufacture during the late 1880s and the early 1890s. A number of firms, notably the French firm of Schneider et Cie, had been experimenting with steel armour but in 1889 a cementation process for hardening the face of steel armour was developed in the USA and in the mid-1890s this process was developed further by the German firm of Friedrich Krupp, whose armour was 3 times more resistant than early wrought-iron armour; this enabled ships to have effective protection over a wider area. All of the major navies adopted Krupp armour and the British armour makers all re-equipped their works to make it.

The major test of the pre-Dreadnoughts took place in the Russo-Japanese war of 1904–05. The major naval powers, all of whom had observers at the battles, studied the actions in great detail and two schools of thought emerged. The first of these felt that a hail of fire from a mixed armament of large guns and lighter, quick-firing guns had been shown to be effective. The opposing camp argued that the larger guns were far more effective and that future battleships should be equipped only with large guns. The supporters of the 'all-big-gun' ship largely won the day over the proponents of the 'hail of fire' approach and this led to the next radical development in battleship design. As with all such changes, it was controversial. Britain was the leading trading nation, with the largest fleet of merchant ships and an empire which stretched round the world. It therefore relied on its navy to protect its shipping. A strong navy was seen as essential for protecting Britain's worldwide interests, but adopting radical new designs threatened its ability to do this as it meant the previous design of ships, in which a huge amount of money had been invested, were no longer as effective. Britain traditionally was a follower rather than an initiator of innovation and relied on its superior industrial base and shipbuilding capacity to respond to new developments and to maintain its naval superiority. However, it was Britain that took the lead in building the next generation of ships, laying down the first all-big-gun ship HMS *Dreadnought* in 1905 and thus beginning a naval build-up which lasted until the outbreak of the First World War.

The period from the mid-1890s onwards was characterised by two themes which will recur throughout this account:

• This was a time of increasing nationalism and changing patterns of alliances. At the beginning of the period, Britain maintained its historic aversion to long-term European alliances, preferring to pursue its own imperial and economic interests. Its traditional imperial and European competitors were Russia and France, and it was against these powers that it measured its naval strength. However, as Britain's industrial dominance was eroded by the growth of the United States and Germany, Britain began to seek among these former competitors friendships and over the period strengthened links first with Japan, then with France, and lastly with Russia. As Germany began to be seen as posing a growing threat to Britain, its position at the centre of Europe meant that the North Sea became a more important theatre than the Mediterranean and the Atlantic, where Britain had traditionally concentrated its naval power.

• Like many nineteenth-century industries, the armament companies had traditionally operated openly across national boundaries, sharing technologies and taking part in international trials. The pages of the *Engineer* and similar publications were full of information about developments in armour and guns, but as nationalism and national rivalries grew, a greater emphasis on secrecy became the norm. One area that became increasingly controversial was the relationship between the armour makers. The world's major armour makers had formed the Harvey United Steel Company, in which they were all shareholders, and the company operated as a pool for income from patents and also as a method of controlling international competition and maintaining prices. At a national level, there were suspicions in the United States, Germany and France that their domestic armour makers were forming cartels and stifling competition on prices. The same fears were expressed in Britain and this book presents new evidence about a pool agreement between the five armour-making companies.

The Battle of Jutland was the major test of the heavily armoured Dreadnought fleets in which the city of Sheffield, although many miles from the sea, played a major building role. The powerful River Don Engine, which drove the armour plate rolling mills at Cammell Laird, is a working reminder of the huge scale of the industrial process involved in making armour. A century after the Battle of Jutland the engine can still be seen at Kelham Island Museum in the city.

1   T. A. Brassey (ed.), *The Naval Annual 1899* (J. Griffen & Co.).

PART ONE

LEARNING THE POSSIBILITIES OF NEW TECHNOLOGIES

INTRODUCTION

The introduction of iron ships into the Royal Navy represented a clear break with the wooden ships of the past. The British decision to build an ironclad ship was taken because the French had done the same, and before the Navy had explored the technology in any great detail. The early years of the ironclad era were therefore ones of experimentation with different methods of making armour and of fixing it on to ships. Not only did Britain have to develop its armour-making capacity, it also had to re-equip its own Royal Dockyards to build and maintain a fleet of iron ships.

The Crimean War, which finished in 1856, had shown that British artillery was inadequate and this led to an increased interest in gun technology, with engineers such as William Armstrong and Joseph Whitworth becoming involved in designing more modern guns. The heaviest guns fitted to the old wooden three-deck battleships fired shot weighing 42 lbs; HMS *Warrior*, launched in 1860, was designed to carry 68-lb guns, but was eventually fitted with ten, even larger 110-lb guns in addition. By the end of the 1860s the increasing use of steel in gun construction meant that guns were able to fire 400-lb shots and by 1880 guns with a 16-inch bore could fire shot weighing 1,684 lbs. William Palliser's invention of chilled iron shot in 1867 meant that such guns were capable of piercing wrought-iron armour 22-inches thick. These rapid advances in the technology of both armour plate and gunnery meant that ship design changed much more swiftly than it had done during the period when navies were made up of wooden ships of the line. The most famous of these ships, HMS *Victory*, was launched in 1765 and was not retired to harbour duties until 1812 — an active service career of nearly fifty years. The *Warrior*, on the other hand, was obsolete by the early 1870s and was placed in reserve in 1875 after an active career of only fourteen years. She was finally decommissioned in 1883.

In this time of rapid development, naval architects and strategists were experimenting with the best way to integrate all the new technologies into naval design, and working out how these developments would effect a naval strategy. As the influential *Engineer* magazine commented in May 1889:[1]

> 'Experience is the foundation of all knowledge.' We have absolutely no experience of the results of naval action between modern fleets, and the consequence is that every man makes his own assumptions as to what would happen. He cannot prove that he is right, his opponents cannot prove that he is wrong; and so the interminable controversy rages and instead of spending our money on a very few types of ship, we spend it on a great many in the hope that in this way we may get what is right.

Certainty may have been in short supply, but no country that had aspirations to be a naval power could afford to do nothing and risk their competitors gaining an edge.

---

1   'An Experimental Warship', Engineer, 3 May 1889, p. 375

CHAPTER 1

NAVAL AND INDUSTRIAL DEVELOPMENT: THE IRONCLADS

THE INTRODUCTION OF ARMOUR PLATE

The era of the ironclads, which began with the launch of the British ship HMS *Warrior* in 1860, led to around twenty-two years of rapid change, and ended with the launch of HMS *Edinburgh*, the first of what are now known as the pre-Dreadnoughts.

During the Crimean War (1853–56) Britain and France put aside their traditional enmity and allied against the Russian threat of expansion into the Black Sea at the expense of the weakening Ottoman Empire, but once the war was over Anglo-French relations deteriorated again. The foreign policy of the French emperor, Napoleon III, was aimed at increasing French influence in Europe; he wanted to oppose nationalistic movements in Germany and Italy that might create powerful blocs and thereby threaten French power.

At the end of the Crimean War the battleships of the world's navies were still built of wood and propelled by a combination of steam engines and sails. The active British navy was made up of twenty-four steam ships of the line, fifteen steam frigates with propellers, eight frigates with paddle-wheels, ten smaller steam corvettes and ninety-two other steam-powered vessels such as gunboats. The fleet also had older sailing ships, including ten sailing battleships and seventeen sailing frigates, eighteen sailing corvettes and eighty-three small sailing vessels. The more powerful and modern battleships and frigates were concentrated in the Mediterranean and the Channel in order to counteract the French fleets.

The French had pioneered the use of armour-clad batteries to bombard the Russian fortifications at Cronstadt during the Crimean War, and they were first used against Fort Kinburn on Russia's Black Sea coast in 1855. The British also built armoured batteries, two of which had iron hulls: HMS *Erebus* was built by Robert Napier's shipyard on the Clyde, and HMS *Terror* at Palmers' on the Tyne. After the end of the war both countries explored the potential of this new technology in seagoing warships, but as the British were the leading sea power they were reluctant to introduce such a radical new technology, which would reduce their numerical advantage.

The French were the first to incorporate the idea of iron armour protection into full-size, seagoing naval ships, and commissioned the wooden-hulled ironclad ship the *Gloire*. The launch of *Gloire* in 1859 destabilised the balance of naval power and caused an invasion scare in Britain, as an ironclad ship could potentially attack British naval bases unopposed. It may be that the French did not intend to start an arms race but wanted rather to influence British policies.[1] Lord Palmerston, the British Prime Minister, took the view that Napoleon III was building up the French navy 'for the purpose of keeping us in check and overaving us upon some occasion.' Britain required defence that would 'enable us to have an opinion on matters which may seriously affect our interests'.[2] Naval expenditure, he said, would take priority over economy and HMS *Warrior*, launched in 1860 in response to the threat poised by the *Gloire*, was the world's first iron-hulled ironclad warship.

The idea of iron-built ships was not new. Isambard Kingdom Brunel's SS *Great Britain*, the first merchant ship to combine an iron hull with screw propulsion, had been launched in 1843. Brunel's later ship, the SS *Great Eastern*, launched shortly before the *Warrior*, was 19,000 tons and 692 feet long, much bigger and heavier than *Warrior*'s 9,137 tons.

The development of such large iron-built ships was made possible by developments in the iron industry.[3] Between 1830 and 1852 the British production of pig iron, which was needed to make wrought-iron, rose fourfold and it continued to rise in the following decades.

---

i.   HMS *Victory* was completed in 1765 and retired to harbour duties in 1812.

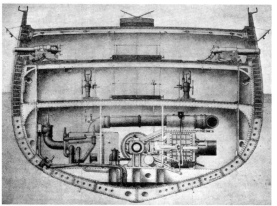

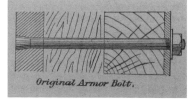

Original Armor Bolt.

TOP: The armoured battery HMS *Erebus* under construction at Napier's yard on the Clyde in 1856.

FAR LEFT: A cross-section of the *Warrior's* hull showing the iron plating and armour with its teak backing. The section also shows the traditional layout of the guns.

LEFT: A cross-section of the skin of the *Warrior* showing (from left to right) the 4½-inch armour plate, the 8-inch outer teak backing, the 10-inch inner teak and the iron hull plating.

A growing understanding of the process as well as the increased availability of raw materials made this rapid increase in production possible. More efficient steam power enabled the mechanisation of the process and allowed larger-scale production.

HMS *Warrior's* sides consisted of iron frames 10 inches deep and 2 feet apart. These were covered in a skin of iron plating, $^{9}/_{16}$th inch thick. On top of the iron plates were two thicknesses of teak backing, the inner layer being 10 inches thick with the grain running horizontally and the outer layer 8 inches thick with the grain running vertically. The armour plate was fastened to the teak backing and the iron plating by 1½-inch bolts with a countersunk head.[4]

Year	British pig iron production (tons)
1830	678,417
1835	940,000
1839	1,248,781
1848	1,998,568
1850	2,249,000
1852	2,701,000
1869	5,446,000
1873	6,566,000

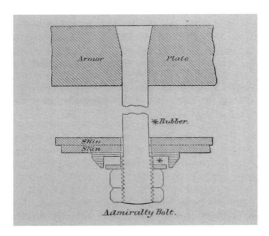 

TOP LEFT: The armour bolt used in later ironclads showing the double nut, washers and the screw thread wider than the bolt shaft.
TOP RIGHT: An early engraving of HMS *Warrior*. The evenly spaced gun-ports along the whole length of the ship show the traditional broadside layout of her armament.

The design of bolt used in the *Warrior* proved not to be very successful as it was prone to leaking. More seriously, if the bolt was hit by a shot the nut tended to break off, as the screw thread was machined into the 1½ inch bolt and this created a weak point. An improved bolt design by Edward Pallister corrected this by adding a rubber washer and having a 'male' screw thread which was wider than the bolt shaft.

The *Warrior's* armour was able to resist the conventional round shot of the period. Tests of the armour plate showed that, at a short range of 200 yards, even a 200 lb ball did not penetrate the plate.

HMS *Warrior* was built as a response to the *Gloire*, and was designed as a fast frigate, even though she was more powerful than contemporary battleships. She was more than 3,500 tons bigger than the *Gloire* and also much longer, faster and more heavily armed.

The *Warrior* brought together a whole series of technical developments and was the most powerful warship in the world when she was launched. In the view of the naval architect and historian David Brown,[5] HMS *Warrior* changed the mindset of British naval architects and led to the rapid changes in the development of the battleship seen over the next few years. However, the direction of naval policy is not decided by designers – it is a political choice and, having commissioned the *Warrior*, Britain had to decide whether to build more iron ships or to stick with a mainly wood-built battle fleet. Wood had a lot to commend it, particularly as the naval dockyards and support systems across the British Empire were equipped to build and maintain wooden rather than iron ships. The changes in construction methods meant that the Royal Dockyards had to re-equip themselves with new machinery and develop the required engineering skills before they could build the new ironclads themselves. For this reason, the first two ironclads, *Warrior* and *Black Prince*, were both built at private yards which had expertise in working with

iron hulls. The *Warrior* was built at Thames Iron Works at Blackwall on the Thames, and the *Black Prince* at Napier's on the Clyde. The first ironclad built in one of the navy's Royal Dockyards, as opposed to a private yard, was HMS *Achilles*, constructed at Chatham and completed in 1864. The *Achilles* improved upon the armour protection of the *Warrior*, which had been criticised as not protecting the full length of the ship at the waterline and leaving the steering gear vulnerable.

The British Admiralty decided that it could not risk its command of the sea by switching completely to iron-built warships. It needed to reinforce its existing battle fleet while the potential of the new iron frigates such as the *Warrior* was assessed. In May 1861 the Controller of the Navy, Rear Admiral Sir Spencer Robinson, proposed that:

> The further building of Line of Battle Ships being for the present suspended, it would be advantageous to erect the frames of such of these ships as are nearly completed, with a view of preparing them for 50 gun frigates to be covered with Armour plating.[6]

It was therefore decided to convert seven wooden battleships that were under construction in the Royal Dockyards into ironclads. This would help with the transition from wood- to iron-working skills and was also a relatively cheap option. The first four of these ships were converted into broadside ironclads with their guns in a traditional layout – the other three were converted into central battery ironclads with a smaller number of larger guns concentrated in a heavily armoured central battery.

MAKING EARLY ARMOUR

The armour for HMS *Warrior* was made at the Thames Iron Works where she was built. In January 1860, a month after the *Warrior's* launch, Mr Hardy of the Thames Iron Works gave evidence to the Committee on Iron about how the armour plate was made. The plates were made by hammering and were 16 feet long,

3 feet wide and 4 ½ inches thick. Each plate weighed 4 tons.[7] His colleague Captain John Ford, who was a director of Thames Iron Works, described the process at a meeting of the Institute of Naval Architects in March 1862:[8]

> The hammered plates manufactured at the Thames Iron Works are made in the following manner:- Scrap iron of the best description is carefully selected, cleaned, piled, and then hammered into a bloom; it is then rolled into bars 6 inches broad, and 1 inch thick; these bars are cut up, piled, and again hammered to the form required; this process being repeated, the plate goes on gradually increasing to the length required.
>
> I confidently believe that scrap iron, rolled and hammered as above described, is decidedly the best material, and superior to any description of puddled iron, from which, all the rolled plates are understood to be made.

Sir William Fairburn and William Pole, who were both members of the Committee on Iron in 1861, reported of the iron plates for the *Warrior* that 'hammering was the first process adopted for the manufacture of armour plates' and that 'it was used by the Thames Iron Company, who built the *Warrior*, and the plates for the ship were made in that way'.[9]

A contemporary account of a visit to the Thames Iron Works describes the hammering of the iron ingots with a steam hammer and further hammering to combine these together into plates 15 feet by 3 feet by 4½ inches. The observers described 'long ranks packed on their edges like cards waiting to be taken to the planing room'. The plates were machined two at a time, the edges made smoother and tongue and grooves cut.[10]

Although the plates for the *Warrior* were hammered, this was not the only technology used for making early armour plates. As well as the Thames Iron Works, the Committee on Iron took evidence from Samuel Beale & Co. of the Parkgate Works in Rotherham. George Grant Sanderson, who was the manager of the armour-making plant, gave evidence to the committee on 29 January 1861.[11] He described Beale & Co. as having made their first iron armour plate over four years previously for HMS *Terror*, the iron-plated floating battery built by Palmer's on the Tyne for which they made 300 tons of 3½- to 4-inch plate. They had made a further 700 tons of 4½-inch plates 'within the last five months'. The ship for which this armour was intended was not identified but according to the dates in the Admiralty return to the House of Commons it is most likely they were made for HMS *Resistance*.[12] Mr Sanderson was questioned about other companies making plates and said that 'I believe ours is the only house that has rolled any of these armour plates.'

He described the process by which the company made the armour:

1. First they puddled Derbyshire pig iron and made it into 12-inch bars. These bars were cut up and mixed with bars made from scrap iron. Both puddled iron and scrap iron were made by hammering.

2. The pile of bars was made from ten layers of bars of alternated puddled and scrap bars together. The puddled bars were generally on the outside.

3. The bars were laid out 'so that they run both left and right and all across'. This produced cross fibres in the iron and Mr Sanderson showed the committee a sample that had a 'uniform character' at the fracture.

4. The bars were then rolled into 'No. 1 slabs' which were 5 feet by 3 feet by 1½ inches thick.

5. The rough iron on the outside of the slab was taken off and four slabs were put together and welded by rolling into another slab 2¼ inches thick.

6. Four of these 2¼-inch plates were then heated and rolled into the final plate.

7. The rollers used by the company were 20 inches in diameter by 6½ feet long. They were linked to the furnace by a railway and the four plates, which had been heated for four and a half to five hours, were pulled out of the furnace by a pair of tongs attached by a chain to the top roller. The plates travelled down an inclined slope to the rollers 'in about half a minute', losing little heat in the process.

8. The rollers had a reverse mechanism and the plates were rolled backwards and forwards for about three minutes until they were the required thickness.

9. The plates were then allowed to cool and the edges trimmed with a slotting machine.

Mr Sanderson told the committee that the largest size of armour plate that they had made to date was 17 feet 8 inches by 3 feet 3 inches by 4½ inches thick. He believed that with his present machinery, he could roll armour 7 inches thick. His current output was about eighteen plates a week weighing around 60 or 70 tons in total.

At the meeting of the Institute of Mechanical Engineers held in Sheffield on 31 July 1861 John Brown, the founder of the Sheffield company of the same name, described the method he used to make 5-ton plates as follows:

> Bars of iron are rolled 12 inches broad by 1 inch thick, and are sheared to 30 inches long. Five of these bars are piled and rolled down to another rough slab. Five other bars are rolled down to a rough slab, and these two slabs are then welded and rolled down to a plate of 1¼ inches thick, which is sheared to 4 feet square. Four plates like this are then piled and rolled down to one plate of 8 feet by 4 feet and 2½ inches thick; and lastly, four of these are piled and rolled to firm the final entire plate. These are thus welded together 160 thicknesses of plate, each of which was originally 1 inch thick […][13]

The final operation of welding the four plates of 8 feet by 4 feet by 2½ inches is a very critical matter. To bring a pile of four plates of these dimensions up to a perfect welding heat all through the mass, without burning the edges and ends of the plate most exposed to the fire; to drag this pile out of the furnace, convey it to the rolls, and force it between them, in so short a time as to avoid its losing the welding heat, is a matter of greater difficulty than those unacquainted with the work would imagine. The intensity of the heat thrown off is almost unendurable, and the loss of a few moments in the conveyance of the pile from the furnace to the rolls is fatal to the success of the operation.

Included in the transactions are three drawings of his rolling mill with a description of the process:

The pile of four plates (A) was heated in the furnace (B) and drawn out by a liberating chain attached to the roller. It travelled on an iron carriage (C) which conveyed the pile to the rollers (D). A small incline (E) lifted up the front of the carriage and enabled the pile to be transferred onto the fore-plate. On the other side of the rollers was a roller frame (F) which was set at an incline to enable the plate to be drawn back through the rollers when they were reversed. The plate was then lifted of the carriage by the crane (G) and placed on a massive cast-iron straightening bed (H) and rolled by an iron cylinder weighing 9 tons. When it was cooled it was lifted by another crane (K) and transferred to the planing machine (L) where its ends and sides were machined.

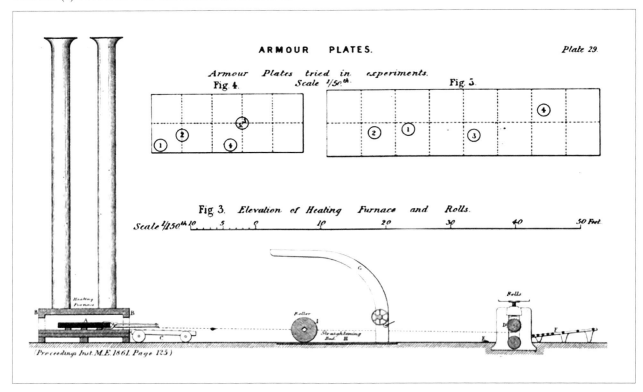

A plan of John Brown's armour rolling mill. In the image a pair of tongs can be seen gripping the pile of plates in the furnace. The tongs are attached to a chain that is linked to the upper roller.

John Brown's description of his rolling process is remarkably similar to that described by Mr Sanderson as being used at Samuel Beale's. The two firms were only about 7½ miles from each other and in 1906 Mr Johnson, an ex-employee of Beale's, wrote to the *Manchester Guardian* refuting the claim that John Brown's had been the first company to roll armour plates.[14] He also claimed that:

> When chief engineer of the Park Gate Works, over 25 years ago, I replaced the original armour plate mill by a larger one for producing ordinary boiler and ship plates, and some of the old hands working for me at the time told me of the Sunday visits paid by officials of the Atlas Works to Park Gate, to make sketches of the rolling mill, the heating furnaces and the apparatus for handling heavy plates.

Whether John Brown's copied Samuel Beale's methods or not there is little doubt that Beale's were the first company to roll armour in Britain. Because rolling quickly displaced hammering as the preferred method of manufacturing armour plates, some people later found it difficult to believe that the armour for the *Warrior* could have been made by this method. Lt E. W. Very, writing in the 1883 *Proceedings of the US Naval Institute* in a paper entitled 'The Development of Armour for Naval Use', claimed that the armour plate around the portholes of the *Warrior* was rolled while the remainder was hammered. He claimed that this showed that 'at this time the superiority of rolled over hammered plates was recognised.'[15] C. E. Ellis, who had been on the board of John Brown's since 1884 and was at the time the firm's managing director, also claimed in a paper he gave at the Institute of Naval Architects in 1911 that the *Warrior*'s armour plates had been rolled.[16] He was informed by a Mr Jordan that as he was:

> intimately connected with the building of the Warrior, I am in a position to say, without doubt whatever, that the armour plates for that vessel were made throughout under the steam hammer. I am perfectly sure of that, because I was present at the Thames Iron Works during the time she was under construction.

Sir William White (an ex-Director of Naval Construction) backed up his statement and also confirmed that Beale's were the first company to roll armour.

However, whatever the views about hammered armour that were held at a later date, the view of the authorities at the time was that plates made by either method could be equally effective. At a meeting of the Institute of Naval Architects in 1862 Sir John Dalrymple Hay, the chairman of the Committee on Iron, compared the quality of the leading four manufactures at the time:

> The Low Moor Company manufacture plates both hammered and rolled; the Thames Iron Works […] manufacture their plates entirely by hammering; Mr Brown of Sheffield, on the other hand, manufactures entirely by rolling; whilst the plates of the Pontypool Works are produced by hammering. Those are the four firms that have produced the best plates, and it is evident there was hardly a shade of difference between them.

INVESTIGATIONS INTO ARMOUR PLATE

The Special Committee on Iron was set up by the War Office and the Admiralty in 1861 to 'inquire into the application of iron for defensive purposes'. As William Fairburn, one of the two engineers on the committee, commented:

> On finishing the *Warrior*, the Government bethought themselves that it would be desirable to do what they ought to have done five years before, namely, to ascertain something about the principles which should guide the design of iron armour. In other words, having already built the ship, they began to enquire how they ought to have built her.'[17]

The membership of the committee was drawn from the services as well as from prominent engineers. It included:

- Captain (later Admiral Sir) John Dalrympole Hay (Royal Navy);
- Major W. Jervois (Royal Engineers);
- Colonel W. Henderson (Royal Artillery);
- Dr John Percy;
- Mr William Fairburn (Engineer & Industrialist, Fellow of the Royal Society);
- Mr William Pole (Engineer, Fellow of the Royal Society); and
- Captain A. Harrison (Royal Artillery), secretary to the committee.

The committee submitted annual reports on its investigations until it was wound up in 1864:

1861	Mechanical properties of specimens of iron and steel plates.
1862	The resistance of different types of shot. Experiments on punching armour plates.
1863	Mechanical properties of iron plates. The manufacture of iron plates. The value of annealing armour plates. The tenacity of cast-iron shot.
1864	The mechanical properties of iron plates. The manufacture of iron plates. General summary of results.

During their investigations the committee looked at the manufacturing methods for armour plate and in particular the comparison of hammered and rolled armour plates.

Iron manufacturers were encouraged to submit plates for trial and carried out a range of mechanical and stress tests on a range of plates. In 1863 and 1864 the committee carried out a standardised set of firing tests at HMS *Excellent*, the navy's gunnery school in Portsmouth. Nine different companies submitted a total of sixty-one plates which were tested using a 68 lb cast-iron shot fired with a 16 lb charge at a range of 200 yards. The results were assessed by the award of a Figure of Merit by Captain R. S. Hewlett, the officer in charge of the firing tests.

By giving a numerical score to the Figure of Merit it is possible to average the score for each manufacturer and thus form a judgement about the comparative quality of the plates they were producing:

Figure of Merit	A1 plus	A1	A2 plus	A2	A3	A3 minus	B1	B2
Numerical score	8	7	6	5	4	3	2	1

It is slightly risky allocating scores to the Figure of Merit scale as we do not know if Capt. Hewlett had, for example, an A4 in his scales. This would mean that the plates in the B category would score lower. However, in spite of this, the opportunity to do an analysis of the performance of the plates is irresistible.

Over the two-year trial the plates show the following results:[18]

4- to 4.5-inch armour plates

Company	1863		1864	
	Number of plates	Average score	Number of plates	Average score
Beale			5.00	4.00
Cammell	1	4.00	2.00	5.00
J. Brown	4	5.00	5.00	6.60
Butterley	1	4.00		
Millwall	1	5.00		
Begbie	4	3.75	3.00	7.00
Thames Iron	2	1.50		

5.5-inch armour plate

Company	1863		1864	
	Number of plates	Average score	Number of plates	Average score
Beale	2	3.00		
Cammell	1	7.00	1.00	8.00
J. Brown	3	5.00	2.00	6.50
Mersey	3	4.67	3.00	5.67
Millwall	4	6.50		
Begbie	4	5.00		
Thames Iron	1	4.00	1.00	2.00

6-inch armour plates

Company	1863		1864	
	Number of plates	Average score	Number of plates	Average score
Millwall			4.00	6.25
Rigby / Beardmore			1.00	7.00

A comparison of the relative scores of the rolled and hammered plates show that the rolled plates had a higher average score for both 1863 and 1864:

Year of test	Rolled	Hammered
1863	5.46	4.67
1864	5.18	4.33

The Committee on Iron did not, however, make a recommendation about whether they preferred rolling or hammering. Their final report states:

> We have directed our attention to the mode of manufacture of armour plates, the principal point being to ascertain whether rolling or hammering was the better process. We have tried large numbers of plates made by both processes, and we have found good plates may be made by either; but we consider, on the whole, the results of experience to be in favour of rolling, as more likely to produce softness and uniformity of quality – hammered plates having generally a tendency to be hard and unequal. At the same time rolled plates appear frequently liable to unsoundness of welding, a defect which has never yet been fully overcome.

Although they concluded that it was better to leave the choice of method to the makers themselves it seems that most armour makers chose to adopt rolling, and it soon became the standard method of manufacture.

THE QUALITY OF ARMOUR PLATE

Because making armour plate was extremely experimental in the early years, the Controller of the Navy[19] drew up a list of nine 'approved' contractors in May 1862. These companies were asked to tender for the armour plate for six further ships and the contracts were awarded as follows:[20]

Ship	Description / type	Company
Achilles	Iron-built frigate.	Samuel Beale Co. Ltd, Rotherham.[21]
Royal Oak		Thames Iron Works & Shipbuilding Co., Blackwall, London.
Ocean	Prince Consort class: converted during building into wooden-hulled ironclads.	Butterley Co., West Alfreton, Derbyshire.
Prince Consort		Samuel Beale Co. Ltd, Rotherham.
Caledonia		Lancefield Forge Company, Glasgow.
Royal Alfred	Converted into wooden-hulled central battery ironclad.	J. Brown & Co., Atlas Works Sheffield.

Only three of these firms were considered to have made plate to a sufficient standard – Samuel Beale of Parkgate in Rotherham, John Brown's in Sheffield and Butterley in Derbyshire.

The difficulty of manufacturing these early armour plates is shown in a report written by the Controller of the Navy for the House of Commons in June 1861,[22] reporting on the manufacture of armour plate for the early ironclad ships *Warrior*, *Black Prince*, *Defence* and *Resistance*. This recorded both the makers of the plates and the number of plates that had failed:

Ship	Manufacturer of armour plates		Mode of manufacture	Plates condemned	
	Company	Location		Number	Dates
Warrior	Thames Shipbuilding Company	London	Steam hammer	5 out of total made	Between 26/4/1860 & 6/9/1860
Defence	Samuel Beale & Co.	Rotherham	Rolling	1 out of 184 plates made	1/5/1861
	A. Fulton	Glasgow	Steam Hammer	0 out of 6 plates made	
Resistance	Samuel Beale & Co.	Rotherham	Rolling	17 rejected after delivery	Between 21/2/1861 & 23/4/1861
				14 rejected at manufacture	Between 5/6/1860 & 12/12/1860
Resistance & Defence	Samuel Beale & Co.	Rotherham	Rolling	33 rejected at manufacture (see note)	Between 21/1/1860 & 11/5/1861
Black Prince	Mr Rigby, Parkhead Forge	Glasgow	Steam Hammer	21(see note)	Between 18/8/1860 & 16/5/1861
	The Lancefield Company	Glasgow	Steam Hammer	3	Between 24/8/1860 & 22/2/1861
	John Brown & Co.	Sheffield	Rolling	10	Between 29/4/1861 & 6/5/1861

Note: Some plates were recorded as fractions and are shown here as failed plates.

FROM BROADSIDE TO BATTERY

The development of wrought-iron armour was matched by developments in guns and projectiles. Between 1863 and 1865 the Royal Gun Factory at Woolwich developed an effective rifled muzzle-loading gun. This fired an elongated shot, which was invented by General Sir William Palliser and which used a chilled iron mould to harden the shot.

Trials of these two developments at the Royal Artillery gun-testing range at Shoeburyness on the Essex coast showed that they could penetrate wrought-iron armour of the same thickness as the calibre of the gun. With these developments in gunnery, a 10-inch gun could penetrate 10 inches of armour plate, roughly twice as thick as the armour plate on the *Warrior* and her immediate successors.

The increased ability of naval guns to penetrate wrought-iron armour is shown right:[23]

As naval guns became more powerful they became heavier and therefore fewer could be carried on each ship. They also needed thicker armour plate to protect them from more effective enemy fire. The response to this was the central battery ship where fewer, larger guns were carried in a heavily armoured box. The initial central battery designs were for small ships but the idea was soon incorporated in designs for battleships. HMS *Bellerophon*, launched in 1865, was the first iron-built battleship of this design.

Year	Weight of gun (tons)	Weight of shot (lbs)	Penetration (inches)
1865	6.5	115,	2.6
1866	9.0	1800	8.8
1866	12.0	256	9.9
1868	18.0	410	11.7
1875	25.0	536	12.5
1869	25.0	614	12.7
1871	35.0	820	13.9
1874	38.0	820	15.7
1879	80.0	1,684	22.5

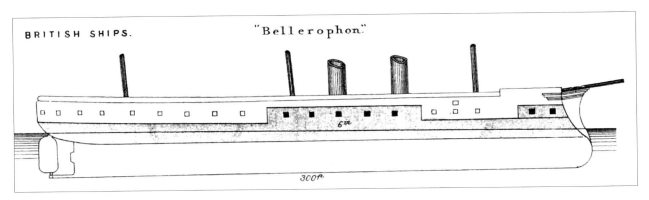

BRITISH SHIPS. "Bellerophon."

HMS *Bellerophon* carried ten 9-inch rifled muzzle-loading guns in her main battery protected by 6-inch armour plates.

THE INTRODUCTION OF THE TURRET

The next development in design was the cupola or turret ship. The concept was patented by Captain C. Coles RN in 1859 and was separately developed by John Ericsson in the USA. After a trial in 1861 in the experimental ship *Trusty*, the Admiralty placed an order for HMS *Prince Albert* in February 1862. She was armed with four 9-inch guns each mounted in a separate turret.

In 1862, at the Battle of Hampton Roads during the American Civil War, Ericsson's design, the USS *Monitor*, equipped with two 11-inch guns in a single turret mounted on a spindle, sank the ironclad CSS *Virginia*. The success of the design had a great influence on many navies, and ships of this type were known as monitors. Later monitors were designed with more turrets and the design was particularly successful for coastal defence as the low freeboard design was not particularly seaworthy.

Because the British needed ships with a wide range to protect their trade interests accross the world, they experimented with turret ships that combined steam and sail. Some of these designs, such as HMS *Monarch*, were relatively successful but they were generally considered not to be very seaworthy and the capsizing of a similar turret ship, HMS *Captain*, in 1870 demonstrated the problems with stability. In order to improve the seaworthiness of the monitor design, Edward Reid, the Chief Constructor of the Navy from 1863 to 1870, developed the concept of the 'breastwork monitor', which had an armoured structure amidships raised several feet above the deck.

At first breastwork monitors were also designed to be used for coastal defence, but the idea continued to be developed and in 1871 HMS *Devastation*, a first-class battleship with an armoured breastwork was launched. She displaced 9,300 tons and was the first seagoing mastless turret ship. She carried four 12-inch guns in two turrets and proved to be a seaworthy vessel.

An alternative approach to the problems was HMS *Inflexible*, which was designed by Edward Reed's successor Nathan Barnaby, with the detailed design being done by William White, who succeeded Barnaby as Director of Naval Construction. The *Inflexible* was laid down in 1874; she carried her four main 16-inch guns in two centrally placed turrets and had a strongly armoured central citadel which contained the engines. The ends were unarmoured but were compartmentalised and cork-filled to keep the ship afloat if the ends were pierced by enemy gunfire. This design was extremely controversial and Edward Reid criticised his successor's design in *The Times*, which led to a committee being set up to review the design.

T. A. Brassey, politician and editor of the eponymous *Naval Annual*, writing in *The Times*, supported the committee's decision to back the design with some suggested modification to the pumps and the cork floatation. He pointed out that the amount of armour protection was inevitably a compromise and that there was no risk-free option. He opposed the addition of more armour as this would reduce the ship's speed and in 'securing additional protection against uncertain fire of naval guns, you may expose a valuable ship to grave risks from other weapons.'[24]

The *Inflexible* was innovative in a number of ways:

- She carried the heaviest armour yet fitted to a British ship. Her central citadel was protected by 12 inches of plate backed by 11 inches of teak and another 12 inches of plate, which in turn was backed by 6 inches of teak.
- She was the first ship to have a horizontal armoured deck.
- She was the first ship to be lit entirely by electric lighting.
- Her hull shape was designed with the aid of an experimental water flow tank. The *Inflexible* was the first ship for which this was the case.

The turret ship HMS *Monarch*. Her four 12-inch guns were housed in two turrets amidships, which had a very limited field of fire because of the superstructure and masts.

HMS *Inflexible* from a C. Cammell & Co. publication promoting the company's armour plate.

THE TORPEDO AND THE 'JEUNE ÉCOLE'

Between the late 1860s, when the early iron warships were constructed, and the late 1880s there were major improvements in naval ordinance with the introduction of armour-piercing shells and self-propelled torpedoes. The effectiveness of armour-piercing shot was demonstrated in the War of the Pacific between Chile and Peru where at the Battle of Angamos (1879) the British-supplied 9-inch Palliser shot pierced the 8-inch wrought-iron armour of the Peruvian *Huascar's* turret. By the end of the 1880s it was thought impossible to protect battleships against modern armour-piercing shells without giving them such heavy iron armour that they became too slow and thus of course vulnerable to attack by torpedo boats.

At the same time there were rapid improvements in torpedo technology. The earliest torpedoes, used in the American Civil War, were known as spar torpedoes and were fitted on a long pole at the front of the attacking craft. The Union Navy successfully used a spar torpedo to sink the Confederate ironclad CSS *Albemarle* in 1864. It was not until the late 1860s that a practical self-propelled torpedo was developed. This was designed by the British engineer Robert Whitehead working in Trieste, Italy. His early experiments had a range of about 200–300 yards but had problems with depth control. This was improved when the depth was measured by a combination of pressure and angle. In 1868 Whitehead demonstrated torpedoes with a range of 700 yards to the Austrian navy, but they could not afford the cost of buying exclusive rights to the technology. The next year Whitehead was invited to England, where there were extensive trials of his torpedoes. In 1870 the Admiralty purchased the rights to manufacture the torpedoes for £15,000 and began production at the Woolwich Royal Gun Factory. France, Germany and China quickly followed the British example in purchasing the rights and began making their own torpedoes.

Parallel to the development of the torpedo was the development of small boats to deliver them. A number of experimental designs were tried before John Thorneycroft persuaded the Admiralty to base a design on his fast launches. The *Lightning* was ordered in 1876 and this design was the basis for subsequent torpedo boats.

In response to this perception of the torpedo as the weapon of the future, a theory of naval strategy developed which was known as the 'Jeune École' (literally the 'Young School'). The idea was developed in France as a strategy to challenge the British navy on a worldwide basis without the commitment of building an expensive battle fleet. It proposed that, rather than the traditional fleet of battleships, navies should construct a fleet of unarmoured cruisers for commerce raiding and torpedo boats for coastal defence and attacking enemy battleships.

The *Jeune École* influenced most navies but the influence of the school on naval strategy reached its peak in France when Admiral Théophile Aube, a leading figure of the *Jeune École*, became the minister in charge of the navy in January 1886. Under his leadership the French built a range of protected cruisers, starting in 1887 with the 4,561-ton *Sfax* and followed by six further classes of protected cruiser, although no armoured cruisers were built. Between 1876 and 1890 France also built a fleet of 128 torpedo boats of around 53 tons or less.

Austria–Hungry was also a great supporter of the *Jeune École* and, under the leadership of Admiral Max von Sterneck, virtually abandoned battleship construction for the seventeen years after 1883. In Germany the navy, under the leadership of General Albrecht von Stosch, had believed in building an ocean-going battle fleet to challenge the British navy and had become the third-largest ironclad fleet in the world after Britain and France. Von Stosch's successor was General Leo von Caprivi, who was a soldier and supported the primacy of the army. Under his leadership the navy turned away from building large battleships in favour of coastal defence ships and torpedo boats.

The British navy, although it had supporters of the *Jeune École* (including John 'Jackie' Fisher, later the First Sea Lord), hedged its bets on cruiser design, building both armoured cruisers and protected cruisers for the protection of its trade. It also continued to build battleships throughout the period.

INDUSTRIAL AND TECHNICAL DEVELOPMENT

Technical developments were gradually taking place that would enable designers to make the breakthrough to the next generation of warships. Critical were developments in steel manufacture and armour making.

Steel for shipbuilding

Making steel was not a new process. Small-scale steel production had been common for many years and was used to make high-value objects such as swords or cutting tools:

- Crucible steel developed by Benjamin Huntsman in Sheffield in the 1740s used small clay pots to make high-quality steel. It increased the quality and quantity of steel it was possible to make, but it remained an expensive and small-scale product.
- The Bessemer process developed in 1856 in Sheffield made larger quantities of steel more quickly, but the quality of the steel was variable. It was suitable for uses such as making rails.
- The Siemens–Martin open-hearth process was developed in 1864 in France. It was a slower process but it gave greater control over the final product as it was possible to test it at intervals, thus producing a more consistent quality steel, better suited for use in high-specification products.

The Bessemer and Siemens processes initially depended on using a non-acidic ore such as haematite, which is found in the Cumberland/Furness area of Britain. In 1878–79 Sydney Gilchrist Thomas discovered that by adding limestone to the more widely available, and more acidic, phosphoric ore the impurities could be separated out as slag, leaving non-acidic steel. Because it was made from 'basic' ore the resulting steel was known as basic steel. This method was used more by the continental producers, who did not have easy access to haematite, whereas British makers tended to use more haematite and scrap iron in producing their steel.

Steel production using Bessemer & Siemens–Martin processes ('000 tons)[25]

	Great Britain	France	Germany
1865	225	40.6	99.5
1869	275	110.0	161.0
1873	588	151.0	310.0
1879	1,030	333.0	478.0

As the technology to make steel on a large scale became more widely used Britain began to lose its place as the premier industrial power. The USA overtook Britain in the amount of iron and steel produced in 1890. Germany followed in 1893 (steel) and 1903 (iron).[26] The new investments and increased volumes of production using the new processes drove down the cost of steel by 80–90% between 1860 and the early 1890s making it economical for large-scale usage.

Associated with increased production levels was the mechanisation of the processes for handling the steel. Large reversing engines and rollers had to be developed for rolling the ingots and machinery for cutting and managing the sheet steel. These developments began in Britain in the 1860s but were taken up and developed by American companies in the 1890s and quickly adopted by German firms.

Steel for shipbuilding began to be adopted later than in other industries due to concerns about the reliability of the product by shipbuilders and insurers. The mercantile insurer Lloyd's began to accept the use of steel in ships and in November 1877 steel-built ships stopped being classified as 'experimental'.[27]

Merchant ships added to Lloyd's register ('000 tons)[28]

	Steel ships	Wrought-iron ships
1880	38.0	487.0
1885	185.0	308.5
1890	913.0	46.0

Small amounts of steel began to be used in warship construction in Britain in the late 1860s, for example in HMS *Audacious*, built at Chatham in 1867–68. The first warship to be built mainly in steel was the French *Redoutable,* a central battery ship built at Lorient taking advantage of the French lead in the Siemens-Martin process. In Britain the first steel naval ships were the dispatch vessels *Isis* and *Mercury,* which were laid down in Pembroke Dock in 1875, close to the Landore Works near Swansea, which had fitted Siemens–Martin furnaces.

Steel was also gradually introduced into boilers and engines from about 1870 onwards, decreasing the engines' weight and increasing their power output.

Compound armour

From the mid-1870s onwards the armour-making firms were experimenting with improved armour. The table of the experiments carried out by Charles Cammell in 1877 shows the nature of the experiments, and that both all-steel and iron/steel compound armours were being explored:[29]

	Thickness	Description	Outcome
Type A	9 inch	9-inch rolled iron armour	Not available
Type B1	9 inch	Subcarburised steel tempered in cold water	Broke up on second shot
Type B2	9 inch	Subcarburised steel not tempered	
Type C	9 inch	Alexander Wilson Patent plates of steel cast between two wrought-iron plates – reheated and rolled	Work stopped July 1877
Type D	9 inch	Alexander Wilson Patent Steel cast on a 12-inch iron plate – reheated and rolled	Not available
Type E	9 inch	Yates patent – cast ingot with hard steel between 2 pieces of mild steel – reheated and rolled	Work stopped on E1; no information on E2
Type F	9 inch	Steel between 2 iron plates – reheated and rolled	Not available

In 1876 the Italians tested a range of armour types from various manufacturers at a test range at Spezia. The plates tested were:

- 22-inch iron armour from C. Cammell;
- 22-inch iron armour from Marrel Frères (France);
- 10- and 12-inch iron sandwich plates from Cammell and Marrell; and
- 22-inch Schneider (France) steel armour.

The plates were tested with 10-inch, 11-inch and 17.7-inch guns firing Palliser chilled shot. Broadly speaking the conclusions were that:

- steel plate is more liable to be destroyed by the fire of guns not capable of completely penetrating it than wrought-iron, which under these circumstances suffers but little; and
- steel, by transmitting the blow of impact through the plate is less liable to let the shot through the backing, while more liable to be stripped off and destroyed itself.[30]

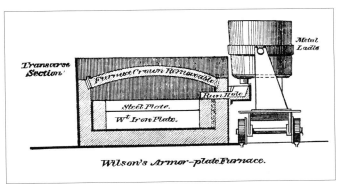

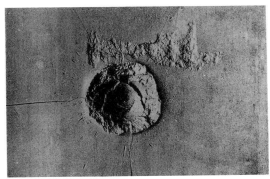

TOP: The trials at Spezia. Note the wire framework in front of the targets to measure the velocity of the projectile.
ABOVE: Charles Cammell's method of fusing the iron and steel together to make the compound armour plate.
RIGHT: Wilson first compound armour plate test.

The *Engineer* magazine concluded that the trials at Spezia had been an excellent experiment 'as a result of which we have learnt more at the conclusion of these experiments as to the relevant behaviour of iron and steel than has probably been learned in any trials hitherto made'.

Both Charles Cammell and John Brown successfully developed compound armour in the late 1870s. Working at the same time they each developed a slightly different technique of fusing a hardened steel face on to a softer wrought-iron backing.

The Cammell process for compound armour was developed by Alexander Wilson, who later became chairman of the company. This involved heating a wrought-iron plate into a mould into which Bessemer steel then was poured. After solidifying, the plate was rolled to the required thickness. This plate was first tested on 1 August 1877 at Shoeburyness. The plate was 3 ft 10 in by 3 ft 8 in and consisted of 5 inches of steel backed by 4 inches of wrought-iron. The 7-inch Palliser projectile only penetrated 3.12 inches into the plate and the back of the plate bulged 0.2 inches. There were four radial cracks in the plate.[31]

John Brown's process was developed by John Devonshire Ellis and was tested on board HMS *Nettle* at Portsmouth. The plates trialled were not penetrated by 250 lb Palliser shot, although they were badly cracked.[32] The process was patented in October 1877.[33] A forged steel plate was placed over a wrought-iron plate with spacers in between them. Molten steel was then poured between the two plates and after cooling the plate was pressed to 3 inches thick.

The new compound armour was 1.9 times more resistant than wrought-iron armour and both John Brown and C. Cammell's quoted prices of around £100 per ton for their compound armour plates. By 1880 compound armour was being produced internationally by a number of firms under licence:[34]

Company	Country	
Chas. Cammell	Sheffield, Gr. Britain	
John Brown	Sheffield, Gr. Britain	
Marrel Frères	France	Under licence from C. Cammell
Petin et Gaudet	St Chamond, France	Under licence from C. Cammell
Terre Noir Works	St Etienne, France	Under licence from C. Cammell
Aciéries de la Marine	St Chamond, France	
Chatillion et Commentry	Montluçon, France	
Dillenger	Saarland, Germany	
Kopline	St Petersburg, Russia	

Endnotes

1. A. Lambert, 'Politics, Technology and Policy Making 1859–1865: Palmerston, Gladstone and the Management of the Ironclad Naval Race', *Northern Mariner*, Vol. 8, No. 13, July 1998.

2. A. D. Lambert (ed.), *Steam, Steel and Shellfire: The Steam Warship 1815–1905* (London, 1992), pp. 51–9. Quoted in Lambert, 'Politics, Technology and Policy Making', p. 14.

3. David S. Landes, *The Unbound Prometheus* (Cambridge University Press, 2003), pp. 96 and 194.

4. E. W. Very, 'The Development of Armour for Naval Use', *Proceedings of the US Naval Institute*, Vol. 9, No. 3, 1833.

5. D. K. Brown, *Warrior to Dreadnought* (Seaforth Publishing, 2010), p. 12.

6. Quoted in Howard J. Fuller, 'Seagoing purposes indispensable to the defence of this country: Policy pitfalls of Great Britain's early ironclads', *Northern Mariner*, Vol. 13, No. 9, 2003; his reference National Archives, ADM 1/5774, does not appear to correspond to a current NA reference.

7. National Archives WO33/11, Transactions and Report of the Special Committee on Iron between 21 January 1861 and March 1862, p. 103.

8. J. Ford, 'On the Manufacture of Iron Plates', *Institution of Naval Architects*, Vol. 3, 1862, p. 144.

9. W. Fairburn and W. Pole, *The Life of Sir William Fairburn* (1877; reprinted 1970, David & Charles Reprints), p. 354.

10. 'A visit to the Iron Clad', *Temple Bar Magazine*, London, August 1861.

11. National Archives WO33/11, Transactions and Report of the Special Committee on Iron between 21 January 1861 and March 1862, p. 86.

12. Report of Controller of Navy's Office to House of Commons, 13 June 1861, © Copyright 2005 proQuest Information & Learning.

13. J. Brown, 'On the Manufacture of the Steel Rails and Armour Plates', Proceedings of the Institute of Mechanial Engineers, 31 July 1861, p. 124

14. *Manchester Guardian*, 13 November 1906, quoted in A. Grant, *Steel & Ships: The History of John Brown's* (London: Joseph, 1950), p. 20.

15. Very, 'The Development of Armour Plate for Naval Use', p. 374.

16. C. E. Ellis, Institution of Naval Architects, *Armour for Ships 1860–1910*, 7 July 1911, p. 338.

17. Fairburn and Pole, *The Life of Sir William Fairburn*, p. 354.

18. Results extracted from National Archive, Committee on Iron reports, WO/10 to WO/15.

19. The Controller was the Third Sea Lord and was in charge of ship design and shipbuilding.

20. David Evans, *Building the Steam Navy 1830–1906* (Conway Maritime Press, 2004), p. 163.

21. A. D. Stacey, 'An Historical Survey of the Manufacture of Naval Armour by Vickers & Sons and their successors 1888–1956' (Cambridge University Archive Vickers Collection 1153 / SIMT MNVK/0006). Evans (see previous note) names the company as Mr Sanderson of Parkgate. Mr Sanderson was S. Beale's works manager.

22. Report of Controller of Navy's Office to House of Commons, 13 June 1861, © Copyright 2005 proQuest Information & Learning.

23. Brown, *Warrior to Dreadnought*, p. 25.

24. T. A. Brassey, *Papers and Addresses*, Vol. 1 (Longmans Green & Co, 1894), p. 333.

25. D. S. Landes, *The Unbound Prometheus* (Cambridge University Press, 2003), p. 262.

26. Landes, *The Unbound Prometheus*, p. 269.

27. *Engineer*, 23 November 1877, p. 373.

28. Landes, *The Unbound Prometheus*, p. 260.

29. Stacey, 'An Historical Survey of the Manufacture of Naval Armour'.

30. Details of the trial at Spezia were published in the *Engineer* on 29 December 1876.

31. *Engineer*, 17 August 1877, p. 120.

32. Ibid., 22 February 1878, p. 125.

33. Ibid., 17 May 1878, p. 358.

34. Stacey, 'An Historical Survey of the Manufacture of Naval Armour'.

CHAPTER 2

THE PRE-DREADNOUGHTS AND THE DEVELOPMENT OF CEMENTED ARMOUR

During the 1870s Britain had built fewer new warships than other major European powers such as France.[1] This was partly because, influenced by the views of the *Jeune École* discussed in Chapter 1, there were doubts about the value of battleships, but the state of Britain's finances may also have played a part.

Although in 1884 Britain still possessed the world's largest navy, the French navy was growing rapidly. The Italians and Russians were also expanding their fleets and Germany was beginning to show an interest in expanding its own navy. The Congress of Berlin in 1878, which ended the 1877–78 Russo-Turkish War and involved all the major European powers, the Ottoman Empire and four Baltic states, ushered in a period of international stability. In this climate Britain's relative naval weakness did not cause undue public alarm but by 1884 the international situation had become more threatening. The relationship with Russia was deteriorating because of conflicting interests in India and Afghanistan; similarly, there was tension with France over Egypt and in the Far East and with Germany over their interests in Africa. To make things more troubling for Britain, Franco-German relations were improving.[2]

In September 1884 the campaigning journalist W. T. Stead wrote a series of articles in the *Pall Mall Gazette*, of which he was the editor, entitled 'What is the Truth about the Navy?' He asked twelve questions, the first three of which were:

1. Our war risks have enormously increased. Has our navy, which is our national insurance, been correspondingly strengthened?
2. Can we or can we not demonstrate beyond all gainsaying our 'irresistible superiority' in armour, guns, speed, and coal-carrying capacity over any combination of fleets which it is reasonable to believe could be brought against us?
3. If at this moment we are in this position, how will it be five years hence, when the ironclads now building are in commission?

He demanded that the Admiralty either state clearly that they were satisfied with the current position, or alternatively admit that there was a problem, and set out a programme to rectify the situation.[3] He concluded that:

1. Our risks have increased, enormously since 1868; our expenditure has slightly diminished.
2. We are just a little ahead of France in ships, behind her in guns, and about equal in armour and speed.
3. We have not sufficient fast ocean cruisers to defend our commerce.[4]

The articles led to public demand that the Royal Navy should be strengthened, to the extent that the Parliamentary Secretary to the Admiralty felt that there was 'sufficient excitement and anxiety felt in the country to prevent the question being shelved or pooh-poohed.'[5] As a result an additional £3 million was added to the naval budget.

The concern about the strength of the navy coincided with technological developments that led to the development of a new class of warships in the mid-1880s. Known at the time as 'modern' battleships, these ships were later known as the pre-Dreadnoughts. They replaced the earlier ironclad battleships and were characterised by the following features:

- They were built of steel with hardened steel armour. This was initially compound armour, later replaced with Harvey armour and then by the even more effective Krupp armour.
- They were powered by triple expansion steam engines fuelled by coal.
- They had a small main battery, usually of four heavy guns.
- They had a secondary battery of lighter, quick-firing weapons.

In the early years of the pre-Dreadnought period there were conflicting views about how best to mount the main armament. The two main options were the turret mounting and the barbette mounting, and both had advantages and disadvantages. A turret offered the most protection to the main guns and their crews, but it was extremely heavy and the additional weight could not be carried high up on the ship. Turret ships therefore had a low freeboard (the height between the deck and the sea) and consequently they were less seaworthy. Barbettes, which were large armoured tubes between

HMS *Edinburgh* showing the large turrets amidships.

The armour layout was:[6]

	Inches of armour	Type of armour
Citadel	18–14	Compound
Bulkheads	16–13	Compound
Conning tower	22–10	Iron
Decks (2)	3 and 3–2½	Iron
Turrets	16 face, 14 side	Compound

Rapid development of the technologies and an uncertainty as to the role that the ships would be required to play led to major debates within the Admiralty about which direction the design of battleships should take. There were those who argued for less armour and more mobility, and others who argued for fewer large guns. The outcome of these debates was the *Admiral* class of battleships.

The *Admiral* class had four 12-inch breech-loading guns mounted in two barbettes. These were located forward and aft and were much lighter than the turrets in the *Edinburgh* class. The secondary battery had six 6-inch guns that were designed to attack the unarmoured portions of an enemy ship.

The armour layout of the *Admiral* class was:[7]

	Inches of armour	Type of armour
Main belt	18–8	Compound Belt reducing to 8 in below top 4 ft
Barbettes	11½–10	Steel 1 in roof and 3 in floors
Bulkheads	16–7	Compound
Conning tower	12	Steel, 2 in roof
Decks (2)	3 and 2½–2	Steel

the guns and the magazines, with the guns mounted on top of them, were lighter and the weight was carried lower down. They therefore had the advantage that the ships had a higher freeboard and were more seaworthy. However, the guns and gunners were more vulnerable.

It took some time for this issue to be resolved and, as we will see, the early pre-Dreadnought ships varied in the mountings they used.

THE EARLY PRE-DREADNOUGHTS

Early examples of the new type of battleship were HMS *Colossus* and HMS *Edinburgh*, both laid down in 1879. Their hulls were of open-cast steel and they had steel-faced compound armour. They carried four 12-inch breech-loading main guns in two turrets amidships. Their secondary armament was five 6-inch guns as well as a number of quick-firing smaller guns.

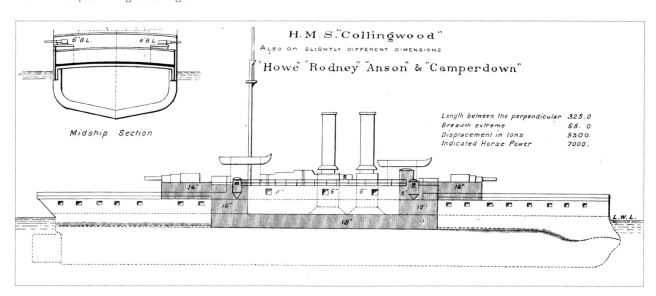

HMS *Collingwood* of the *Admiral* Class.

DEVELOPMENTS IN ARMOUR PLATE

From 1875 the British government encouraged armour manufacturers to develop steel armour. Whitworth's in Manchester produced thin steel plates but the only company able to produce steel armour suitable for warships was the French firm Schneider of Le Creusot in eastern France. In 1886 Schneider was making steel armour plates 22 inches thick and with a carbon content of about 0.4%.

Up to the end of 1887 the total amounts of steel and compound armour manufactured were:[8]

Country	Compound armour (tons)		Steel armour (tons)
	Cammell's 'Wilson' patent	John Brown's 'Ellis' patent	
England	24,358	17,959	
France	14,387		19,309
Germany & Russia	10,375		
Totals	49,120	17,959	19,309
	67,079		

On a worldwide basis the number of firms making armour plate was relatively small; the majority were making compound armour based on the Cammell (Wilson) patent:[9]

Compound armour		Steel armour
Wilson patent	Ellis patent	
C. Cammell (Sheffield)	J. Brown (Sheffield)	Schneider & Cie (Le Creusot, France)
Marrel Frères (Rive De Gier, Loire, France)		
La Compagnie Anonyme des Forges (Chatillion & Commentry, France)		
La Compagnie des Hauts Forneaux (St. Chamond, France)		
Dillinger Works (Germany)		
The Imperial Ijora Works (St Petersburg, Russia)		

In 1888 C. Cammell & Co. submitted the first British all-steel plate for an Admiralty trial aboard HMS *Nettle* at Portsmouth. This trial was for both compound and steel plates and the following firms submitted plates:[10]

Firm	Location	Type of armour
C. Cammell & Co.	Sheffield	'Wilson' compound
J. Brown & Co.	Sheffield	'Ellis' compound
C. Cammell & Co.	Sheffield	Solid steel
Spencers	Newcastle	Cast steel, unwrought
Vickers	Sheffield	Solid pressed steel
Firths	Sheffield	Rolled steel
Jessops	Sheffield	Cast steel compound
J. Brown & Co.	Sheffield	Solid steel
Armstrongs	Newcastle	Steel
Whitworths	Manchester	Steel

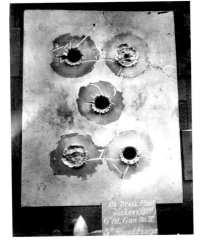

Vickers submitted a 10½-inch steel plate on 6 September 1888 (see picture at right) with a carbon content of 0.34%. The results of this trial, using 6-inch projectiles at a distance of 30 ft was:[11]

Shell & type		Effect on front of plate	Effect on back of plate and backing
1	Holtzer	Plate punched through, shell rebounded intact.	3-inch hole in back. Star-shaped cracks.
2	Holtzer	Penetrated plate 13 inches, shell rebounded intact.	1.8-inch deep bulge in back of plate, small crack.
3	Palliser	Entered plate and broke up leaving front piece in plate. Shell broke up.	3-inch deep bulge in back of plate, small crack.
4	Palliser	Entered plate and broke up leaving front piece in plate. Shell broke up.	0.85-inch deep bulge in back of plate, no cracks.
5	Holtzer	Penetrated through plate with tip just reaching backing, shell rebounded intact.	Hole in bulge 1.5 inches in diameter in back of plate, 8 cracks.

As a result of the successful testing of its plates, Vickers laid down an armour plate works at the River Don Works, which was operational by 1892.

At this stage homogeneous steel armour was considered about equally as effective as compound armour. In 1889 Schneider's, which were generally the pioneers in steel armour at this time, introduced nickel steel armour that contained around 4% nickel. In 1891 Charles Cammell's produced nickel steel armour plate 3 to 4 inches thick for the first time in Britain. The addition of nickel to the carbon steel improved the resistance of the armour and it was considered to be 2.2 times superior to wrought-iron armour.

FINANCIAL PROBLEMS AND SPENDING REDUCTIONS

In the latter part of the 1880s the British government was experiencing budgetary problems. Colonial military expenditure had increased due to problems in Afghanistan[i] and Africa.[ii] Disagreements with Russia in 1878 and 1885 had increased expenditure. As neither Liberal nor Conservative governments wanted to increase taxes, this meant that the country ran substantial financial deficits from the late 1870s to the mid-1880s.[12]

	Deficit	Surplus
1874/5		£595,833
1875/6		£509,920
1876/7		£439,807
1877/8	-£2,640,197	
1878/9	-£2,291,817	
1879/80	-£2,840,698	
1880/1		£933,363
1881/2	-£1,650,294	
1882/3		£98,178
1883/4		£205,600
1884/5	-£1,049,772	
1885/6	-£2,642,543	
1886/7		£775,998
1887/8		£2,378,000
1888/9		£2,798,740
1889/90		£3,221,001

By the end of the 1880s technical developments had reduced the costs of building an effective and seaworthy battleship. The introduction of the triple expansion steam engine in place of the previous compound engines had increased engine efficiency and the maximum power output. Increased use of nickel steel allowed thinner plate to be used, with associated weight savings, and this meant that the ships could have a higher freeboard, making them more seaworthy. The development of quick-firing guns for the secondary armament also increased protection against torpedo craft.

THE NAVAL DEFENCE ACT AND A NEW BUILDING PROGRAMME

W. T. Stead was not alone in his concerns about whether the navy was strong enough. In 1887 Sir William White, the newly appointed Director of Naval Construction (DNC) wrote a memo identifying seventy-two ships which would become obsolete within the following five years and outlining a £9 million programme of replacement. This memo stimulated a debate about the strategic role of the navy, as opposed to a budget-driven approach, which had been the previous practice.

A report on the naval manoeuvres of 1888[13] by Admirals Symonds, Hornby and Alcester, which was presented to parliament, concluded that the navy was 'altogether inadequate to take the offensive in a war with only one great power […] and […] supposing a combination of two great powers to be allied as her enemies, the balance of maritime power would be against England'. This report added to pressure from the politician and naval officer Captain Lord Beresford, who had resigned as Fourth Sea Lord on the Board of the Admiralty after leaking an internal report that was critical of the ability of the British fleet to mobilise quickly in an emergency. He continued to campaign for a stronger navy from the back benches of the House of Commons. As a result of these pressures Lord George Hamilton, the First Lord of the Admiralty, introduced the Naval Defence Act in March 1889. This Act formalised the traditional two-power standard for the first time, stating 'our establishment should be on such a scale that it should be at least equal to the naval strength of any two other countries'. The standard was to be measured in terms of battleships 'of the newest type and most approved design' and they were to be larger than the foreign equivalents in order to allow them to be given comparable armament and protection, with more powerful engines for higher speed.

The government was able to fund this programme as Britain's financial position had improved due to a reorganisation of the national debt, resulting in the annual servicing costs of the debt being much lower.

The Act authorised a programme of building seventy ships, including ten battleships, over the five-year period between 1889 and 1894 at a cost of £21.5 million. It was hoped that the Act would have two effects: firstly, to reduce the costs of building the ships by spreading the funding over five years so that building was not halted if funding ran out in any year; and, secondly, to deter other countries from competing with the British naval building programme. It

---

i   Second Anglo-Afghan War, 1878–80.

ii   Anglo-Xhosa war 1877–79; Anglo-Zulu War 1879; First Boer War 1880–81; Mahdist War (Sudan) 1881–89.

was hoped that 'the mere enunciation of this scheme will show them the utter futility of their desire'.[14]

Sumida[15] and Brown,[16] writing about the Naval Defence Act, both concluded that it was a success in terms of finance and shipbuilding but that, perhaps unsurprisingly, it did not have the restraining effect on rival nations that Hamilton had predicted. Instead, it could be argued that it triggered a naval arms race that continued up to the First World War. The two next largest naval powers, France and Russia, who signed a treaty of alliance in 1891, each laid down twelve battleships between 1889 and 1893 and announced plans for five more in 1894. During the same period Britain built ten battleships under the Naval Defence Act and planned three more under the Estimates of 1892/93 and 1893/94. This left the country short of the 'two-power standard' as set out by the First Lord.

The Admiral class were felt to have had a number of problems – not least in their low freeboard which meant that they were not very seaworthy – and reports of naval manoeuvres expressed concern that it did not 'appear as if the Admiral class will be very steady gun platforms in bad weather'.[17] Various improvements in the design were considered for the new battleships built under the Act. In November 1888 a meeting was called to consider the main design features. The issues to be decided were:

• Should the ships have turrets or barbettes?
• What should be the main and secondary armaments? How should the guns be arranged?
• What height of freeboard should the ships have? The weight of the turrets precluded a high freeboard turret ship.
• What armour protection should the ships have?
• What speed would the ships be required to achieve?

The result of these discussions was a programme in the 1889 Estimates to build seven Royal Sovereign class battleships. These were to be high freeboard barbette ships with a displacement of 16,000 tons. They were armed with four 13½-inch guns and a secondary armament of ten 6-inch guns. Their armour plate was mostly compound armour with some use of Harvey armour or nickel steel armour on the upper belt.[18]

	Inches of armour	Distribution
Main belt	18–16–14	240 ft long, 3 ft above waterline, 5½ ft below
Upper belt	4	150 ft long (Harvey in Royal Sovereign, nickel steel in other ships)
Barbettes	17–16–11	Armoured down to height of main belt, thinner armour inside bulkheads
Bulkheads	16 –14	Forward barbette thicker
Conning tower	14 –12	
Decks (2)	3 and 2½	Middle and lower
Main deck casement	6	Upper deck 6-inch guns only protected by splinter shields

The turret-versus-barbette argument was not resolved and so one ship, HMS Hood, was built with twin turrets instead of barbettes. Because of the weight of the turrets she had a much lower freeboard (11¼ feet compared to 19½ feet) and was much less seaworthy. She was the last of the old-style turret ships to be built by the British navy.

Two 2nd-class battleships, HMS Centurion and HMS Barfleur, built as part of the Naval Defence Act programme in the 1890 Estimates, took the first steps towards the modern turret and had a 6-inch armour shield over the barbettes to protect the gun crew. This was, however, not complete and was open at the back.

	Inches of armour	Distribution
Main belt	12–10–9–8	200 ft long, 2½ ft above waterline, 5 ft below
Upper belt	4	
Barbettes	9–8–5	
Bulkheads	8	
Screen bulkheads	3	Harvey armour
Conning tower	12	
Decks (2)	2–2½	Middle and lower
Casement	4–2	Faces and sides
Turrets	6	Faces and sides

CEMENTED ARMOUR AND THE HARVEY PROCESS

In 1889 Hayward Augustus Harvey, the owner of Harvey United Steel Company of the USA, completed his experiments on treating steel to make it more resistant.

Harvey experimented with carburising (or cementing) the face of a 10½-inch Creusot steel plate and holding it at a high temperature equivalent to that of molten cast iron for two to three weeks. A high-carbon substance such as bone charcoal was packed against the face that was to be hardened, with a non-carboniferous material on the other side. The resulting plate had a carbon content on the face of 1–1.1%, which tapered off further into the plate and was about an inch deep.

When the heating process was finished the plate was quenched or sprayed with running water to produce a hardened surface on the side of the plate with the higher carbon content.

Firing trials were carried out by the US Naval Ordinance Board at Indian Head Proving Ground in October and November 1891 on high- and low-carbon steel plates treated by the Harvey process. Two American companies, Bethlehem Iron Co. and Carnegie Phipps Co., manufactured the plates. The test showed that the plates were superior to both Schneider carbon and nickel steel plates tested previously.

Shortly after the introduction of the Harvey process, Carnegie Steel in the USA discovered that the resistance

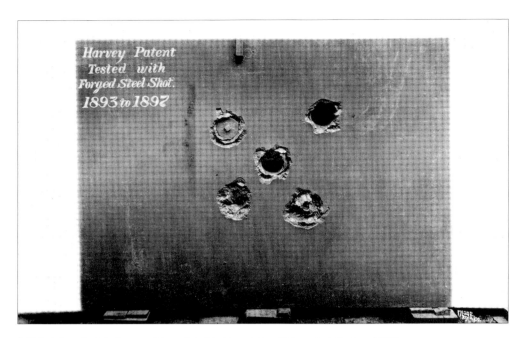

A 5.9-inch Harveyised steel armour plate made by John Brown & Co., which was tested in August 1893.

of the plates could be improved by reforging them after cementation. The plates were reheated at a low temperature and the thickness was reduced by 10–15%. This process was known as double forging.

Harvey took out a British patent in 1891 and a legal judgement by Sir Richard Webster QC concluded that 'none of the previous patents would enable anyone to produce any such Armour Plates as have been produced by Mr Harvey'.[19] John Brown & Co. challenged this patent on the grounds that Capt. John Tresidder had perfected a method of high-pressure sprinkling of hardened plates. The company felt that 'Mr Harvey was not an armour plate maker: if he had been he would have omitted from his specification all details of the well-known process of cementation and at the same time elaborated the description of the chilling, where the difficulties really exist.'[20] A comparison of the two types of plate in the *Engineer* concluded that, although the tests were not identical, the Ellis–Tresidder plates were of an equivalent standard to the American Harvey plates.[21] In the end the Harvey Company bought the Tresidder patents for Britain and Europe from John Brown's and the Harvey Company of New York similarly acquired the American rights to the Tresidder process and the Société Harvey acquired the French rights.[22] The Tresidder chilling process and the Harvey cementation processes were thus combined.

Charles Cammell & Co. and Vickers, Sons & Co. took up both the Harvey patent and the John Brown patent, at first using carbon steel and later nickel-carbon steel. In 1892 Vickers submitted a 10.5-inch 'Harvey' armour plate to HMS *Nettle*. During this test all the Holizer and Palliser shot was shattered and the rear of the plate showed 'five smooth bulges' and no penetration of the plate. Cammell's

10.5-inch plate showed equivalent results.[23] Thinner 6-inch plates from Vickers were not as successful and two of the three trial plates broke up.

In order to manufacture the Harvey armour the armour manufacturers invested in new plant and machinery. John Brown invested in a new forging press, bending press and rolling mill. Vickers also invested in new machinery at the River Don Works. Armstrong Whitworth invested in a modern armour plate mill at Openshaw in Manchester. The other two firms making Harvey armour were William Beardmore of Glasgow and, as we have seen, C. Cammell of Sheffield.

The first British ship to use Harvey armour for most of her protection was HMS *Renown*, an improved *Centurion* design, laid down in 1893. She was designed with a view to increasing the protection from high-explosive medium-calibre shells. She also had a sloped armoured deck behind the belt as opposed to the previous practice of having a flat armoured deck across the top of the belt. The armour arrangement can be compared to that of the previous class of ship:

	Inches of armour		
	Centurion / Barfleur	*Renown*[24]	
Main belt	12–10–9–8	8–6	250 ft long
Upper belt	4		
Barbettes	9–8–5	10–6	
Bulkheads	8	10–6	
Screen bulkheads	3	6	
Conning tower	12	9	
Decks (2)	2–2½	3–2	Middle deck sloped
Casement	4–2	6–4	
Turrets	6	6	

The effect of the introduction of Harvey armour is seen in the weight of armour carried by the *Centurion* and the *Renown*. In spite of having a higher level of protection the *Renown* carried only about 2,400 tons of armour compared to 4,280 tons on her predecessor.[25]

THE *MAJESTIC* CLASS BATTLESHIPS

At the end of the five-year Naval Defence Act programme the government agreed in 1894 to a further five-year programme. Lord Spencer, speaking at the Cutlers' Feast in Sheffield, laid out the Liberal government's policy for the navy as: 'we must maintain and uphold the sea power of this country. We have interests round us in every sea; we have important dominions and large colonies in every quarter of the globe. These large interests need the protection of the British Fleet.'[26]

The Spencer programme was in response to foreign battleship-building programmes and the perceived threat of Russia in the Mediterranean, which had been triggered by the visit of a Russian squadron to Toulon. The programme placed orders for seven new battleships as well as twenty cruisers. When the government fell in 1895 the incoming Conservative/Unionist government ordered a further five battleships.

The first of the new ships under the Spencer programme were the *Majestic* class of nine battleships. The principal developments of these ships from the *Royal Sovereign* class were:

- the introduction of 12-inch guns in place of the previous 13½-inch guns. These were designed by Vickers and were the first wire-wound guns. They were markedly superior to the older type;
- the general use of Harvey cemented armour in place of compound armour;
- a deeper side armour belt of uniform thickness backed up by a sloped armoured deck; and
- a complete armoured shield covering the main armament mounted on the barbettes.

The *Majestic* class carried 5,912 tons of armour laid out as shown:[27]

	Inches of armour	
Main belt	9	220 ft long, 15 ft deep. Upper edge at main deck level
Barbettes	14–7	Thinner below armoured deck
Bulkheads	14 and 12	Forward and aft
Conning tower	14	
Decks (2)	3 on flat, 4 on slope lower deck 2	Outside citadel
Casement	6 face, 2 sides and rears	
Turrets	10½ faces, 5½ sides, 2 floor and roof	

HMS *Mars*, a *Majestic* class battleship built by Laird Brothers of Birkenhead between 1894 and 1897.

Endnotes

1. *Conway's All the World's Fighting Ships 1860–1905*, Vol. 1, p. 282; quoted in Jon T. Sumida, *In Defence of Naval Supremacy, Finance Technology and British Naval Policy 1889–1914* (Naval Institute Press, 2014), p. 11.
2. A. J. Marder, *The Anatomy of British Sea Power, A History of British Naval Policy in the Pre-Dreadnought Era, 1880–1905* (Archon Books, 1964), p. 120.
3. W. T. Stead, 'What is the Truth about the Navy?', *Pall Mall Gazette*, 15 September 1884.
4. W. T. Stead, 'The Responsibility for the Navy?', *Pall Mall Gazette*, 30 September 1884.
5. Marder, *The Anatomy of British Sea Power*, p. 122.
6. R. A. Burt, *British Battleships 1889–1904* (Seaforth Publishing, Barnsley, 2013), p. 26.
7. Ibid., p. 28.
8. *Facts Concerning Armour 1888*, Book from English Steel Corporation Library, SIMT 3144, p. 120.
9. Ibid., p. 4.
10. Ibid., p. 133.
11. Copies of official reports and photographs of government trials. Vickers, SIMT Archive MNVK 0001.
12. Sumida, *In Defence of Naval Supremacy*, Appendix Table 1; data from Sidney Buxton, *Finance and Politics: An Historical Study 1789–1885* (Augustus & Kelly, 1966; first published in 1888).
13. Marder, *The Anatomy of British Sea Power*, p. 132.
14. Lord G. Hamilton, Hansard, HC Deb 7 March 1889 (series 3), Vol. 333 c1191
15. Sumida, *In Defence of Naval Supremacy*.
16. Brown, *Warrior to Dreadnought*.
17. *Engineer*, 1 March 1989, quoting from the Parliamentary paper 'Extracts from the Report of the Committee on the Naval Manoeuvres of 1888'.
18. Burt, *British Battleships 1889–1904*, p. 78.
19. Stacey, 'An Historical Survey of the Manufacture of Naval Armour'.
20. John Brown and Company Limited, Atlas Works Sheffield; Shipyard and Engineering Works Clydebank, 1903. Held in SIMT Library ref: 1572.
21. *Engineer*, 16 September 1892, p. 241; 14 October 1892, p. 329.
22. John Brown and Company Limited, Atlas Works Sheffield.
23. Stacey, 'An Historical Survey of the Manufacture of Naval Armour'.
24. Burt, *British Battleships 1889–1904*, p. 128.
25. Ibid., pp. 109 and 125.
26. T. A. Brassey (ed.), *The Naval Annual 1894* (J. Griffin & Co.), p. 501.
27. Burt, *British Battleships 1889–1904*, p. 145.

CHAPTER 3

KRUPP ARMOUR AND THE LATER PRE-DREADNOUGHTS

Although the pre-Dreadnoughts are generally described as a group, there were a number of significant changes in both thinking and design. During the early 1890s there was both a revival of belief in the battleship as the major naval weapon and technological developments to enable these ideas to be realised. The change in naval thinking was almost entirely down to the publication by Alfred Mahan of his books *The Influence of Seapower on History 1660–1783* in 1890 and *The Influence of Seapower upon the French Revolution and the Empire* in 1892. The introduction of Krupp cemented armour complemented the change in naval thinking and enabled the creation of a new generation of battleships capable of realising the new ideas.

MAHON AND THE GROWTH OF 'NAVALISM'

Alfred Theyer Mahan was a United States naval officer who developed his ideas on seapower by applying the lessons he drew from the Punic Wars between the Romans and the Carthaginians. He argued that the Roman side owed their success to their naval power and applied these principles to a study of more recent Anglo-French conflicts, concluding that naval power was the most decisive factor in the rise and fall of nations. Mahan linked naval policy and operations to their political and economic context and he believed that in democratic societies the development of strong navies required a coalition of interests to support them.[1]

Although Mahan was the most well-known naval writer, he was not alone in arguing for a strong navy; in Britain Admiral Phillip Colomb, an instructor at the Royal Naval College, argued in his book *Naval Warfare: Its Ruling Principles and Practice Historically Treated* that a fleet of battleships was the key to the command of the sea and thus victory in war. In Britain public support for Mahan's and Colomb's ideas was orchestrated by the Navy League. The idea for this organisation was first put forward in January 1892 by a writer using the pen name 'Civis' in a letter to *The Times*. The idea was taken up by Spencer Wilkinson in an article in the *Pall Mall Gazette* in October 1894. The paper received a lot of support for the idea and in January 1895 the Navy League was formed with the original aims as follows:[2]

1. To spread information, showing the vital importance to the British Empire of naval supremacy upon which depend its trade, empire and national existence.
2. To call attention to the enormous demands which war would make upon the Navy, and to the fact that the Navy is not at present ready to meet them.
3. To secure the appointment of a single professional advisor, responsible to the cabinet, upon the maritime defence of the Empire, who shall hold office for a term of years, and whose opinion as to the sufficiency of the preparations covered by the Estimates shall be communicated to Parliament.
4. To urge these matters upon public men and, in particular, upon candidates for Parliament.

The third clause proved somewhat controversial and it was replaced with a milder alternative which read 'To call attention from time to time to such measures as may be requite to secure adequate preparation for the maritime defence of the Empire'. The league published the *Navy League Journal* to promote their views and established Trafalgar Day as a popular pro-navy festival. Although the League membership was only 15,000 in 1901, it had many prominent supporters and its propaganda influenced the debates on naval affairs and provided fertile ground for successive naval scares.

THE DEVELOPMENT OF KRUPP ARMOUR

The first ships of the German Imperial Navy had their armour made in Britain, but by 1878 German firms were manufacturing wrought-iron plates for the later gunboats of the *Wespe* class.

When in 1889 the German navy ordered the four 10,000-ton battleships of the *Brandenburg* class, the firm of Dillinger, who had a licence from Cammell's to manufacture compound armour, expected to get the orders. However, in order to encourage competition the government encouraged the firm of Friedrich Krupp AG to enter the market. They promptly reached an agreement with Dillinger to fix prices and split future orders.[3]

Under this agreement Krupp's would be responsible for armour plate research and development for both firms. They had been experimenting with armour production since 1862 but had not pursued this line of work. In 1875 Alfred Krupp, the head of the firm, began further experiments working with both wrought-iron and mild steel but he had difficulty in making the surface of the plates hard enough. He continued his work with steel plates, using a variety of alloys and different methods of carbonising, quenching and heat-treating the steel. In 1886 the company produced a 15-cm (6-inch) plate which withstood fifty-six shots from a 10.5-cm (3.94-inch) gun. Alfred Krupp's view of this was that 'such a result must, to the whole body of practical men, probably appear unattainable, I am nevertheless a long way from satisfied.'[4] After Alfred Krupp's death in 1887 the work was continued and experiments were conducted in hardening the plates in rapeseed oil at 920 °C and tempering it at 66 °C. Krupp's went on to experiment with gas carburisation instead of using charcoal. A plate of this type that had had water sprinkled on the front was exhibited at the Chicago World Fair in 1893. The problem with this approach was, however, that raising the temperature of the face to a high enough temperature to ensure hardening risked over-tempering the back, causing deterioration in the fibrous structure of the steel.

Dr H. H. Burton described the essential qualities of steel for armour plate as being that:[5]

> The alloy contents should be sufficient to allow the necessary degree of hardening to take place in the centre of the plate [...] When tempered after hardening, the steel should be capable of developing maximum toughness at the highest tensile levels practical.

To create an alloy with these properties Krupp's used steel alloyed with nickel and chromium. Chromium had been used as an alloy of steel for a number of years for various purposes, and it was known that this produced harder steel. It also had the advantage that it slowed the critical cooling speed of the resulting alloy. The steel finally used had a composition of 0.3% carbon, 3–4% nickel and 1.75–2% chromium.

Krupp's found that they could control the final tensile strength of the plates between 170 and 364 lbs per square foot by the amount of hardening and tempering they used on the plates. The structure was completely fibrous throughout the thickness of the plates, which meant that it was more elastic and resistant to spalling[i] and cracking. Following trials in 1894 and 1895 this process was patented and adopted by all the major international armour-making firms under a licence. The detailed process for making Krupp armour was as follows:[6]

1. The ingot was cast with a small runner head.
2. The plates were rolled from the ingot directly. After rolling, the head and about a third of the plate was cut off under the press while the plate was still hot.
3. The plates were allowed to cool on supports and when they were cold they were either surfaced or chipped to remove the scale.
4. The plates were then placed in pairs in a carburising furnace with powdered charcoal between them. They were heated for two days and then maintained at the required temperature for eight or nine days.
5. They were then placed individually in a reheating furnace and straightened or bent to the required shape.
6. The plates were then placed again in a reheating furnace and when they reached a suitable hardening temperature they were quenched, usually in rapeseed oil.
7. While the plates were still warm they were again placed in a reheating furnace for tempering.
8. When they were cool the plates were cut to size and any machining and drilling was carried out. A test piece was left attached to the plate.
9. The plates were then placed in a final hardening furnace and the face was raised to a high temperature while the back was kept as cool as possible.
10. When the face reached the required temperature the plates were withdrawn from the furnace and sprinkled with high-pressure water on both sides. This made the high-carbon face very hard and the low-carbon back tough.
11. After sprinkling, final adjustments to shape were made at a temperature that was not high enough to remove the face hardness. The edges of the plate were ground off at this stage.
12. The test pieces (see stage 8) were then cut off and tests for tensile strength and bending were carried out as well as an examination of the structure.

The British armour plate manufacturers took out licences for making the new Krupp armour and began making and testing plates. Thicker 12-inch plates proved more difficult to make than thinner armour and there was a period of trial and error while the manufacturers perfected the process. By 1898 the manufacturers were able to meet the Admiralty's request for plates weighing 480 lbs per square foot or 12-inch plates.[7]

TESTING ARMOUR PLATE

The effectiveness of armour plate was generally measured by testing its resistance to shells fired at it. The force of the shell, and thus the minimum resistance of the plate, was measured by the thickness of wrought-iron plate that a shell fired at a certain velocity could penetrate. Over the years various empirical formulae were used such as:[8]

---

i   Spalling occurs when the armour plate flakes due to the shock wave caused by the impact of the shell.

- Gâvre, which gave low results at all shell velocities;
- Fairburn and Maitland, which gave lower results at high shell velocities; and
- the Tresidder and Krupp, which broadly agree, had the best fit with the trial results in the 1890s. The Krupp formula gives more emphasis to the weight of the shell than the Tresidder formula.

Captain T. J. Tresidder, who was an engineer at John Brown, devised the formula that was most commonly used in British tests. This result was coupled with the Figure of Merit, which is the ratio between the thickness of wrought-iron it is calculated the shell could pierce, and the actual thickness of the trial plate.

The Tresidder formula is expressed as:

$$t2=wv3/d \times 1/log-1\ 8.8410$$

Where:

t is the thickness of wrought-iron that could be perforated;

w is the weight of the projectile in pounds;

v is the striking velocity in feet per second; and

d is the diameter of the shot in inches.

The test results of Cammell's,[9] John Brown's[10] and Vickers 12-inch Krupp cemented armour plate are shown in the table:

	Thickness of plate (ins)	Holtzer shot weight (lbs)	Striking velocity (ft / sec)	Perforation of iron (note 1) (ins)	Figure of Merit
Cammell 1	11.66	719.75	1,846	23.50	2.02
Cammell 2		718.50	1,866	23.70	2.03
Cammell 3		719.25	1,859	23.50	2.02
J. Brown 1	11.6875	714.00	1,852	23.65	2.01
J. Brown 2		714.00	1,856	23.70	2.02
J. Brown 3		714.00	1,849	23.60	2.03
Vickers 1		721.50	1,860		
Vickers 2	11.69	714.00	1,868	23.60	2.02
Vickers 3		715.00	1,860		

The results for a plate made by Krupp itself in 1898,[11] and described as a 'champion' plate, provide a comparison against which the British plates can be measured:

	Thickness of plate (ins)	Holtzer shot weight (lbs)	Striking velocity (ft / sec)	Perforation of iron (note 1) (ins)	Figure of Merit
Krupp 1	11.8	718	1,917	24.5	2.08
Krupp 2		714	1,979	25.6	2.26
Krupp 3		715	2,066	27.5	2.33

Note 1: calculated by the Tresidder formula

Testing the Tresidder formula against the results given by the *Engineer* gives similar results:

	Engineer figure for perforation	Check using Tresidder formula
Cammell plates	23.50	23.33
	23.70	23.69
	23.50	23.57
J. Brown plates	23.65	23.35
	23.70	23.42
	23.60	23.29
Krupp plates	24.50	24.90
	25.60	26.00
	27.50	27.80

Note: Vickers results are not compared, as the figure given in the *Engineer* is an average of the three shots.

By 1898 all three Sheffield armour-making firms, Charles Cammell, John Brown and Vickers, Sons & Maxim had re-equipped their armour-making works to manufacture Krupp armour.

There was criticism of the British method of testing armour plate in the *Engineer* in 1898. They complained of the difficulties in comparing results from different countries and noted that:

> [the] Americans test their plates up to complete perforation, which is undoubtedly far the most satisfactory method of investigation. The trials in England, and so far as we have been furnished with reports in Germany also, have only extended to proving that a plate has completely defeated a certain severity of attack.[12]

By not testing the plate until it was perforated the Europeans did not therefore get a measurement of the true strength of the plate, merely an understanding of the fact that the plates could resist forces up to a certain level without knowing how much they could exceed this by.

THE IMPACT OF KRUPP ARMOUR ON SHIP DESIGN

The Krupp process meant that armour was now around three times as effective as the wrought-iron fitted on the early ironclads.

This technology gave naval architects the opportunity to re-explore the balance between armour protection, guns and propulsion machinery. In 1895 the DNC, Sir William White, submitted a report on the details of two Japanese battleships (the *Fuji* and the *Yashima,* which were being built at Thames Iron Works and Armstrong Whitworth). He suggested that these powerful battleships required the British Far Eastern Squadron to be strengthened. He proposed building a class of battleships that would be able to pass through the Suez Canal. The resulting *Canopus* class ships were 1,950 tons lighter than the *Majestic* class but had the same armament and a slightly higher speed. They achieved this by incorporating a number of new features, including the introduction of Krupp's armour, which was around 30% more effective than Harvey armour for the

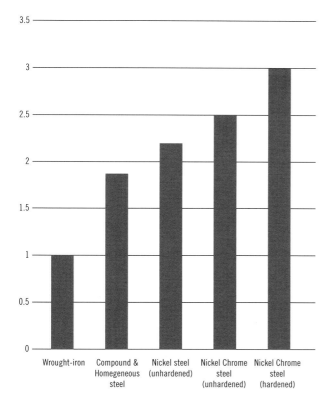

same weight, and the introduction of Belleville water tube boilers, which were licensed from France. Compared to the previous cylindrical boilers, these boilers produced steam at a higher pressure and enabled engines with smaller cylinders to be fitted. It was hoped that these would save weight and prove more economical.

The armour for the *Canopus* class was:[13]

- Belt armour: 6 inches thick and covering a length of 196 feet. The top of the belt was at main deck level and was 9 feet above the waterline. It extended to 5¼ feet below the waterline. A 2-inch thick belt of nickel steel armour ran forward to the bows.
- The barbettes had a 10-inch front and a 12-inch back, reducing to 6 inches below the level of the belt.
- The main bulkheads ran from the belt to the barbettes and were 10, 8 and 6 inches forward and 12, 8, and 6 inches aft.
- The main armament turrets were 8 inches thick with 2-inch roofs.
- The *Canopus* class were the first British ships to have two armoured decks: the main deck had 1-inch steel armour and the middle deck 2-inch steel armour.

The secondary casements and conning tower were of Harvey armour.

The next class of ship ordered under the 1897 Naval Estimates was the *Formidable* class of battleships. These were built to respond to the larger Japanese battleships currently being built and also needed to be larger to accommodate

the new Mark IX 12-inch 40-calibre gun designed by Vickers, which was stronger, heavier and took a greater charge of cordite to give greater muzzle velocity. The *Formidable* class were in effect improved *Monarchs,* but with Krupp rather than Harvey armour and with Belleville water tube boilers.

The initial Estimates for 1898 were for three battleships of the *Bulwark* class but there was concern that the Russians were building ships of the *Peresviet* class of battleships that were reported to be capable of 18 knots. It was agreed that Britain needed to respond to this threat but there was some concern about the ability of the armour manufacturers to produce enough Krupp armour for these new ships. In January 1898 Sir William White reported that in his view:

> The production of armour could be made sufficient in 1898/9 and later years to permit an extended programme of construction for battleships and armoured cruisers [...] The pinch of armour supply comes in this year and arises from the concurrent influence of labour difficulties and of change of quality of armour, which needs reconstruction of plant and large additions to machinery. This reconstruction is now fairly in hand, and several firms are now using every means to perfect and extend their appliances, as well as increase their output.[14]

In May of that year the First Lord of the Admiralty, George Goschen, the Controller of the Navy (Third Sea Lord), Admiral Wilson, and the DNC, Sir William White, toured the three Sheffield armour works to see the investments that had been made.[15] The following week the *Engineer,* reporting on their visit, said that 'in the armour plate departments extensions and alterations are proceeding with great rapidity. The process of altering to the Krupp armour, as required by the British Government is now well advanced and new contracts will be of this type of ships clothing.'[16]

As a result, it was decided to order three ships of the *Duncan* class to be started towards the end of the year, and eventually after the French and Russian shipbuilding plans were known it was decided to increase the size of the class to six ships – five of which were laid down in 1899.

Armour protection for the *Formidable* and *Duncan* classes was:[17]

	Formidable class (inches of armour)	Duncan class (inches of armour)
Main belt	9	7
Fore / aft belt	2 and 1	3–5 and 1½
Barbettes	12–6	12–8–6
Bulkheads	12–10–9	12–10–9
Conning tower	14–2–3 (Krupp)	14
Turret face / sides	10–8	8
Decks	2½–3	2½–1
Casements	6	6 in faces, 2 in backs

In the 1900 Naval Estimates two *Queen* class ships were ordered which were developments of the *Bulwark* classes, with the same armour layout. One of these, HMS *Queen,* had cylindrical Babcock and Wilcox boilers. The change to the new boilers was the result of a long controversy that had led to a committee of enquiry being set up to look at the problems with the Belleville boilers. The 'Boiler Committee' had taken a favourable view of the American Babcock and Wilcox boiler, which had an established track record with the US navy and in merchant ships.[18]

THE LATER PRE-DREADNOUGHTS

The next class of British battleships, ordered under the 1901/02 programme, carried a heavier secondary armament. This was in response to the USS *New Jersey* and the Italian *Bennedetto Brin.* The design was a departure from the basic *Majestic* type that characterised the generation of previous pre-Dreadnoughts and was mainly influenced by:[19]

- the adoption by foreign navies of an intermediate 8-inch battery in addition to the 12-inch and 6-inch armaments;
- criticism that existing British battleships were under-gunned for their displacement; and
- improvements in the armour protection that had reduced the effectiveness of 6-inch guns.

This class of eight ships carried the traditional main armament of four 12-inch guns but had an intermediate armament of four 9.2-inch guns. Orders for the armour plate for the *King Edward VII* class of battleships are recorded under the British pool arrangement of 1903 and show that the armour plate orders were spread among the five armour plate makers.[20] For example, for HMS *Africa*, which was the last battleship built at Chatham Dockyard, Armstrong Whitworth made the gun-shields for the 12- and 9.2-inch guns and the torpedo director towers. Cammell Laird made the main and splinter bulkheads, the side and bow armour, the 9.2- and 12-inch barbettes and the conning tower.

The armour scheme for the *King Edward VII* class was generally the same as the *Bulwark* class but was modified to take account of the different armament.[21]

	Inches of armour	
Main belt	9–8–7	Covering a longer area and carried up above the main deck
Fore / aft belt	3 and 2	Generally slightly thickened
Barbettes	12–8–6	
Bulkheads	12–10–8	
Conning tower	12–10	
Turret face / sides	12–10–8	
9.2 in turret	4	
Decks (3)	1½ , 1, 2½–1	Upper deck armour added
Casements	6	

HMS *King Edward VII.*

The last class of British pre-Dreadnoughts were the *Lord Nelson* class of two ships in the 1904/05 Estimates. These ships were the result of a review of the design of British battleships carried out under a new DNC, Phillip Watts. A review of battleship armament and armour found that:[22]

- 6-inch guns had relatively little destructive effect on the armour of new battleships;
- the impact of heavy shells was very destructive and the lightly armoured secondary guns were nearly always badly damaged and would probably be destroyed before getting into range; and
- heavier armour protection was needed over a larger area of the ship to protect against heavier main armaments.

The Controller of the Navy, Admiral Sir William May, had commissioned studies which suggested that heavier armour and larger guns were needed in the next class of ships to be ordered as the *King Edward VII* class had been criticised for being too large and not having enough firepower. A range of designs was considered. The initial designs combined 12-inch, 9.2-inch and 6-inch guns with various armour combinations but in the later designs the 6-inch guns were dropped in favour of more 9.2-inch guns. At one stage an armament of all twelve or sixteen 10-inch guns was considered but was not carried forward.

It was decided to increase the overall displacement of the ships from 14,000 tons to around 16,000 tons, and in November 1902 a decision was made to increase the side armour protection from 9 to 12 inches. The design process was a long one and as a result the ships were not ordered in the 1903/04 programme; in fact, construction was not started until discussion on the next generation of battleships, the *Dreadnought*, had begun in late 1904. Admiral Fisher, the incoming First Sea Lord, tried to get the *Lord Nelson* and the *Agamemnon* cancelled[23] but it was decided to continue with their building although this was delayed because gun mountings for the ships were diverted to the *Dreadnought* project.

The armour scheme for the *Lord Nelson* class was:[24]

	Inches of armour	
Main belt	12–8	Thickness increased
Fore / aft belt	3–4	Thickness increased aft
Barbettes (12 in)	12–3	Reduced to 3 inches within citadel
Barbettes (9.2 in)	8	
Bulkheads	8	Aft bulkhead not extended below middle deck
Conning tower	12	
Turret face / sides	13½–12	Sides increase to 12 inches and rears to 13 inches
9.2 in turret	7–3	
Decks (3)	1½, 4–2, 3–1	Thickness on middle deck slopes increased
Casements		

The armour plate orders for the *Lord Nelson* class were split among four of the five armour plate companies:[25]

- Armstrong Whitworth made the plates for the 12-inch and 9.2-inch gun-shields and sighting hoods for the *Lord Nelson*.
- Beardmore made bulkheads, deck armour, bow protection, 12-inch barbettes and conning towers for the *Agamemnon*.
- Cammell Laird made bulkheads, 12-inch barbettes, side belt, bow protection, deck armour and conning towers for the *Lord Nelson*.
- Vickers made 9.2-inch shields and sighting hoods for the *Agamemnon*.

The fifth firm, John Brown's, was not given any orders for armour plate for this class of ship.

The *Lord Nelson* class, which overlapped with the building of the *Dreadnought*, was an attempt by the Admiralty to move ahead of developments in other navies rather than to respond to them. Battleship design was, however, developing so fast that the step change from the pre-Dreadnought battleship to the much superior *Dreadnought* rendered the *Lord Nelson* and *Agamemnon* out of date before they were completed.

THE TEST OF BATTLE

There were a number of minor naval conflicts during the pre-Dreadnought era, all of which were studied by the Admiralty as well as other navies and the conclusions were built into future designs. The major naval engagements of the period, involving modern pre-Dreadnoughts, took place as part of the Russo-Japanese War of 1904 and 1905. The origins of the war lay in the two countries' conflicting interests in Korea and Manchuria, and their desires to expand their influence and territories in those areas.

Britain and Japan were both concerned about Russian expansion in the Far East and by the end of the nineteenth century this shared interest brought the two countries closer together. In 1902 they signed the Anglo-Japanese

Alliance, which recognised their interests in the region and allowed either signatory to intervene in China and Korea to protect their vital interests.

Japan had been building up its naval strength since 1897 and had commissioned a whole new fleet of six pre-Dreadnoughts, eight armoured cruisers and eight protected cruisers. Vickers helped to develop the Japanese steel and armour industry but, in spite of this, armour production was limited and most of their battleships were built in Britain.[26]

Ship[27]	Date	Armour	Based on	Builder
Chin-Yen	1884	Harvey	Captured from China	Stettin (Germany)
Yashima	1897	Harvey		Armstrong
Fuji	1897	Harvey		Thames Iron Works
Shikishima	1900	Harvey	British *Majestic* class	Thames Iron Works
Hatsuse	1900	Harvey	British *Majestic* class	Armstrong
Asahi	1900	Harvey	British *Formidable* class	John Brown,
Mikasa	1902	Krupp	British *Formidable* class	Vickers

The battleships were also equipped with modern Barr and Stroud range-finders from Britain. The comparative naval strength at the beginning of the war was:[28]

	Russia		**Japan**
	Pacific fleet	Other	
Battleships	7	20	7
Armoured cruisers	8		10
Protected cruisers	14		17

There were two major naval battles during the war. The first was the Battle of the Yellow Sea (or Shantung), which took place in August 1904 between the Japanese fleet and the Russian Pacific fleet. The second naval battle at Tsushima in May 1905 involved the Russian Baltic fleet after it had sailed 18,000 miles around the Horn of Africa to relieve Port Arthur, which was besieged by the Japanese army.[29]

The latest pre-Dreadnoughts, into which so much investment in new technology had been poured, had never been tested in combat. Naval strategists, from all the major naval powers, were therefore understandably keen to study both of these battles to look for any lessons that they could draw from the conflict about the future direction of their own navies. Britain in particular was interested in the performance of the British-built Japanese battleships.

At the Battle of the Yellow Sea the Japanese battleships began firing at a range of 8,000 to 11,000 yards.[30] At this range the quick-firing 6- and 8-inch guns were ineffective and it was the 12-inch guns which inflicted the damage. The Japanese admiral, Togo, tried to 'cross the T' by sailing his line of battleships across the front of the Russian line, a tactic which would enable his complete fleet to concentrate their fire on the leading ships of the Russian line. This tactic had been tried at the British naval manoeuvres of 1901 and was adopted by the Japanese naval staff the following year. The Russian admiral managed to counteract this Japanese manoeuvre a number of times and eventually they were able to get past the Japanese fleet and tried to escape. The Japanese fleet was able to use its superior speed to close the range to between 7,500 and 7,800 yards and opened fire, hitting the Russian flagship *Cesarevitch* (see illustration below) and killing the Russian admiral. The Russian fleet then dispersed. The flagship, two protected cruisers and four destroyers fled to various neutral ports, where they were interned. The remainder of the Russian fleet sailed to Port Arthur where they were sunk in the harbour by artillery from the besieging Japanese army.

Details of the damage to the *Cesarevitch* were reported in Brassey's *Naval Annual* of 1905:

Diagram number	Description
1	Hit the starboard side and tore a hole 6½ ft sq. but did little damage inside the ship.
2	Hit the side armour and caused a hole 3¼ ft sq.
3 & 13	Hit sides of front and rear turret but caused no damage.
4	Hit the starboard side of the conning tower. This killed five crew and caused the helm to become jammed because of somebody falling against it.
5	Hit the foot of the foremast and killed Admiral Vitgeft.
6, 7 & 8	Hit the funnels.
9	8-inch shell passed through the superstructure and damaged the boat deck.
10	8-inch shell hit in front of the aft 6-inch gun making a hole 4 ½ ft sq.
11	HE hit the roof of the after turret, bulging the roof and killing one man inside the turret.
12	HE shell blew the chart room to pieces.
14	Hit the starboard side 7 ft underwater, the plates and frames were bent and about 150 tons of water entered the ship.
15	HE shell hit the upper deck ripping of planking.

A much larger number of smaller shells were reported to have done no damage.

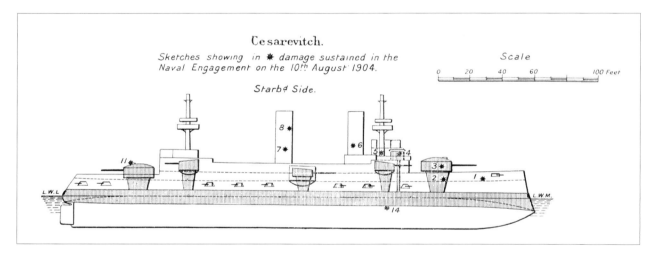

At the Battle of Tsushima, the Russian fleet consisted of thirty-eight ships, which included eleven battleships, three armoured cruisers and five protected cruisers. Of these, three of the battleships were small costal defence ships and the three armoured cruisers were small ships built in the 1880s. The main Russian strength lay in four *Boridino* class battleships of 13,599 tons and the *Oslabya* of 12,600 tons, all of which were built at St. Petersburg.

Admiral Togo set sail to meet the Russian fleet with a force of four battleships and eight armoured cruisers and when the fleets met on 27 May the Japanese managed to 'cross the T' twice before the Russians turned away and tried to head for the Russian base of Vladivostok. They were unable to do this because their maximum speed was 9 knots compared to 15 knots for the Japanese fleet. With the two fleets on a parallel course the action took place at a range of between 7,000 and 7,650 yards. The Japanese gunnery was superior and the *Oslabya* was the first Russian ship to be sunk. Three of the *Borodino* battleships were also sunk and the last of the four, the *Orel*, surrendered along with three of the small coastal defence battleships.

The main conclusions that were drawn for the two major naval battles of the war were related to the importance of guns and of speed.

The damage inflicted on the *Orel* at the battle of Tsushima.

The relative importance of big guns

Unlike the naval engagements in the Sino-Japanese and the Spanish–American wars, the quick-firing guns had done little damage to armoured ships. The importance of the 12-inch guns was demonstrated by an analysis of the hits on the Russian *Borodino* class battleship *Orel* at the Battle of Tsushima.[31]

Novikoff-Priboy, who was a seaman aboard the *Orel*, collected the accounts of many of his fellow sailors while they were in Japanese captivity. He described the effect of the large-calibre shells hitting the *Orel*:

> The enemy high-explosive shells were veritable aerial torpedoes. Of course, as the range increased, the shooting became less accurate, but whatever reached its mark was destructive. The shells did not perforate the armour of our ironclads, but wrought havoc in the upper works, putting guns out of action, destroying the means of communication, starting fires, scattering wounds and death.[32]

Calibre of shell	Number of hits	Weight of shells	
		(lbs)	Percentage
12 inch	5	4,200	38.8%
10 inch	2	980	9.0%
8 inch	9	2,250	20.8%
6 inch	39	3,400	31.4%

Although the larger 12-inch guns proved more effective at long range than expected, there were also supporters for the concept of the 'hail of fire' from smaller quick-firing guns. These included the ex-DNC, Sir William White, who had

retired in 1902, and the US naval strategist Admiral Alfred Mahan. Based on a detailed plot of the battle prepared by US observers, Lt Commander Sims, an influential naval officer who was serving as Director of Target Practice and was later appointed a naval adviser to the president, argued that these conclusions were based on incorrect information.

The importance of speed

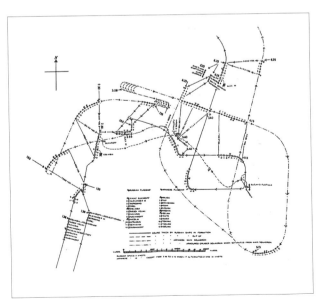

A US plot of the Battle of Tsushima, drawn by Lt R. White (USN), who was an observer at the battle. The plot was used to calculate the 'rate of change of range' at different stages of the action and showed that the majority of hits occurred when the rate of change of range was low.

At both the naval battles of the war the Japanese fleet had an advantage of speed. This enabled them largely to control the way the battles were fought, and meant that the Russian fleet could neither avoid combat nor retreat when required.

William Sims argued that the faster fleet always has:

the great advantage of being able to:

1. Refuse or accept battle.
2. Choose his own range.
3. Control the rate of change of range.
4. Control the compass bearing, thus taking advantage of the weather conditions that favour his own gun fire.[33]

The extent to which these conclusions about the naval engagements of the Russo-Japanese War influenced the development of the 'all-big-gun' battleship, such as the *Dreadnought*, or whether they merely demonstrated trends that had been apparent for some time is debatable. Certainly naval thinkers had been contemplating such ships for some time and the Italian naval architect Vittorio Cuniberti had published an article in the 1903 edition of *Jane's All the World's Fighting Ships* entitled 'An ideal battleship for the British Navy', which was published before the Russo-Japanese War and argued for a fast ship carrying twelve 12-inch guns.[34]

Endnotes

1. Marder, *The Anatomy of British Sea Power*, p. 49.
2. Ibid., p. 49.
3. L. Sondhaus, *Naval Warfare 1815–1914* (Routledge, 2001), p. 165.
4. As quoted (without attribution) in Stacey, 'An Historical Survey of the Manufacture of Naval Armour'.
5. Ibid., Dr. Burton was Research Director at the English Steel Corporation.
6. I have found a number of descriptions of the process, not all of which are the same. I have therefore chosen to use the process described in ibid.
7. *Engineer*, 4 November 1898, p. 438
8. *Engineer*, 24 April 1896, p. 429.
9. Test date 29 September 1898, reported in the *Engineer*, 11 November 1898, p. 470; Brassey 1898, p. 371.
10. Test date 21 July 1898, reported in the *Engineer*, 21 October 1898, p. 402; Brassey 1898, p. 367.
11. Test date 19 July 1897, reported in the *Engineer*, 19 November 1897, p. 493.
12. *Engineer*, 18 November 1898, p. 501.
13. Burt, *British Battleships 1889–1904*, p. 178.
14. Ibid., p. 206; report of a meeting on the construction programme held in the First Lord's room on 7 January 1898.
15. *Engineer*, 20 May 1889, p. 491.
16. Ibid., 27 May 1899, p. 515.
17. Burt, *British Battleships 1889–1904*, pp. 190 and 232 respectively.
18. *Engineer*, 22 March 1901, p. 296.
19. Burt, *British Battleships 1889–1904*, p. 265.
20. SIMT, Armour Plate Pool ledgers, M560 are discussed further in Chapter 9
21. Burt, *British Battleships 1889–1904*, p. 267.
22. Ibid., p. 312.
23. K. McBride, '*Lord Nelson* and *Agamemnon*', in J. Jordan, *Warship 2005* (Conway, 2005), p. 66.
24. Burt, *British Battleships 1889–1904*, p. 320.
25. SIMT, Armour Plate Pool ledgers, M560
26. T. A. Brassey (ed.), *The Naval Annual 1905* (J. Griffin & Co.).
27. The Japanese spellings are taken from ibid., p. 109.
28. Sondhaus, *Naval Warfare 1815–1914*, p. 188.
29. Ibid., pp. 187–92.
30. Adm. Sir C. Bridge, 'The Russo-Japanese Naval Campaign of 1904', in Brassey, *The Naval Annual 1905*, p. 152.
31. Brown, *Warrior to Dreadnought*, p. 175.
32. A. Novikoff-Priboy, *Tsushima: Grave of a Floating City* (G. Allen & Unwin Ltd, 1937), p. 172.
33. William S. Sims papers, Box 96, Manuscript Division, Library of Congress, Washington DC.
34. *Jane's All the World's Fighting Ships*, 1903, pp. 407–9.

CHAPTER 4

THE 'ALL-BIG-GUN' BATTLESHIP

The *Dreadnought* was the outcome of a process of development that covered a number of fields. The development of Krupp armour, discussed in Chapter 3, meant that more protection could be provided for less weight, and parallel developments in a number of other fields were equally influential on the development of the next generation of battleships.

THE DEVELOPMENT OF LONG-RANGE GUNNERY

In order to be effective over longer ranges two technologies need to be developed: the ability of the guns themselves to propel the shells accurately over a long distance, and the ability to aim the guns quickly and keep them on target. Rapid development was taking place in both these areas.

The guns

Over the period of the pre-Dreadnoughts the power of the guns fitted to battleships increased significantly. This was due to a combination of an improvement in the propellant and the techniques of manufacturing the guns themselves.

The early breech-loading (BL) 12-inch guns used quick-burning powder as a propellant. The force of this explosion meant that the pressure on the base of the shell was at its maximum before the shell started to move, fell almost at once and decreased rapidly as the shell neared the muzzle of the gun. The guns were therefore thick at the breech to contain the explosion and were short, as there was no benefit in a longer length.

The invention of cordite, which was a mixture of nitrocellulose, nitroglycerine and petroleum jelly, meant that the speed of burning could be more easily controlled and the pressure maintained all the way along the barrel. Cordite was introduced into the British navy in the early 1890s and it meant that the guns needed to have a larger chamber and could be longer to maximise the time the pressure was on the shell thus increasing muzzle velocity. The British used wire-wound guns to increase the strength of the barrel and the development of the technology over the pre-Dreadnought period is shown in the table below:[1]

Gun	Length	Ships to which it was fitted	Weight (tons)	Shell weight (lbs)	Muzzle velocity (ft sec)	Muzzle energy (ft tons)	Energy per ton of gun (ft tons)
12-inch Mark VIII	35 calibre	*Majestic* class *Canopus* class	46	851	2,362	38,027	718
12-inch Mark IX	40 calibre	*Formidable* class *Bulwark* class *Duncan* class *King Edward VII* class	50	851	2,474	36,285	724
12-inch Mark X	45 calibre	*Lord Nelson* class	58	851	2,894	49,575	853

Armstrong's, among other firms, had been producing guns for many years and had developed the guns for HMS *Warrior* in 1860. They and Vickers were now making an increasing contribution to the designs of the guns fitted to the pre-Dreadnoughts and gun design and manufacture was no longer restricted to the Royal Gun Factory at Woolwich, which now had to buy the forgings from private manufacturers.

The diagram below shows the inner (rifled) and outer 'A' tubes, the wire winding and the 'B' tube and jacket covering on the outside. The 'B' tube and jacket are fastened together by the 'C' hoop.

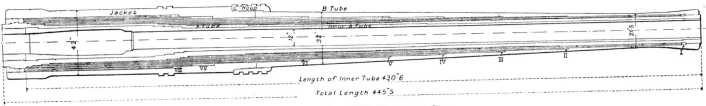

FIG. 1.—12-IN. MARK VIII. WIRE-WOUND GUN.

Over 100 miles of 0.25 × 0.06-inch wire strip was wound round the 'A' tubes. The 'B' tube was then heated in a vertical furnace and fitted over the wire.

The Mark VIII barrel had a life of around 220 rounds, after which it had to be sent back to an ordinance factory to have the lining replaced.

Gunnery

At the beginning of the ironclad era the largest naval guns had a maximum effective range of about 700–1,000 yards.[2] At this range the trajectory was virtually flat and the time of flight was only a few seconds so the navy adopted the practice of horizontal fire – firing 'on the roll'.[3] By the late 1880s the range of guns had increased but their effective firing range in good conditions was still only around 2,000 yards. At this range the trajectory was still virtually flat and guns continued to be laid horizontally.[4] With horizontal firing at short range there was no need for range-finding and no effective scheme was developed.

The introduction of quick-firing guns, as their name suggests, increased the rate of firing by combining the shell with the propellant in a brass case with a primer in its base. This meant that there was only one thing to load into the gun, whereas the previous system that involved loading the shell, then the propellant, in a cloth bag and then the percussion mechanism to ignite the propellant. In quick-firing guns the brass case also sealed the breech allowing a lighter, cone-shaped breech mechanism that was easier and quicker to use.

Although small-calibre quick-firing guns had been in use for a number of years as a defence against torpedo boats, the first larger-calibre quick-firing guns on a battleship were the ten 40-calibre 6-inch guns of the secondary armament of the *Royal Sovereign* class which were agreed in August 1888.[5] The guns were wire-wound and were designed by the Elswick Ordinance Company (owned by Sir W. G. Armstrong, Mitchell & Co.) and manufactured by the Woolwich Royal Gun Factory. They were capable of firing between five and seven rounds per minute, and extra ammunition needed to be carried.

The new quick-firing guns were capable of greater accuracy over a longer range, and so the question of range-finding was referred to the Director of Naval Ordinance (Captain John Fisher) in 1889. He concluded that a 'simple and easily manipulated range-finder suitable for use on board ship would be a great advantage'. After two years of discussion an advertisement was published for a range-finder 'capable of measuring up to at least 3,000 yards with a maximum error of 3%'.[6] A committee was set up to evaluate the four responses, which were tested on the cruiser *Arethusa*. A device designed by Archibald Barr and William Stroud, two professors of engineering and physics at the Yorkshire College in Leeds,[i] was selected and was found to be accurate to 1%. The range-finder worked by measuring the angle between two lines to the target from lenses 4½ feet apart.

The firm of Barr and Stroud was then set up in Glasgow in 1893 to manufacture the range-finders. In November 1893 they exhibited their range-finder at Armstrong's artillery range at Silloth in Cumberland (now Cumbria) to observers from several European countries, the USA and Japan. The *Engineer* reported that 'the visitors amused themselves by taking the distances of all the surrounding objects. The ease with which the instrument was understood and manipulated was most remarkable and the visitors were fairly astounded by the accuracy of these readings.'[7]

Although reading the range might have been easy at the Silloth range it was more complicated on a moving ship, with the potential additional complication of poor weather conditions. As ranges of guns increased, gunnery officers needed a way to measure range accurately over a longer distance, calculate the range as the direction of the target changed, and adjust the direction (known as the deflection) to allow for the time the shell was in flight.

In 1902 Lt Dumaresq invented a trigonometric device (named the Dumaresq) into which could be entered the course and speed of the firing ship and the target (which had to be estimated) and the bearing of the target. From these the slide rule calculated the change of range rate and the deflection. In 1904 the Admiralty commissioned Vickers to produce the 'Vickers clock', which could generate ranges independently of observations of the target. The clock was powered by a clockwork motor that could be set at certain speeds depending on the change of range rate. The pointer was then set to the initial range and the clock generated the range at any given moment, provided of course that the target did not alter the change of range rate by altering course!

By 1903 Admiralty firing trials had shown that the effective range of large-calibre guns had increased to 8,000 yards and in 1904 they issued a requirement for a range-finder that was accurate to 1% at 7,000 yards and could take ranges up to 10,000 yards with a proportionally increased error. Although the trials of the two competing range-finders did not take place until

---

i   Now the University of Leeds. Barr later moved to become the Regius Professor of Civil Engineering and Mechanics at the University of Glasgow.

1906, the search for such an instrument shows the range at which the Admiralty expected battles to be fought at the time when the *Dreadnought* was being designed.

As a result of the trials a Barr and Stroud range-finder with a 9-foot base was selected, twice the width of the original model.

New techniques in gunlaying and training

In 1898 Captain Percy Scott, captain of the protected cruiser HMS *Scylla* and considered the 'father of modern gunnery', altered the gun-sights of his quick-firing guns. He fitted telescopic sights that were independent of the recoil of the gun instead of the open sights with which they had previously been fitted. He also changed the gearing on the elevating mechanism so that the guns were easier to train. His gunlayers were then trained in keeping the guns aimed continuously, by changing the elevation to counteract the ship's roll and pitch and the direction to counteract the ship's yawing. As a result of these changes and the training in continuous aiming, the *Scylla*'s score in the Annual Prize Firing rose to fifty-six hits out of seventy shots (80%). This was six times better than she had previously achieved. Scott repeated his performance in HMS *Terrible* in 1901 with larger 6-inch guns. It was not possible to transfer this methodology to the 12-inch guns as they could not be trained quickly enough, and the mechanisms could not respond fast enough. In April 1904 Scott was made captain of *Excellent*, the navy's gunnery school, to spread his methods across the navy.

The Annual Prize Firing, a test for British naval gunnery, took place between 1884 and 1904. Ships steamed at low speed on a set course and fired at a stationary target at ranges of between 1,400 and 1,600 yards. The success rate was rarely more than 50% of hits to shots fired.

Scott was appointed Inspector of Target Practice in February 1905 and changed this system to a gunlayer's test and battle practice. In the new test gunners shot at a stationary target at a range of 2,000 yards; in battle practice firing was from a ship steaming past a stationary target at a range of between 5,000 and 7,000 yards.

Scott was a strong believer in director firing, in which all the big guns were controlled from a central point. He encountered much resistance on this but it was eventually adopted and British Dreadnoughts began to be fitted with this system from 1914 onwards.

The introduction of turbines to large ships

The idea of producing power from the spinning of turbine blades had occurred to more than one engineer. It was, however, the Honourable Charles Algernon Parsons who patented the idea in 1884. Ten years later he set up the marine Steam Turbine Co. at Wallsend on the River Tyne and applied for a patent for 'propelling a vessel by means of a steam turbine, which turbine actuates the propeller or paddle shaft directly or through gearing'. The company built the yacht *Turbina*, initially with a single turbine and propeller, but later fitted with three turbines: one high pressure, one intermediate pressure and one low pressure. Each turbine drove a separate propeller. The trials of the *Turbina* were attended by Sir William White (the DNC) and the navy's Engineer-in-Chief, Sir John Durston. Parsons later showed off the *Turbina*'s speed at the Diamond Jubilee Fleet Review of 1897.

After Parsons had demonstrated the effectiveness of the marine turbine, the Admiralty ordered a destroyer, HMS *Viper*, powered by two high-pressure and two low-pressure turbines each driving a shaft. The *Viper* achieved 31.5 knots over six runs on its trials. Armstrong's also built a destroyer powered by turbines and sold it to the Admiralty; unfortunately, the *Cobra* sank on its trials due to structural weaknesses in the hull.

The turbines proved that they were effective in smaller vessels but it remained to be seen if they could be equally effective in larger vessels. Their key weakness was that the turbines were only efficient when spinning at high speed and this gave the ships fitted with them a high fuel consumption.

A MOMENTUM FOR CHANGE

Changes in offensive and defensive technologies led to a rethink about battleship design in all the major navies and contributed to a number of develpopments:

- The increasing range of torpedoes meant that fleet actions had to be fought outside the range of torpedoes. It was thought that by 1905 the effective range of torpedoes would be around 6,000 yards.

- Because of the introduction of range-finders, long-range gunnery had become practical. Exercises in the Mediterranean in 1899 suggested that it would be possible to hit targets at 8,000 yards.

- The best method of ranging guns at long range was to fire salvoes of at least eight guns. These were easy to observe and when the salvo straddled the target the exact range could be determined.

- The reports of the first battle of the Russo-Japanese War at Port Arthur showed that the heaviest guns did the most damage and were the most accurate at long range. The Battle of Tsushima in 1904, after *Dreadnought* had been designed, confirmed these conclusions.

- British fleet manoeuvres in 1901 in the Mediterranean showed the advantage of speed in enveloping the enemy and concentrating the full weight of the fleet's fire. This was also demonstrated in 1904 by Admiral Togo at the Battle of Tsushima.

In Britain the Chief Constructor, Henry Deadman, who was standing in for Sir William White while he was ill, suggested in

1902 that Britain should build ships of such size and cost that other powers would be unable to match them.[8] His idea was not supported by the Controller of the Navy, Admiral W. H. May. Philip Watts, who succeeded as DNC, and the Assistant Director J. H. Narbuth also suggested that an all-big-gun armament was adopted. Their ideas were likewise rejected.

In Italy the naval designer Colonel Vittorio Cuniberti put forward a proposal for a fast, all-big-gun battleship. When his ideas were rejected he published a paper that was printed in the 1903 edition of *Jane's All the World's Fighting Ships*: 'An Ideal Battleship for the British Fleet'. This argued for an armament of twelve 12-inch guns and a speed of 24 knots. Within the 17,000 tons displacement he advocated, this was probably impractical using reciprocating engines.[9]

In the United States, Lt Matt Signor published a paper in the 1902 US Navy Institute *Proceedings* in favour of a big-gun battleship with six 12-inch and six 10-inch guns.[10] In the debate that followed his proposals, gunnery expert Professor P. R. Alger argued for an armament of eight 12-inch guns. The 12-inch gun was also favoured by the US General Board for war games in 1903 and 1904.

Lt Commander William Sims, the US Director of Target Practice from 1902 to 1909, was requested by President Theodore Roosevelt to comment on Thomas Mahon's article[11] on the Battle of Tsushima.[ii] Mahon had argued that the battle demonstrated the case for smaller ships with a mixed armament. William Sims used the opportunity to present the case for the all-big-gun battleship.[12] His conclusions were that:

1. We should design our battleships so that they will at least equal those of our possible enemies in all of their principal fighting qualities – speed, gun power and protection.
2. Subject to the above requirements, it is always desirable to increase the speed a certain reasonable amount at the expense of an equivalent weight in gun-power – that a certain increase of speed is, in reality, an increase of battle gun-power.
3. It is always desirable to substitute heavy turret guns, such as 12 inch, for the equivalent weight of the usual intermediate guns, 6 inch etc. In other words the all-big-gun battleship affords the greatest possible capacity of effective hitting.
4. In order to simplify fire control and attain its maximum efficiency, all the main battery guns of ships of whatever type should be of the same calibre.
5. For similar reasons, all of the torpedo defence guns should be of the same calibre.
6. Very important tactical advantages are obtained by the concentration of many heavy guns on each large vessel of high speed, and by the intense concentration of fleet gun-fire, due to the compactness of the fleet.

7. The tactical advantage of size, speed and diminished numbers are of much greater importance than any advantages to be obtained from an increased number of smaller and slower vessels that can be built for the same total cost.

An amended version of the letter was circulated by the Naval Institute within the US Navy and was later published.

These developments in naval thinking led to a number of countries developing programmes for an 'all-big-gun' battleship. In 1904 the Admiralty received information that:

1. The United States Navy had designed two ships of 16,000 tons with eight 12-inch guns. They had originally wanted to design a larger ship with ten 12-inch guns but were prevented from doing so by Congressional limits on the size of battleships.
2. As a result of their experience in their recent war both Japan and Russia were planning battleships with eight or more 12-inch guns. Japan had ordered two 'all-big-gun' battleships in 1904, before the Battle of Tsushima.

DESIGNING THE *DREADNOUGHT*

Admiral Jackie Fisher is often described as the driving force behind the *Dreadnought*. While we have seen that the move towards an 'all-big-gun' battleship was happening internationally, Fisher was certainly a key driving force in shaping ideas about the form the new ships would take and in ensuring that Britain was the first to launch such a ship.

When he became the new First Sea Lord Jackie Fisher set up a Committee on Designs. Fisher chaired the Committee and the other members were:[13]

Rear Admiral Prince Louis of Battenburg	:	Director of Naval Intelligence
Rear Admiral Sir John Durstan	:	Engineer-in-Chief of the Fleet
Rear Admiral Sir Alfred Winsloe	:	Commander Submarine and Torpedo Flotillas
Captain H. G. Jackson	:	Controller
Captain J. R. Jellicoe	:	Director of Naval Ordinance
Capitan C. E. Madden	:	Naval Assistant to the Controller
Capitan Reginald Bacon	:	Naval Assistant to the First Sea Lord
Phillip Watts	:	Director of Naval Construction
Professor J. H. Biles	:	Naval Architecture, Glasgow University
Lord Kelvin	:	Engineer
Sir John Thornycroft	:	Shipbuilder
Alexander Gracie	:	Fairfield Shipbuilding
A. E. Froude	:	Superintendent, Admiralty Experimental Works, Haslar
W. H. Gard	:	Chief Constructor, Portsmouth Dockyard

---

ii   Known in the USA as the Battle of the Sea of Japan.

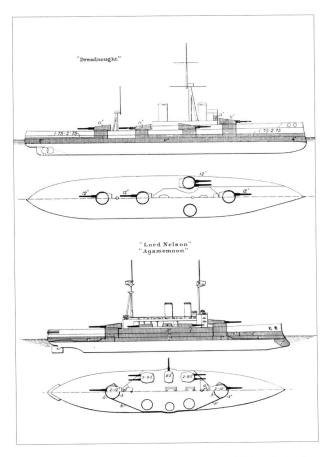

The layout of the *Dreadnought* compared to the earlier *Lord Nelson*, showing the heavier guns and lighter armour protection.

A range of options for the layout of the armament was considered; the final design that was agreed on had ten 12-inch guns in five twin turrets. Three of the turrets were on the centre line with a twin turret on either side.

The armour protection was lighter than that of the *Lord Nelson* class as, in line with Jackie Fisher's thinking, the emphasis was placed on firepower and speed. The principal differences in the armour protection were:

- The thickness of the main belt was reduced by 1 inch as the ship was longer and the additional weight was considered too heavy.
- The upper level of the belt was omitted, as there was no secondary armament to protect.
- Upper deck armour was omitted and middle and lower deck armour increased.
- The rear turret protection was decreased slightly.
- Longitudinal bulkheads were fitted to protect the ship from an internal explosion if hit by a torpedo.

Initially it had been proposed that the *Dreadnought* should be fitted with reciprocating stream engines, but these were abandoned in favour of steam turbines. The main advantages of this were:

- Savings were achieved in space, weight and costs.
- They were easier to operate and needed fewer crew.
- They had better fuel economy at high speed.
- They had a reduced risk of battle damage as they were fitted lower in the ship.

The *Dreadnought* was fitted with four Parsons direct-drive reaction turbines, two high-pressure turbines for high speeds and two low-pressure turbines for cruising. How radical this decision was can perhaps be seen in the fact that Vickers, Maxim & Sons, which won the contract to make the machinery for HMS *Dreadnought*, did not take out a licence for making Parson's turbines until 22 September 1905 and signed the contract for the *Dreadnought*'s machinery on 17 October 1905.[14]

Endnotes

1. Brassey (ed.), *Naval Annual 1905*, p. 388.
2. P. Padfield, *Guns at Sea* (Hugh Evelyn, 1973)
3. Sumida, *In Defence of Naval Supremacy*, p. 71.
4. Padfield, *Guns at Sea*.
5. Burt, *British Battleships 1889–1904*, p. 77.
6. Sumida, *In Defence of Naval Supremacy*, from 'Range-finders for Naval Service', Admiralty Gunnery Branch, MRPQ/DNO July–Dec 1899, Nat Lib Min Def., p. 9.
7. *Engineer*, 1 December 1893, p. 502.
8. R. A. Burt, *British Battleships of World War I* (Seaforth Publishing, 2012), p. 21.
9. Sumida, *In Defence of Naval Supremacy*, p. 47.
10. N. Freidman, *US Battleships* (Annapolis, 1985), quoted in Brown, *Warrior to Dreadnought*, p. 187.
11. Proceedings of the United States Naval Institute, June 1906.
12. William S. Sims papers, Box 96, Manuscript Division, Library of Congress, Washington DC.
13. Brown, *Warrior to Dreadnought*, p. 189.
14. Vickers Board Minutes, Minute Book 5, CU1363, pp. 195 and 197.

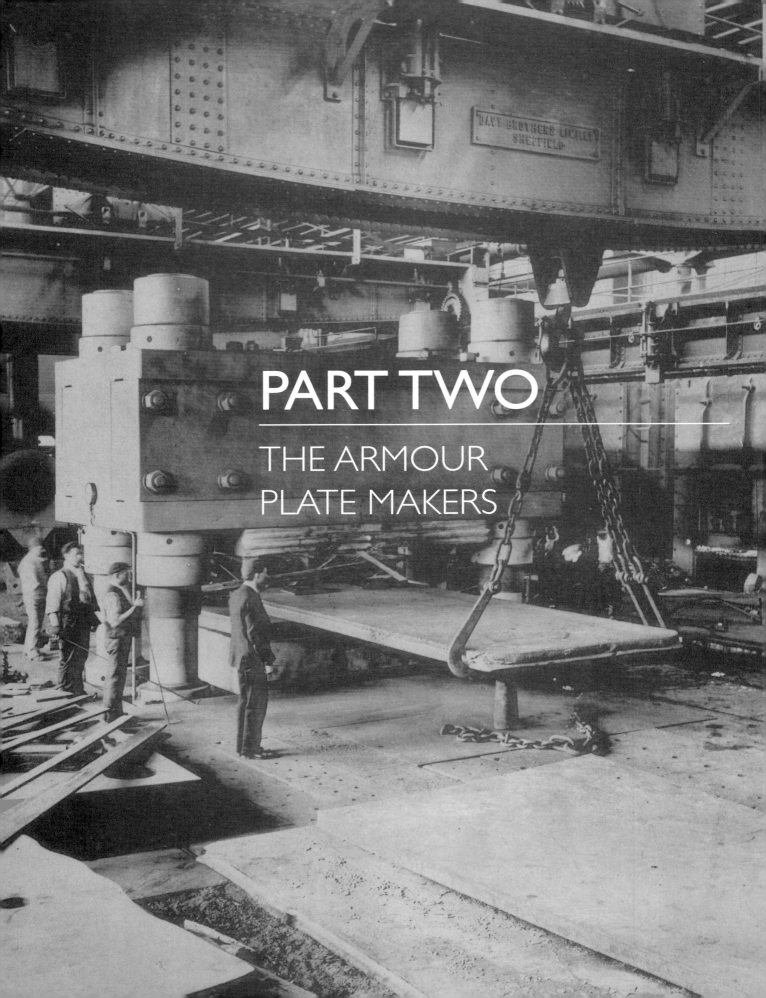

PART TWO

THE ARMOUR PLATE MAKERS

INTRODUCTION

In the 1880s there were two main armour makers in Britain, both based in Sheffield. Both John Brown's and Charles Cammell's companies manufactured compound armour to their own patents, but of the two, Charles Cammell were the most successful and their patent was the one that was most widely adopted by foreign navies and armour makers. In the latter part of the nineteenth century, with the advent of steel armour, Vickers, Sons & Maxim began to manufacture armour as well and by the early twentieth century they had grown to become the dominant producer, playing a leading role in improving the quality of armour plate. Armstrong Whitworth and William Beardmore later joined these three Sheffield companies in the armour plate business. By the beginning of the First World War all of these five companies had expanded the range of their activities and each was able to provide a complete range of armaments from shipbuilding to guns and shells as well as the armour plate that is the main subject area of this book.

Even though Armstrong Whitworth manufactured armour at Openshaw in Manchester and William Beardmore made theirs at Parkhead in Glasgow, the centre of the armour-making industry was in Sheffield, miles from the sea. The iron industry had developed in Sheffield because water from the Pennine hills provided water power for the early manufacturers. As iron and engineering became larger and steam power replaced water the Sheffield companies built larger works close to each other in the flatter Lower Don Valley area of the city, where they were served by the railway network, which enabled them to transport their armour plates to the shipyards on the coasts.

CHAPTER 5

THE SHEFFIELD IRON MAKERS

At the beginning of the age of armour plate there were a range of firms involved in its production, and this continued up to the 1880s. However, as armour plate became more sophisticated, and the Harvey and Krupp patents introduced complex cementation processes, higher levels of investment and engineering knowledge were required to manufacture the latest types of armour. By the beginning of the twentieth century, the number of manufacturers had contracted to five firms, all of whom had specialised armour plants with expensive investment in specialised machinery. The Sheffield iron and steel companies of John Brown and Cammell Laird were early entrants into the armour-making business and dominated the industry in the latter years of the nineteenth century. They were later joined by a third Sheffield firm, Vickers, Sons & Maxim, and the three Sheffield companies, all situated within a short distance of each other in the lower Don Valley, continued to play an important role in armour manufacture up to the end of the First World War.

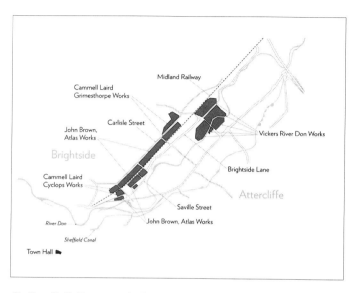

The three Sheffield armour works clustered together in the Lower Don Valley, north-east of the city centre.

JOHN BROWN & CO.

The development of the company

John Brown was born just off Fargate, in the centre of Sheffield, in 1816. At the age of fourteen he started working for Earle Horton & Co., which manufactured files and cutlery. He became a salesman for the company, travelling throughout the country. In 1838 he decided to set up his own steelworks and started in a small foundry at Orchard Street in the centre of the city. He patented a conical spring and buffer for railway carriages and, based on the success of this, the business expanded. In 1853 he purchased the 3-acre Queen's Works in Savile Street and renamed it the Atlas Works where he centralised all his activities. In 1859 he bought more land on the north side of the Midland railway line.

In 1856, after six years of experimentation, the engineer and inventor Henry Bessemer announced in a paper to the British Association for the Advancement of Science that he had found a new way of making steel in large quantities. He decided to divide the country into five 'iron districts' and to license his process to one company in each district for a price of £10,000. John Brown's were one of these five companies. Bessemer had also set up a factory himself in Sheffield next to the Atlas Works. John Brown and John Devonshire Ellis, one of the two new partners whom John Brown had brought into the business, decided to invest in a large Bessemer plant at the Atlas Works and by 1859 they had given up the production of steel from puddled iron. From 1860 onwards John Brown's pioneered the introduction of steel rails in place of iron rails and gained large orders from abroad. They had greater difficulty in persuading British railways of the advantage of steel rail and apparently substituted a steel rail for an iron one in in the middle of the night, later pointing out its improved performance to the railway company. By 1865 steel had been adopted by British rail companies and John Brown's had gained a large share of the market.

When he took on new partners in 1859 the firm became a limited company, John Brown & Company. By 1864 it had expanded its armour plate business, which required large investments in new equipment, resulting in the company experiencing cashflow problems. Apparently it was dependent on the goodwill of a Mr Barber, the manager of the Sheffield Banking Company, who advanced sufficient funds to pay the workforce on a week-by-week basis.[1] When the Limited Liability Companies Act was passed the directors took advantage of this to form a limited liability company, John Brown & Co. Ltd, with a capital of £1m. The directors of the new company were:

The three previous directors:

John Brown	Chairman
John D. Ellis	Managing Director
William Bragge	Managing Director

Plus:

James Ashbury	Based in London
E. L. S. Benzon	Based in London
John Cheetham MP	Vice Chairman & Manchester industrialist
James Holden	Based in Manchester
Henry Ponchin	Industrial Chemist from Manchester
Charles Stewart	Partner in rail engineering firm in Manchester
Benjamin Whitworth MP	Owner of a cotton factory near Manchester

J. D. Ellis, Chairman of John Brown from 1870 to 1906 and a key figure in the armour plate industry.

John Brown was a prominent figure in Sheffield and he became mayor of the city in 1861 and Master Cutler in 1865–66.[i] It has been suggested that he found working within the constraints of a public company difficult[2] and in 1870, after disagreements about expansion, he left the company. He undertook not to set up any new firm within 50 miles of Sheffield but in 1873, with his nephew George Brown, he formed the steel company Brown, Bayley and Dixon & Co., based only half a mile away from Atlas Works. This company later became Brown, Bayley Steel Works.

The new public company expanded during the early 1870s under its new chairman, John Devonshire Ellis, and it took interest in iron ore mines in Spain as well as buying two collieries in South Yorkshire. As the decade progressed there was an increase in foreign competition in the iron and steel business. As a result, the wages of the workforce were reduced by 12.5% and hours were also reduced. In 1879 no dividend was paid to the shareholders.

In 1890 the armour plate business picked up after the passing of the Naval Defence Act in 1899 (see Chapter 2); Captain Tolmie John Tresidder, who had been the manager of the armour plate works, and was probably the country's leading expert on armour plate, was appointed to the board.

By the end of the nineteenth century the Atlas works was producing about 94,500 tons of iron and steel products a year, made up as follows:[3]

	Tons per year
Armour plates	10,000
Forgings	5,000
Flues	2,000
Castings	2,500
Railway material	20,000
Pig iron	45,000
Other	10,000

John Brown's were now making a large number of marine products for both warships and merchant steamers. As well as armour plate they made boilers, flues, tubes, engine shafting and forgings. In 1899 John Brown's decided to purchase the shipyard of Clydebank Engineering and Shipbuilding Co. on the Clyde to provide it with an outlet for all of these marine products. The yard cost the company £933,925.

In 1902 John Brown's and Thomas Firth and Sons, another major Sheffield steel firm, exchanged shares. Firth's were well known for their production of shells and in particular the Firth armour-piercing 'Rendable shell', which they first produced in 1903.

The two remained separate companies with one nominee from Firth's on the John Brown Board of Directors and two nominees from John Brown's on Firth's.[4] This arrangement lasted until 1930 when they merged to form Firth Brown.

ARMOUR MAKING

John Brown's were one of the first British firms to begin making iron armour plates and submitted their first successful armour plate in 1861. John Brown's interest in the subject was aroused during a trip to France where he observed the *Gloire* being built. Following the death of J. D. Ellis, the former chairman of John Brown's, the *Manchester Guardian* published a letter from James Johnson. He disputed the *Guardian's* claim that John Brown had rolled the first British armour and claimed this honour for Samuel Beale & Co. of Park Gate Iron Works in Rotherham. He said that when he was chief engineer at Beale's the company replaced their armour plate mill with a larger plant for rolling ordinary boiler and ships' plates. He claimed that 'some of the old hands working for me at the time told me of the Sunday visits paid by officials of

---

i   The Master Cutler is head of the Company of Cutlers of Hallamshire and acts as an ambassador for Sheffield industry.

the Atlas Works to Park Gate, to make sketches of the rolling mills, the heating furnaces and the apparatus for handling the heavy plates.'[5]

John Brown's first rolling mill for armour had rollers 24 inches in diameter and was driven by two beam engines of 300 horsepower. This mill was able to roll the early plates commissioned for ships such as HMS *Black Prince*, which had 4½-inch armour, but as the demand for thicker armour grew the company spent £250,000 on installing a new rolling mill with 32-inch rollers. The first plates rolled by this mill in April 1863, witnessed by the Lords of the Admiralty, were 12 inches thick and 20 feet long.[6]

As production increased in the new plant the number of people employed in the armour works increased from 200 in 1861 to 4,000 by 1867 while the size of the site had grown to 21 acres.

John Brown's were responsible for a number of important developments in the armour-making process:

• In 1871 J. D. Ellis began experimenting with cementation of the face of iron armour but the results were disappointing and the patent was allowed to lapse.

• In 1877 they patented their own system of fusing iron and steel plates to make compound armour by a slightly different method than that adopted by Cammell's.

• The Tresidder chilling process[7] developed in 1891 was a method of hardening the surface of armour plate by spraying it with high-pressure water. The patents for this process were bought by the Harvey companies and combined with Harvey's original process to make Harveyised plates.

CAMMELL LAIRD

The development of the company

Charles Cammell was born in Hull in January 1810 and moved to Sheffield in about 1830. He worked as a salesman for the firm of Ibbotson, based at the Globe Works, which made files and cutlery. He left the company when trade declined in 1837 and set up his own steel and file-making company with the brothers Thomas (the bookkeeper and accountant at Ibbotson's) and Henry Johnson. The company was known as Johnson, Cammell & Co. As trade picked up the firm prospered, making products for the expanding rail industry. In 1849 the firm opened a London office. The huge growth in the mileage of railway track in Britain in the 1840s provided a base on which the company, like other Sheffield firms, could expand their operations and they were one of the first to build a new works in the Lower Don Valley. The Cyclops works covered 2 acres between Savile Street and the new railway line and was opened in 1845.

When Thomas Johnson died in 1852 Cammell formed a short-lived partnership with the railway engineer Edward Bury which only lasted three years. The firm was reconstituted as Charles Cammell & Company in 1855.[8] The firm continued to expand and had a network of overseas agents in New York, Philadelphia and Boston. Four years later they had also opened offices in Berlin, Copenhagen, St Petersburg, Moscow and Hamilton (Canada). The adoption of the Bessemer steel process and the growth in the export trade meant that they outgrew their existing premises and in 1861 they acquired additional land at the Cyclops Works, increasing the size of the site to around 20 acres. They took out a licence for the Bessemer process, which was now being licensed more widely, and built a new works and steel rail mill. In addition the firm built another new works on Grimesthorpe Road in 1863, a mile north-east of the Cyclops Works. In 1864 they acquired the steelworks at Penistone near Sheffield.

In 1863 Cammell's began producing their own puddled iron at the Cyclops Works and within a three-year period had built forty-two furnaces. The rapid expansion of Charles Cammell & Co. required a large amount of investment. In order to gain greater access to the necessary capital the company converted to a limited company in 1864 and the following year it became a publically limited company with a capital of £1 million. The new company was known as Charles Cammell & Company Ltd. The new board of directors consisted of eleven people: Cammell himself as chairman, three men from the south-east of England, one from Doncaster, one from Liverpool, four from Manchester, and the managing director, George Wilson. Wilson was a relative and protégé of Charles Cammell (Cammell had sponsored his schooling from the age of nine and had put him through university), who had joined Johnson Cammell on leaving university in 1851 and had risen rapidly through the firm.

Cammell's began the process of switching from Bessemer steel to the more efficient Siemens open-hearth process in 1867 and over the next few years this led to large scale production at the Grimesthorpe Works. The company sought to reduce costs and increase its security through the purchase of mines as well as acquiring additional ironworks. By 1885 the company consisted of:

- Cyclops Steel and Iron Works, Sheffield (the company's headquarters);
- Grimesthorpe Ordnance, Tyre and Spring Works, Sheffield;
- Yorkshire Steel Works, Penistone;
- Derwent Steel and Iron Works, Workington;
- Old and New Oaks Collieries, Barnsley; and
- iron ore mines, near Whitehaven.

As so much of Cammell's production went into naval shipbuilding there were clear advantages in being able to build the ships as well as arm them. John Brown and Vickers had already acquired shipyards and there was a risk that Cammell's might be placed at a disadvantage. Cammell's identified the company of Laird Brothers, which had been founded in 1824 and begun shipbuilding at Birkenhead in 1828, as a possible partner. It had become John Laird, Sons & Co. in 1860 when the founder's two sons joined the board and after the retirement of the founder, William Laird, it changed its name again to Messrs Laird Brothers.

Laird's was in need of additional capital to expand its operations and also bought most of its armour plate from Cammell's. A merger was therefore advantageous to both sides and in October 1903 the Cammell shareholders agreed to the purchase of Laird's. The new company which was formed was called Cammell Laird & Company. It had a capital of £2.5 million compared to Laird's £450,000 prior to the merger.

Armour making

In 1863 Charles Cammell's followed the lead set by their neighbour John Brown and began making wrought-iron armour plates in response to demand from the Admiralty. They submitted their first two rolled armour plates of 4½ and 5½ inches to HMS *Excellent*, the Royal Navy's gunnery school in Portsmouth, which were tested on 13 November 1863; both were awarded an Order of Merit of A1.[9]

The photo on the right is labelled as being for the *Lord Clyde*. In actual fact the distribution of the indentations from the test shells exactly matches one of the plates that Cammell's submitted to HMS *Excellent*, the navy's gunnery school in Portsmouth, for testing on 13 November 1863. The plate was made by rolling and was 15 feet 7 inches long and 3 feet 5 inches tall. The test consisted of it being fired at eleven

A 5½-inch wrought-iron plate made by C. Cammell and tested on 13 November 1863. This was probably the first armour plate sent for testing by the company.

times by a gun firing a 68 lb cast iron shot, at a range of 200 yards. The officer in charge of the tests, Captain A. Cooper Key, said that the plate was tough and capable of withstanding repeated blows in the same vicinity. He awarded the plate the highest Figure of Merit, A1, which can be seen, which can be seen on the plate. The section of the plate that has been cut out of the bottom right corner was used for testing the mechanical properties of the plate. The mislabelling is perhaps due to the company not wishing to say that the plate was 'for the *Lord Clyde*' until they had seen how it performed (Cammell's described it as 'experimental' when they were submitting it for testing). In 1864 Cammell's won their first orders of armour plates for the *Lord Clyde* and the *Royal Alfred*, both wooden-hulled ships with armour cladding.

Cammell's continued to invest in their armour-making plant. In 1868, although the company had allocated £25,000 investment for the Grimesthorpe armour works, the Admiralty complained about the armour for HMS *Captain* which they said had been inadequately planed. Cammell's had no alternative but to respond to the Admiralty's complaints or risk losing the business. George Wilson advised the board that:

> There is no alternative but to meet the demands made upon us by adopting the means of finishing our Armour as we are able to roll it, and thus to keep faith with our deliveries, for unless this be done, the Admiralty will, we are assured, immediately proceed to encourage others to re-enter the trade and thus create anew such competition as will again result in low and almost un-remunerative prices.[10]

As competition in the rail industry increased at home and other countries increased their own manufacturing base, the attractions of special steels, particularly armour plate, became more apparent. The fact that the two major armour plate makers (Charles Cammell and John Brown) were neighbours in the Don Valley in Sheffield made co-operation between the companies easy and enabled them to maintain high profit margins. The *Engineer* magazine reported rumours circulating in the press that the high cost of armoured ships was due to the fact that the two firms 'actually contrive not to compete with each other.'[11]

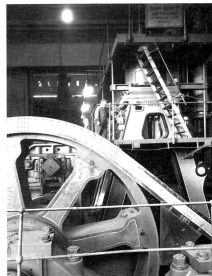

ABOVE: The heavy plate mill circa 1898.

RIGHT: The River Don Engine was installed to drive Cammell Laird's armour rolling mill in 1904. After fifty years at the Grimesthorpe works it was transferred to the British Steel Corporation's River Don Works and in 1978, at the end of its working life, it was reinstalled as a working exhibit at Kelham Island Museum.

In 1876 Alexander Wilson, the brother of George Wilson, who was by then chairman of the company, developed compound armour, a major step forwards from wrought-iron armour. For a period Cammell's compound armour was the dominant form of armour used by most of the world's navies, in spite of challenges from steel armour made by Schneider, and John Brown's rival patent for compound armour. The invention of Harvey armour in 1891, however, put an end to Cammell's period of technical leadership in the manufacture of armour plate. Harvey armour was rapidly succeeded by Krupp armour and Cammell's rolled its first Krupp armour plate in 1896.

At a meeting on 25 November 1903 the board agreed to expenditure on a new armour mill 'not exceeding £50,000'[12] and the *Engineer* magazine reported on the installation of the mill in July 1905, noting that:

> An important development is taking place at Messrs. Cammell Laird & Co [...] where the old armour rolling mill is being replaced by one of the latest type. Messrs. Davy Brothers, Limited of Park Ironworks, Sheffield are building the plant, and the work is being carried out as rapidly as possible.[13]

The armour rolling mill was in the Grimesthorpe Works and was 310 feet long, 64 feet wide and 50 feet high; it had five bogie furnaces for reheating the plates. The mill's rollers were 14 feet wide by 48 inches in diameter. It was powered by a 12,000 HP steam engine, which is still running and is housed in the Kelham Island Industrial Museum in Sheffield. The new mill rolled armour plate for the new Dreadnought battleships.

VICKERS

The development of the company

The firm of Vickers, Sons & Maxim had its origins in Sheffield in the firm of Naylor & Sanderson. In 1829 the firm split for family reasons, one part becoming Sanderson Brothers & Company. The other part was formed by George Naylor, the son of the senior partner in the old company, and his brother-in-law Edward Vickers. The firm had two other partners, Charles Congreve and John Hutchinson, neither of whom was active in running the business. The firm was named Naylor, Hutchinson, Vickers & Co. They rented a works at Mill Sands and another at Wadsley Bridge, and Edward Vickers built up investments in the railways, which enabled him to take control of the company. Two of Edward Vickers' sons, Tom and Albert, were sent to Germany to receive a technical education.

In around 1841 the firm became Naylor, Vickers & Co. and with the help of a new American partner, Ernst Benzon, were successful in taking advantage of the railway boom in the USA. Having survived a collapse of confidence in the American railway boom in 1857, the firm temporarily suspended payments to its creditors but resumed payments in full the following year. The firm bought land in Sheffield's Lower Don Valley in 1863 and built a new factory complex, the River Don Works, covering 15 acres. Soon afterwards the company split into two, one side consisting of the manufacturing activity, based in Sheffield and run by Edward Vickers with a capital of £155,000, and the other, run by Ernst Benzon, concerned with trading activities. In April 1867 Naylor, Vickers & Company converted from a private company to a limited liability company and changed its name to Vickers, Sons & Co.

Although the American market for steel and railways diminished, Vickers expanded in other areas and in 1868 entered the marine engineering market, making their first marine shafting in that year and casting their first screw propeller in 1872. They continued to expand at the River Don Works with additions in 1872; in 1874 the site was expanded by the purchase of an additional 13 acres of land. They also installed one of the first Siemens furnaces in Sheffield,[14] the design of which was modified by Tom Vickers, who was playing an increased role in the technical development of Vickers having taken charge of this side of the business in 1856 at the age of twenty-two. They also installed a large steam hammer made by the Sheffield firm of Davy Brothers, and in 1882 their first forging press was installed.

In 1887 there was a general downturn in trade and to deal with this Vickers followed the Sheffield companies of Charles Cammell, John Brown and Thomas Firth & Sons into the armaments business. They had already begun this process by producing steel for ordinance, and Tom Vickers had patented a method of cooling such steel in 1862, but this was a minor part of their business. In 1887 the Admiralty was looking to expand capacity for making armour plate and Vickers decided to lay down an armour plant and began the process of converting themselves from a steel maker to an armament firm. As part of this transformation they made two key purchases. In 1897 they acquired the Naval Construction and Armaments Company Ltd of Barrow; this yard had an established reputation for building naval ships and had just completed HMS *Powerful*, a 14,200-ton protected cruiser, and the smaller 5,600-ton second-class cruisers *Juno* and *Doris*. The Barrow firm were looking for outside investment and W. G. Armstrong Mitchell & Co. had been considering buying the company to expand their shipbuilding business on the Tyne. Armstrong's decided not to proceed and Vickers took advantage of this opportunity to acquire their own shipbuilding capacity. The second purchase was the Maxim Nordfelt Guns and Ammunition Co., of which Albert Vickers had been the chairman since 1884. Maxim's manufactured light guns at their Erith factory but had been experiencing financial problems due to receiving an uneven level of orders.

The purchase of both of these companies was facilitated by the financier Lord Rothschild and was financed though the issue of £1.25 million debenture capital. The new expanded firm was renamed Vickers, Sons & Maxim Ltd and had works in Sheffield, Barrow, Crayford (Maxim), North Kent ironworks (shells) and the machine-gun works at Erith. It also had ammunition factories in Birmingham and Dartford and two gun-testing ranges, the largest of these being at Eskmeals, north of Barrow. The company embarked on an expansion of these works with the Barrow shipyard expanding from 13 to 25 acres and the workforce doubling to 10,000 people. In 1898 the Barrow yard received an order for its first battleship, HMS *Vengeance*, and in 1902 another order was received for one of the *King Edward VII* class of battleships – the 16,350-ton HMS *Dominion*.

At Sheffield the River Don Works was increased to an area of 60 acres and there was also expansion at Erith, where as well as light guns the breech mechanisms for all Vickers guns were manufactured.

Armour making

Vickers submitted their first armour plates for government tests in 1888, shortly after Cammell's submitted the first British steel armour for testing. Vickers submitted 10½-inch steel armour plates for three trials at HMS *Nettle* in Portsmouth on 6 September 1888, 22 February 1889 and 3 June 1891. The trial results were recorded by the company in a specially bound volume, now in the library at Kelham Island Museum in Sheffield.[15] These trials were a success and, on the basis of the first test, the *Engineer* wrote that 'if Messrs. Vickers, Sons & Co take to armour plate making their establishment will become a veritable arsenal […] and with this solid steel plate they have given proof of their ability to supply armour.'[16]

Endnotes

1.   A. Grant, *Steel & Ships, the story of John Brown's* (Michael Joseph, 1950), p. 22.
2.   K. Warren, *Steel Ships and Men* (Liverpool University Press, 1998), p. 42.
3.   John Brown and Company Limited, Atlas Works Sheffield; Shipyard and Engineering Works Clydebank, 1903. Held in SIMT Library, ref: 1572.
4.   *Engineer*, 27 February 1903, p. 227.
5.   *Manchester Guardian*, 13 November 1906, quoted in Grant, *Steel & Ships*, p. 20.
6.   John Brown and Company Limited, Atlas Works Sheffield.
7.   Ibid.
8.   Grace's Guide to British Industrial History (www.gracesguide.co.uk).
9.   Report of the Special Committee on Iron, 1863, National Archive, WO113/13, p. 140.

10. Cammell Board Minutes, Wirral Archives, 5 September 1868 and 8 October 1868, quoted in Warren, *Steel Ships & Men*, p. 46.
11. *Engineer*, 27 March 1874, p. 226.
12. Cammell Laird Board Minutes, Minute Book 7, 25 November 1903, Wirrall Archive Service, p. 430.
13. *Engineer*, 14 July 1905, p. 37.
14. *Engineering*, 5 January 1872, p. 8.
15. Copies of Official Reports and Photographs, Vickers 1891, SIMT MNVK0001.
16. *Engineer*, 14 September 1888, p. 216.

CHAPTER 6

THE SHIPBUILDERS: ARMSTRONG WHITWORTH AND BEARDMORE

Unlike the three Sheffield companies, neither W. G. Armstrong, Whitworth & Co. nor William Beardmore & Co. began life as iron and steel makers. W. G. Armstrong's began as an engineering company and developed into a major gun-maker and ship building company. William Beardmore's began life as a shipbuilding company with an associated ironworks. After entering the armour-making business at an early stage they soon stopped making armour and concentrated their energies on shipbuilding.

Like the Sheffield companies, both sought to integrate their operations; but unlike the Sheffield companies, which bought shipyards, Armstrong's and Beardmore's developed armour-making plants so they could also become integrated armament providers able to provide all the components for naval warships.

W. G. ARMSTRONG, WHITWORTH & CO.

The development of the company

William Armstrong was born in 1810 in Newcastle and, although his main interest was engineering, he was articled as a solicitor in 1828, becoming a partner in the firm of Donkin, Stable and Armstrong in 1835. Between 1838 and 1844 he trained as an engineer in his spare time; in 1846 he gave up the law in favour of a full-time career in engineering and set up the Newcastle Cranage Company to design cranes using hydraulic principles.

Initially Armstrong's cranes were made by another firm but 1847 he set up the firm of W. G. Armstrong & Co. at the Elswick Engine Works. It had a capital of £19,500 plus the value of £3,000-worth of patents, held by Armstrong himself. The directors of the company were William Armstrong, the appropriately named Armourer Donkin (his legal partner), Addison Parter (the mayor of Newcastle), Richard Lambert and George Criddas. The company built a factory at Elswick, between the Newcastle-to-Carlisle railway line and the river Tyne, and manufactured hydraulic equipment, cranes and bridges. Starting with about twenty employees the company had grown to 400 employees by 1851 and in 1852 the annual output of cranes was seventy-five. In the same year they exhibited a model of a hydraulic crane at the Great Exhibition for which they won a Prize Medal.

In November 1854, the Crimean War Battle of Inkerman demonstrated that the weight of the artillery being used by the British army at that time made it difficult to manoeuvre on the battlefield and Armstrong became interested in the problem 'more as an amusement for his leisure than for any other reason.'[1]

In December 1854 William Armstrong gained an interview with the Duke of Newcastle, the Secretary of State for War, and the next year the company manufactured their first gun, a three-pounder breech-loading gun with a rifled steel lining.[2] Armstrong was suspicious of the newly introduced Bessemer steel and the process he used to make his gun barrels was to twist iron bars around a steel barrel and then shrink them onto it. The barrel was rifled using a lathe.

In 1858, after the Crimean War, an official committee was set up to decide what sort of rifled gun the British army should adopt. Armstrong's and their Manchester competitor Joseph Whitworth & Co. each submitted a gun for the committee to consider. As a result of the trials the Armstrong system was adopted. In March 1859 General Peel, the Secretary of State for War, reported to the House of Commons that the Armstrong gun was 'fifty-seven times [more] accurate as our common artillery'. He also remarked that 'the carriages had been very much improved, and their introduction into the Navy would greatly diminish the number of men required to work the guns.'[3] As a result of the competition the company became a large supplier of the British army as it re-equipped after the Crimean War.

Following the results of the trials the government appointed William Armstrong as the Engineer for Rifled Ordinance and Superintendent of the Royal Gun Factory at Woolwich. As the factory at Woolwich was not equipped to make Armstrong's design of rifled gun, the Elswick Ordinance Company was established with government funding, but Armstrong, as a government employee, had no financial interest in the company. The company received guarantees from the government that it would provide work to keep the works fully occupied but the agreement had a termination clause, in the event of which the government would pay compensation of £85,000.

The protected cruiser *Esmerelda*, built for the Chilean navy by W. G. Armstong's and armoured by C. Cammell's.

In spite of the success of the Armstrong guns in tests, the rivalry between Armstrong and Whitworth continued with supporters of both designs arguing their cases in the press; in 1863 another committee of enquiry was set up to review the two systems. In October 1862 the government wrote to the Elswick Ordinance Company saying that it did not intend to place any further orders with them and as a result William Armstrong resigned from his government position, as he felt that his loyalty lay with the investors in the Elswick companies. By April 1863 all ordinance work had been transferred to the government works at Woolwich and the government agreed to pay the Elswick Ordinance Co. compensation of around £65,000.

Following the cancellation of the contract, the Elswick Engine Works amalgamated with the Elswick Ordinance Factory and became Sir W. G. Armstrong & Co. There were seven directors of the new company of whom three were from the original company – Armstrong, George Cruddas and Richard Lambert – and two were from the Ordinance Works, George Rendel and Andrew Noble. Two new directors, William Cruddas and Percy Westmacott, were added to the board.

The ordinance business received only about £60,000-worth of orders from the British government over the next fourteen years but continued to expand overseas, becoming one of the first international arms suppliers. This search for markets encouraged Armstrong's to look at the naval market and in 1867 they subcontracted the building of the gunboat *Staunch* to Charles Mitchell's at their Walker Yard on the Tyne. As the demand for these gunboats increased, Armstrong's began to consider developing their own shipbuilding capacity and in 1882 Sir W. G. Armstrong & Co. agreed a merger with Charles Mitchell & Co., which had been shipbuilders on the Tyne since 1852. The first ship built by the new company of Sir W. G. Armstrong, Mitchell & Co. was the *Esmerelda*, which was laid down in 1881 and was an influential, steel-built, protected cruiser for the Chilean navy. Because Armstrong's could not manufacture their own armour the cruiser's compound armour plates were provided by Cammell's.

This design fulfilled the requirements of the followers of the *Jeune École* (see Chapter 1) for a fast cruiser designed for the 'guerre de course' or commerce raiding. Part of the success of this design was its relative cheapness and, based on the demand from foreign navies,[i] the company expanded its naval business, building a new yard at Elswick, which was completed in 1884. Orders from the British navy were, however, slow in arriving and Armstrong's relied strongly on their export business. It was not until 1889 that the yard built its first battleship for the British navy, HMS *Victoria*. At this point Armstrong's was the world's sixth largest shipbuilder[4] and was continuing to grow. The company had, by this time, developed into an integrated armaments business, able to build all types of naval ships and to equip them with both engines and ordinance. It could not, however, provide the armour for the ships and this had to be supplied by the Sheffield armour-making firms.

In 1897 Sir W. G. Armstrong, Mitchell & Co. had considered an amalgamation with the Naval Construction and Armaments yard at Barrow. Apparently the First Lord of the Admiralty, Lord Grochen, had been pressurising the company to build

---

i   They received orders from Austria, Italy, China, Spain, Romania, Argentina, Norway, Portugal, Turkey, Brazil and the USA.

an armour plate works at Barrow. In order to try and facilitate this, the chairman of the company, Lord Devonshire, approached Armstrong's with a view to them making a joint investment in an armour works. Part of the attraction of these proposals for Armstrong's was that they feared that Whitworth's, whom they still regarded as their major rival, might form an alliance with the Barrow company, thus providing them with shipbuilding capacity. However, after some discussion the scheme fell through and instead Armstrong's decided to merge with its historic competitor for making ordinance, Joseph Whitworth & Co. The new combined company become Sir W. G. Armstrong Whitworth & Co.

Joseph Whitworth & Co. had been established by Joseph Whitworth in Manchester in 1833 as a tool-making company but by 1860 they had diversified into making small arms and artillery under their own name and also as the Manchester Ordinance and Rifle Co. In 1880 the company began a phased move to a new site in the Openshaw area of the city. The company was a major producer of machine tools and produced equipment for the manufacture of armour. In 1893 they had exported a 10,000-ton hydraulic press and several 120-ton cranes to the American company Carnegie Steel, based in Pittsburgh.

Armour making

Joseph Whitworth had begun experimenting with thin steel armour plates in the late 1870s and had submitted an armour plate for trial on HMS *Nettle* at Portsmouth in 1877, but the results of this (as well as plates submitted by other companies) were described as 'disappointing' by the *Engineer* magazine.[5] The plate was described as being of relatively soft steel. However, it was the invention of Harvey cemented armour in the United States that encouraged Armstrong Whitworth to invest in a major armour-making plant at their Openshaw site.

In 1907 the Openshaw armour plant, which by then employed 4,500 people, was expanded,[6] creating an additional 500 jobs:

- An additional 60-ton Siemens furnace and a 60-ton travelling crane were added.
- A new 12,000-ton casting press was fitted, capable of pressing 125-ton ingots.
- Three additional cementation furnaces were added.
- The plate-grinding shops were lengthened by around 250 feet and new machinery was installed.
- The armour plate erecting shops were extended by a similar amount and four 50-ton travelling cranes were also added, each with a span of 60 feet.

WILLIAM BEARDMORE & CO.

The development of the company

William Beardmore & Co. was originally founded by David Napier, a Glasgow marine engineer who was trained at the Greenhead factory at Camlachie in Glasgow, where he later became a partner. Between 1813 and 1815, in partnership with his father John, he built his own works at Camlachie but in 1822 he moved to Lancefield foundry on the banks of the Clyde. His cousin Robert Napier took over the management of the Camlachie factory and in 1835 he also leased the Lansfield foundry when David Napier decided to move to London. The foundry was rented for £500 a year with the option to buy it within the first seven years for £20,000.[7]

In 1841 David Napier bought the Parkhead Forge in Glasgow from John Inglis Reoch. The price of £2,800 was comparatively high for the area,[8] which suggests that the forge was a successful business. By 1847 the forge, like many Glasgow firms, encountered problems. The directors of the Edinburgh and Glasgow Bank, the company's bankers, reported 'the past year has been one of the most disastrous ever known in the commercial world' and in November and December 1847 alone there were twenty-six insolvencies of major Glasgow firms. As a result of the problems David sold the forge to Robert Napier for £6,500; he bought it on behalf of his sons James and John, although it continued to be managed by William Rigby, who later married Robert Napier's daughter, Jane. The forge was later expanded by the purchase of an additional 4 acres of land.

In 1856 the shipyard in Govan was expanded in anticipation of winning work from the Admiralty, and the company carried out a series of experiments in making armour plate. At the Admiralty's request the company prepared an outline design for HMS *Warrior* and were subsequently asked to tender for building the ship, but they were only given one week to prepare their tender and the Thames Iron Works, based at Blackwell in London, won the contract. However, on 6 October 1859 Napier's heard that they had won the contract for the building her sister ship HMS *Black Prince* at a price of £35.25 per ton.[9]

HMS *Black Prince*, sister ship to the *Warrior*, built at Charles Napier's yard on the Clyde.

The company experienced a number of problems due to the size of the ship, and it took around twice as long to build as planned, with the Admiralty initially refusing to meet the increased costs. *Black Prince* was launched on 27 February 1861, but the armour plates still had to be made. They were not fitted until the end of the year, after which the ship was towed to Portsmouth for fitting out. The cost overruns for building the ship meant that Robert Napier & Co. had to borrow £130,000 from their bankers. Napier complained bitterly that the Thames Iron Works claim for compensation for increased costs in building both ships had received better treatment that his company, implying that this was because they were based in London.[10]

In 1860, in order to help with the company's growing financial problems, Robert Napier agreed to sell the Parkhead Forge to William Rigby for £30,000 payable over fifteen years. To help him overcome the difficulties in making the forgings and plates for the *Black Prince*, William Rigby brought in William Beardmore, a friend who had worked with both himself and Robert Napier on a number of engineering projects. In 1861 the two men formed a partnership to run the Parkhead Forge, operating under the name of Messrs Rigby & Beardmore. In 1863 William Rigby died and his wife inherited his share of the business. The idea of floating a public company was considered but instead William Beardmore and Jane Rigby formed a new partnership until 1872.

Although Parkhead continued to expand, Robert Napier & Sons was in financial difficulties due to increased competition from companies such as Randolph Elder & Co. (formed in 1864), William Denny & Bros (1845) and J. & G. Thompson (1852), which were all set up on the Clyde by former Napier employees. Robert Napier was in need of additional capital and it seems he persuaded his daughter to withdraw from her partnership with William Beardmore and to invest the proceeds in his company. As a result, in 1871 William went into partnership with his brother Isaac, who had been managing the company's forge, setting up W. & I. Beardmore. The new partnership then continued to expand the business, buying additional land for the purpose. In 1877 William Beardmore died at the age of fifty-four and his son, also called William, inherited the business. William Beardmore junior was born in 1856 and had begun his apprenticeship at Parkhead at the age of fourteen. At the time of his father's death he was studying metallurgy and chemistry at the Royal School of Mines in London and he became his uncle Isaac's junior partner.

In 1886 Isaac retired from the company and William Beardmore junior become the sole partner. The trustees of his father's estate were sceptical about his ability to run the company at such a young age and reserved the right to restrict capital investment in the firm if required. From the beginning of his partnership with Isaac, William had begun to invest in Siemens open-hearth furnaces for making steel plates and as trade picked up after 1887 this investment began to pay off. For the company of Robert Napier & Sons Ltd the opposite was the case and they were still suffering from the large losses they had incurred on the *Black Prince*. By 1894 the firm was unable to meet their commitments but they managed to survive until 1898 when William Beardmore bought the goodwill for £200,000. By 1894 the firm was unable to meet their commitments, but they managed to survive until 1898 when William Beardmore bought the goodwill for £200,000. He leased the Govan Yard and the Lancefield Works and planned further expansion in the area with the aquisition of a 75-acre site at Dalmuir. They also bought into the firm of J. Thorneycroft, well known for their skills in building torpedo boats and torpedo boat destroyers.

This pace of expansion, however, had its costs and Beardmore's had been forced to borrow heavily to pay for these new acquisitions. They decided to bring in fresh capital through the formation of a public company. William Beardmore approached Sir Edward Cassel, a leading financier who had worked with Vickers on several of their acquisitions, about an amalgamation with Vickers. In December 1901 William Beardmore reached an agreement with Vickers that both Vickers and himself would hold £750,000-worth of shares in the new public company, William Beardmore & Co. Ltd. William Beardmore himself became a director of Vickers (he attended his first board meeting in August 1902) and received 362,500 Vickers £1 shares (valued at £3 each) plus up to 27,000 additional shares equal in value to half of Beardmore's profits the previous year.[11] As part of the deal Beardmore's became a member of the Harvey United Steel Company and the Steel Manufacturers Nickel Syndicate.

Part of the reason the Vickers company gave for the deal with Beardmore's was that they wished to prevent them entering the market for large naval guns and they tried to persuade Armstrong's to take a third share[12] in Beardmore's; Armstrong's successfully resisted this approach.

Armour making

The company's first venture in armour plate making was for the battery HMS *Erebus,* built for the Crimean War. This had 4½-inch wrought-iron armour that was made from welding 1¼-inch plates together under two newly installed steam hammers, Tubal and Vulcan. They also made the armour plate for the *Black Prince*. But as the technology advanced Beardmore's ceased making armour in 1865–66 and did not start again until 1888, when they laid down a new mill capable of making and rolling all steel armour. This plant was opened in 1890 and Beardmore's submitted three test plates for trial just before the Harvey Company and John Brown's pioneered new methods of hardening steel plates. In 1893 the company manufactured a steel plate and sent it to the Harvey Steel Company to be 'Harveyised', but this was not a success. They continued to develop their works over the next few years and in 1895 they obtained a licence for the Harvey process made the armour plates for the cruiser HMS *Terrible*, built by J. & G. Thomson at Clydebank.[13]

Between 1896 and 1898 Beardmore's modernised their armour shop and installed a 12,000-ton press for armour making – at the time the largest in the world. The *Engineer* acknowledged Beardmore's history of making hammered plates, but described the works as 'the introduction to Scotland of what is virtually a new industry viz., the production of armour plates in their most difficult character, such as casement plates, conning towers, gun shields, ammunition trunks, torpedo tubes etc.'.[14]

They developed a process for making nickel-chromium armour plate which was similar to the Krupp process but produced armour on which the face was not as hard but the back was tougher[15] – and when the company amalgamated with Vickers they obtained a licence to produce armour by the Krupp process, becoming one of the five major armour-making companies supplying the Admiralty with armour plate.

Endnotes

1. K. Warren, *Armstrongs of Elswick* (Macmillan, 1989), p. 12.
2. J. D. Scott, *Vickers – A History* (Weidenfeld & Nicolson, 1962).
3. Hansard, HC Deb, 4 March 1859, Vol. 152 cc1319.
4. Warren, *Armstrongs of Elswick*, p. 23.
5. *Engineer*, 21 December 1877, p. 436.
6. Ibid., 4 January 1907, p. 21.
7. James Napier, *Life of Robert Napier of West Haldon* (W. Blackwood and Sons, 1904), p. 88.
8. J. Hume and M. Moss, *Beardmore – The History of a Scottish Industrial Giant* (Heinemann, 1979), p. 14.
9. Napier, *Life of Robert Napier*, p. 211.
10. Ibid., p. 213.
11. Vickers Board Minutes for 13 January 1902 and 2 June 1902, Vol. 5, CU1363, pp. 30 and 53.
12. Ibid., 25 May 1907, Vol. 5, CU1363, p. 260.
13. Hume and Moss, *Beardmore: The History of a Scottish Industrial Giant*, p. 14, quoting *Engineering*, 1909.
14. *Engineer*, 7 February 1896, p. 130.
15. Ibid., 25 November 1898, p. 524.

CHAPTER 7

THE COST AND PRICE OF ARMOUR PLATE

In both Britain and the USA there was a general concern that government was paying too much for armour plate and that the armour plate makers were collaborating to keep the prices high. In the USA Congress initiated enquiries into the price of armour in 1897, 1906 and 1913, and in Britain the Parliament Estimates Committee investigated the price of armour in 1913, taking evidence from several senior officials at the Admiralty. Although this book is primarily about the British armour plate industry, the American enquiries are important because they are more comprehensive and open in their approach, whereas British documents are much more guarded and the officials seem less willing to share information with politicians.

THE PRICE PAID FOR ARMOUR IN THE USA

The first modern armour purchased in the USA was 600 tons of compound armour authorised by Congress on 5 August 1882. This was ordered from the two Sheffield firms of Charles Cammell and John Brown to be fitted to the double turret monitor *Miantonomah*. The price of £112.94[1] per ton included transport of the plate from Sheffield to New York.

Following this order, the US naval building programme expanded and in 1886 the Navy Department issued an invitation to US steel makers to tender for the production of 6,700 tons of armour plate as well as 1,300 tons of gun forgings. Only two companies tendered for the armour plate order, the Bethlehem Iron Company of Pennsylvania, quoting an average of £113.02 per ton, and the Cleveland Rolling Mill Company of Ohio, which quoted an average of £123.45 per ton. The contract was awarded to Bethlehem Iron, which undertook to build a plant with a capacity of 300 tons per month, and to produce the first plates within a period of two and a half years. At the suggestion of the Navy Department the company signed contracts with the prominent French armour plate company of Schneider & Co. to provide assistance in producing steel armour plates. Bethlehem Iron delivered their first armour plates in autumn 1891.

From 1890 the contracts for armour were changed to include the use of nickel steel plates, with the US government providing the nickel.

As the demand for armour plate increased to around 14,000 tons, the Navy Department entered a separate contract with Carnegie, Phipps & Co. (later the Carnegie Steel Company) of Pittsburgh, for the production of 6,000 tons of armour.

In February and March 1893 the department entered into new contracts with the two companies for the production of armour, 3,562 tons to Bethlehem Iron and 2,928 tons to Carnegie. The prices in these contracts were:

	Price per ton	
Armour	$515–$725	£106–£149
Armour appurtenances	$325–$650	£67–£134
Splinter bulkheads	$500	£103
Average price	$561.86	£115.60
Additional cost for Harvey process (average)	$57.54	£11.80

An additional cost of £2.30 per ton was paid directly by the Navy Department to the Harvey Company for the use of the Harvey process as the Navy Department had signed a royalty agreement with the Harvey Company in March 1892, which was amended in April 1893.

In December 1895 the US Senate directed its Committee of Naval Affairs to inquire whether the price paid by the government for armour plate was fair and reasonable. As part of the Naval Appropriations Act of 10 June 1896, it directed the Secretary of the Navy, H. A. Herbert, to 'examine into the actual cost of armour plate and the price for the same which should be equitably paid.' The Act forbade any new contracts being agreed until after they had received the report.

The secretary's report was submitted in January 1897[2] and included the department's first investigation into the cost of making armour plate. It included a detailed analysis of the actual costs of making armour which formed the basis of the reports estimate of the price per ton the government should pay for armour plate:

	Price per ton	
Labour and materials	$197.78	£40.61
10% allowance for plant maintenance	$50–$60	£10.27–£12.32
Sub total (rounded)	$250	£51.33
Profit allowance (50%) (see note)	$124	£25.67
Add cost of nickel	$20	£4.11
'Equitable' price	$395	£81.11

Note: The profit level was set at what was seen as a generous level as it was felt that the manufacturers were not guaranteed regular orders and the plants may not always be fully used. A higher profit margin, described as 'equitable', was intended to encourage the manufacturers to stay in the business.

Further contracts for a total of 3,000 tons of Harvey armour were signed with the two companies in 1896. The price for these contracts was:

	Price per ton	
Armour	$515.40–$628.40	£105.83–£129.03
Armour appurtenances	$400.00	£82.14
Splinter bulkheads	$450.00	£92.40
Average price	$553.34	£113.62

The prices excluded nickel and royalty and also allowed for the adoption of Krupp armour, at an additional price, if the tests on this were successful.

As a result of the report Congress passed an Act on 3 March 1897 which limited the price that it would approve for armour to £61.85 per ton. This was around £20.58 per ton less than the report suggested was a fair price. The Navy Department sought tenders for 8,000 tons of armour plate from Bethlehem and Carnegie at this price, but both companies declined to tender. The Illinois Steel Company offered to make armour at £49.48 per ton but demanded a guarantee of orders of between 6,000 and 12,000 tons per year for the next twenty years which the department was not prepared to agree to. As a result, Congress raised the minimum price to £82.47, in line with the report's recommendation, and the department was able to sign contracts with Bethlehem and Carnegie for 7,587 tons of armour plate. These contracts included an obligation that the plates would be re-forged and, for the first time in the US, the companies were expected to source their own nickel. The department also agreed to reimburse the companies for any royalty costs.

In March 1899 the department asked for tenders for 24,000 tons of armour. They received one bid of £92.40 per ton from a company with no manufacturing plant to make the armour and did not accept this tender. In August and October of that year contracts for 2,268 tons were signed with Bethlehem and Carnegie at the same price as the 1898 contracts.

In June 1900 the department asked for tenders for the following:

- 31,000 tons of Class A armour (face hardened and 5 inches or more thick);
- 3,600 tons of Class B armour (face hardened and less than 5 inches thick);
- 1,150 tons of Class C armour (non-face hardened nickel steel armour); and
- bolts and nuts designated class D.

Bethlehem and Carnegie both bid the same amount for half the order. They quoted £91.37 plus £9.24 royalty per ton for Class A, £82.13 plus £2.30 royalty for Class B and £82.13 for Classes C and D.

The Midvale Steel Company of Pennsylvania, which was originally founded by William Butcher, who was a director of the Sheffield Company of William & Samuel Butcher (whose original premises at Butcher Works still exist in the centre of the city), also tendered, at a price between £108.83 and £89.93 for Class A plates and between £78.03 and £77.62 for Class B plates. The prices varied depending on the size of the contract awarded to them.

A conference was called with the three bidders but the Midvale Steel Company withdrew and an agreement was reached with the other two companies. This was for Class A armour which was specified as 'being required to be face-hardened, manufactured and treated by the so-called "Krupp process"'. Class B armour was specified as being 're-forged and face-hardened by the so-called "Harvey process"'.

The prices agreed were:

	Price per ton	
Class A	$420	£86.24
Class B	$400	£82.14
Class C	$400	£82.14

For the Class A armour the companies were to be reimbursed by the department for a royalty of £5 for the Krupp process as per an agreement signed by the companies in September 1898. In September 1902 this reduced to £4.10 for armour produced from January 1900; the government took responsibility for paying £2.30 for the Harvey process. For the Class B armour, the government also took responsibility for paying £2.30 for the Harvey process.

A further tender process for 15,000 tons of armour in January 1903 resulted in the two companies being awarded contracts under the same terms. The contract specified reforging for Class A plates. A further tender process in October 1903 saw identical bids being received from Bethlehem and Carnegie at the same price as previously but Midvale Steel Company re-entered the process with the lowest bid for £81.89 for Class A, £80.64 for Class B and £79.22 for Classes C and D. There was considerable debate about offering any of the order to Midvale, even though they were the lowest bidders. They had no established armour plant and it was felt that they did not have the experience in the 'art of armour manufacture' and that this would cause delays. The US Bureau of Ordinance intervened and as a result Midvale received around a third of the total order. The price for the Bethlehem and Carnegie armour averaged £85.82 per ton and for Midvale the average cost was £81.68 per ton.

In January 1905 the three companies again tendered for 8,000 tons of armour. Bethlehem and Carnegie proposed that they would produce armour at the same price as before but to a higher quality able to stand up to a more severe ballistic test. The department set up a board to review the armour makers' ability to meet the orders and this board recommended giving Bethlehem around two thirds of the order and Carnegie about one third. In the end it was decided to split it three ways with the Midvale contract being conditional on them demonstrating that they could deliver the orders on time. The price agreed with the three companies was:

	Price per ton	
Bethlehem	$411.13	£84.42
Carnegie	$402.22	£82.59
Midvale	$395.75	£81.26

In July 1906 a further round of tenders was received. For the first time the Bethlehem and Carnegie companies offered different prices:

	Class A	Class B	Class C	Class D
Bethlehem	£78.56		£72.15	
Carnegie	£76.29			
Midvale	£71.34	£71.13	£70.93	£70.72

All of the bids included the costs of royalties.

The government proposed to the companies that it would award half to the Midvale Steel Company and a quarter each to the Bethlehem and Carnegie companies. The prices received by each company were to be those of the lowest bidder. The three companies accepted the contracts on those terms and because of the mix of armour types the average contract prices were £71.04 to Carnegie, £71.01 to Bethlehem and £71.03 to Midvale.

Based on the records set out in the previous section it can be seen that the price of armour plate fell from £126.80 per ton in 1887 to £71.13 per ton in 1906, while at the same time the complexity of the manufacturing process increased as armour plate changed from compound plate to Krupp cemented plate. This trend is shown in the table:

Year	Brown / Cammell	Bethlehem	Carnegie	Midvale
1882	£112.94			
1883				
1884				
1885				
1886				
1887		£126.85		
1888				
1889				
1890			£123.26	
1891				
1892				
1893		£133.09	£135.38	
1894				
1895				
1896		£121.17	£121.65	
1897				
1898		£84.72	£84.64	
1899		£84.32	£84.41	
1900		£90.09	£90.09	
1901				
1902				
1903		£90.77	£89.57	£81.69
1904			£91.97	
1905		£89.17	£85.30	£81.27
1906		£71.02	£71.04	£71.03

From these figures it seems fairly clear that both the Bethlehem Steel Co. and the Carnegie Steel Co. collaborated over the price of armour plate and it was not until a third competitor, the Midvale Steel Co., entered the field that the US government was able to lower the price it paid for its armour plate.

However, this situation did not remain the same and it seems that the three companies now in the field began to collaborate. In response to a resolution passed by the Senate on 27 May 1913 that called for a new investigation into the cost of armour plate, the Secretary of State for the Navy, Joseph Daniels, reported that since the previous Senate intervention armour prices has risen from £71 per ton in 1906 to £86.42 per ton in 1907 and then to £91.37 per ton the previous year.

He pointed out that government policy of dividing the amount of armour plate required into three roughly equal contracts meant that the firms 'had not overlooked the advantage of putting in bids practically of the same figure and at the same rate'. The firms themselves argued as much.[3] H. M. Deemer, secretary of the Midvale Steel Co., wrote saying that this uniformity 'is entirely due to the Navy Department's long established policy'. E. G. Grace, the president of the Bethlehem Steel Co., made the same point, writing that:

In view of the practice of dividing orders equally between the firms at the price of the lowest tender [...] it has come to be understood by every manufacturer that the naming of a lower price by him would merely lower the price that he and each one of his competitors would receive for part of the order.

The secretary, Joseph Daniels, argued that the only way for the US government to control the cost of armour was for the government to build it own armour plant. He quoted costs for setting up an armour-making plant capable of making 10,000 tons per year, which was about half the US annual requirement at that time, as being £1,738,400. The costs were calculated by the Chief of the Bureau of Ordinance who estimated that it would cost £64.48 per ton and that after interest of 4% on the capital invested the armour plant would save the government £287,474 If the government decided to build a plant with a capacity of 20,000 tons per year he estimated that the cost per ton would be £57.29 and the saving £625,697.

The secretary thought these figures sufficiently convincing to recommend a further investigation into setting up a government plant and he sought Congressional support to examine the armour-making companies' books in detail to work out the costs more exactly.

It is perhaps not surprising that the companies found a way of getting round this system of tendering, as the government had devised a system that gave no advantage to the company making the lowest tender and they would receive exactly the same amount of work as the other two companies.

AMERICAN ESTIMATES OF THE COST OF MAKING ARMOUR PLATE

In 1905–06 the US Navy Department, at the request of Congress, held a second enquiry into the cost of armour plate. With the help of the naval officers based at Bethlehem Steel and Carnegie Steel the Assistant Secretary of State of the Navy drew up a report, which was published in December 1906. In this report the officers attempted to calculate the cost of each stage of the manufacturing process and thus the overall cost of making armour.[4] In order to make comparisons with the prices paid by the British Admiralty, US figures have been converted to pounds sterling at an exchange rate of $4.85 to the pound.[5]

The summary table shows the decreasing weight of the metal as it goes through the manufacturing process and the increasing value, in terms of labour and materials. A full breakdown of the manufacturing process and the value at each stage is shown in Appendix A.

	Weight of ingot (tons)	Cost per ingot	Cost per ton
Furnace charge:	54.24	£680.56	£12.55
Metal poured:	50.44	£711.69	£14.11
Ingot in pit:	47.92	£745.79	£15.56
Ingots forged:	44.15	£708.24	£16.04
Slab:	27.81	£743.19	£26.72
Plates for carburising:	26.98	£845.00	£31.32
Bending and rectifying:	20.00	£871.42	£43.57
Machining and erecting:	20.00	£915.10	£45.76
Shipping:	20.00	£917.16	£45.86
Company charges:		£15.15	
TOTAL	20.00	£932.31	£46.62

American enquiries from what they considered reliable sources indicated that the price the US government paid for armour plate was lower than other governments:

	Price per ton	
	Average for all armour	Krupp armour
Japan	£82.47	£82.47
Austria	£92.58	£114.85
Italy	£107.42	£113.40
Germany	£92.78	£92.78
France	£117.32	£117.53
Britain	£129.07	£140.41
USA	£71.32	£71.34

British armour plate costs and price

There does not appear to be any evidence in the Admiralty archives that the British government carried out any such comprehensive exercise into the price of making armour plate in Britain. The American estimates were largely based on the knowledge of the armour-making process of the Inspectors of Ordinance, based at the armour works. The British Admiralty certainly had access to a similar level of experience through its network of Admiralty Overseers, one of whom was based in Sheffield to supervise the work of the city's three armour makers.

Vickers, Sons & Maxim kept a series of accounts for the River Don Armour Works and these accounts for the years 1902 to 1914 show the 'factory costs' of producing armour plate for the Admiralty.

Year	Tons produced	Factory costs	Cost per ton
1902	3,759	£154,206	£41.02
1903	2,422	£94,943	£39.21
1904	2,786	£85,749	£30.78
1905	1,751	£63,778	£36.43
1906	446	£19,071	£42.75
1907	1,985	£68,446	£34.49
1908	1,773	£62,320	£35.15
1909	1,322	£59,955	£45.38
1910	2,130	£118,317	£55.56
1911	3,450	£140,317	£40.31
1912	3,582	£124,517	£34.76
1913	8,272	£288,983	£34.91
1914	11,067	£382,683	£34.58

The figure for 1906 equates well with the American estimate for the same year of £45.86 (excluding company charges) per ton shown earlier in this chapter. To work out a realistic selling price additional non factory costs, taken from the Vickers accounts, plus a profit margin need to be added:

	Cost per ton
Vickers factory cost for 1906	£42.75
Transport costs to shipyards	£0.53
Royalties on patents	£3.47
Proportion of central company costs	£0.37
Capital costs, depreciation etc. (from US figures)	£13.53
Sub total	£60.65
'Equitable profit' of 50% (from US figures)	£30.33
Realistic selling price	£90.98

This calculation suggests that in 1906 a figure of around £91 per ton would be a reasonable price for armour plate. In actual fact, in 1906 Vickers invoiced the Admiralty for an average price of £116.29 per ton for finished armour plate.

THE FRENCH GOVERNMENT AND THE PRICE OF ARMOUR

In a report to the French Chamber of Deputies in 1912 entitled 'The price of Armour and the Guerigny Works, Necessity for State Works', M. Painlove, a Deputy in the Chamber, made an interesting case for the relationship between the government and the private arms manufacturers.[7] The French government had set up an armour plate factory at Guerigny in 1904, but it was initially only capable of manufacturing thin armour plates. In 1909 they had decided to extend the capabilities of the plant to manufacture thicker plates but by 1912 it had not succeeded in making any plates and it was hoped that it would become operational by 1914.

The report argued that the French manufacturers operated a syndicate of suppliers, which fixed prices and divided orders among themselves. M. Painlove argues explicitly that the existence of such a syndicate was only natural and that 'it may readily be realised that it is desirable for the sake of rapidity and economy in construction that the various works should arrange between themselves to take those portions which correspond to their respective powers of production.' However, it was only advantageous 'if the two parties in question act with moderation and sincerity, but it is, however, a disadvantage if the state is obliged to submit without defence to the industrial conditions imposed.' The relationship could only be advantageous if the government was able to discuss a realistic price for armour plate 'with authority'. This, he argued, meant that the government had to press on with setting up the Guerigny plant even though it had been described as a place where 'millions have been sunk under the pretext of economies rendered impossible by the very enormity of the expenses'.

In the report the author quotes the price of various types of armour being paid by the French government:

	Vergniaud	Jean Bart
Class	Danton class	Courbet class
Date of tender	29 Oct 1907	Aug 1910
Company	Schneider	Forge et Acièries de la Marine
Gun shields	FF2.93 per kilo £118.20 per ton	FF3.05 per kilo £123.04 per ton
Barbette	FF 2.93 per kilo £118.20 per ton	FF2.60 per kilo £104.50 per ton

This was the part of the report that interested the Admiralty, as it was in the middle of the Select Committee hearings into the 1913 Naval Estimate and was under pressure to justify the cost of armour in relation to prices paid by other governments. In a handwritten file note Rear Admiral Moore, the Third Sea Lord, commented – possibly with some satisfaction – that it appeared 'that the cost of armour in France is about the same as in England, it is certainly not lower'.

BRITISH NEGOTIATIONS ON THE PRICE OF ARMOUR

In June 1910 the Admiralty began discussions about reaching an agreement on the price of armour plate with the five armour plate makers. An allocation of orders for armour plate for battleships of the Orion class, the first of the super-Dreadnoughts, had been placed with the firms from December 1909. These ships, which were part of the 1909 Estimates, were the Monarch, Conqueror and Thunderer. Orders for armour for the battlecruiser Princess Royal were also placed at same time.

These orders had been placed on the understanding that a new set of agreed standard rates would be negotiated with the armour plate manufacturers and would apply retrospectively to the orders that had just been placed. On orders placed after 24 December 1909 a new 15%

discount would apply, as opposed to the 10% discount that was applied on orders before December 1909. These discounts may have been related to the expiry of the Harvey and Krupp patents, but no direct connection is made in the available correspondence.

The proposed new agreement was intended to cover not only armour plate but also gun shields, which had previously been excluded and paid for in a lump sum rather than in a price per ton. The Superintendent of Contract Work indicated that the Admiralty did not want the agreement to go beyond the ships of the 1911/12 programme, but the armour firms held the opposite point of view and wrote that 'in view of the concessions they are now making, Their Lordships will see their way to maintain this standard price for at least five years.'[8] This suggests that both parties thought that the trend in armour plate prices was downwards, with the sellers keen to fix prices for a longer period and the buyers feeling that they could lower prices again at the next round of negotiations.

In their joint letter to the Admiralty, signed by senior directors from each of the five companies, the armour makers agreed to send representatives to a meeting to assist in 'fixing the proposed schedule of net prices [...] for the purpose of obviating the necessity of calling for tenders for the main supplies of each ship'. The conference was held on 28 July 1910 and it appears that the price of standard Krupp cemented armour was largely agreed. The five armour plate firms clearly got together after the conference to co-ordinate their response and all appear to have written letters on 8 September to the Director of Naval Contacts over certain types of armour. The disagreements concerned gun shield roof plates and sighting hoods and tapered armour.

The firms wanted between £3 and £5 per ton for the additional work required for making plates that tapered from one thickness to another while the Admiralty proposed to pay only an additional £1 per ton. In earlier negotiations in 1909 on the price of armour, the armour plate makers had refused to reveal the cost of making armour plate and they were therefore not really able to present a detailed case for a higher price for tapered armour without revealing the details of their manufacturing costs – a weakness which it seemed the Admiralty exploited, as they stuck to their guns over the price in spite of a joint letter from the five firms reiterating their case.

The prices per ton that were eventually agreed for some of the main elements of ship armour were:[9]

Weight	Type of armour plate		
	Belt	Bulkhead	Barbette
480 lbs	£96	£92	£97
400 lbs	£96	£92	£97
320 lbs	£94	£92	£95
280 lbs	£94	£92	£94
200 lbs	£93	£92	£93
120 lbs	£85	£84	£88

More details of the schedules are shown in Appendix B.

The list of prices for standard quality armour plate was reissued in July 1913[10] for the 1912–13 and 1913–14 programmes of shipbuilding. Although there were some alterations, such as 520 lb armour being added, the prices for the weights and types of armour used in the table above remained the same.

Endnotes

1. Converted from US dollars via http://www.measuringworth.com/datasets/exchangepound/result.php.
2. *Cost and Price of Armor Plate*, Report of the Secretary of the Navy, 1897, New York Public Library 659499A.
3. Letter from the Secretary of the Navy to the Committee of Naval Affairs, 63rd Congress 1st Session, Document 129, 14 July 1913, p. 5.
4. Letter from the Acting Secretary of the Navy as to the Cost of Armor Plates and Armour Plant, Doc 193, 59th Congress 2nd session, p. 34 onwards.
5. http://www.measuringworth.com/datasets/exchangepound/result.php.
6. Vickers Accounts, 1905 and 1906, Sheffield Archives 1988/50, Box number 13562.
7. Report of the French Chamber of Deputies, No. 1880, 1912, on the Budget (Minister of Marine) by M. P. Painlove (Deputy), Translated in National Archives ADM116/3456.
8. Letter signed by the five armour firms dated 3 June 1910, ADM 116/3456.
9. National Archive, ADM 116/3456.
10. Ibid.

CHAPTER 8

RINGS AND CARTELS

As is the case with all articles whose manufacture requires very expensive machinery, armor plate is peculiarly susceptible to monopoly, and it is indeed doubtful whether there is any other manufactured article which can be so easily controlled by a trust or combination to keep up prices. The peculiarities of armor plate and the costly equipment necessary for its manufacture makes plain the opportunity afforded for combinations among the few wealthy corporations capable of undertaking its manufacture. There has been much evidence that the opportunity for such combinations has been taken full advantage of, both in this country and in foreign countries building armoured ships of any considerable size.

Joseph Daniels, Secretary of the US Navy [1]

Together with their European and American counterparts, all the British armour plate companies were active in forming trade associations, cartels, price-fixing syndicates and patent pools. Many of these were known of at the time and they caused a significant amount of controversy in both naval and political circles. As J. D. Scott says, in his history of Vickers, which was commissioned by the company: 'It was a period of cartelization, of the forming of trade associations, price fixing syndicates and patent pools. All the great European industrial concerns, as well as many in the USA, were deeply involved, Vickers among them.'[2]

The existence of these 'arrangements' at an international level was an important factor in the branding of the armour plate companies as merchants of death – providing armaments to foreign countries for profits and thus stoking regional arms races and conflicts. This line of argument was influential during and immediately after the First World War when writers such as Walter Newbold (*The War Trust Exposed*, 1915; *How Europe Armed for War*, 1916), and H. Robertson Murray (*Krupp and the International Arms Ring*, 1915) were keen to explore the causes of a conflict that had cost so many lives, and to prevent it happening again.

One of the outcomes of this concern was the Royal Commission on the Private Manufacture of Arms and Trading in Arms. The Royal Commission was set up in 1935, chaired by Sir John Bankes and, over twenty-two sessions, took evidence from a wide range of people. The terms of reference of the Royal Commission were:

- To consider and report upon the practicability and desirability (both from the national and international point of view) of the adoption (a) by the United Kingdom alone, (b) by the United Kingdom in conjunction with the other countries of the world, of a prohibition of private manufacture of and trade in arms and munitions of war, and the institution of a State monopoly of such manufacture and trade.

- To consider and report whether there are any steps which can usefully be taken to remove or minimize the kinds of objections to which private manufacture is stated in Article 8 (5) of the Covenant of the League of Nations to be open.

- To examine the present arrangements in force in the United Kingdom relative to the control of the export trade in arms and munitions of war, and to report whether these arrangements require revision, and if so, in what directions.

In the USA similar sentiments led to the formation of the Nye Committee,[3] which was set up by the US Congress in 1936 to investigate the munitions industry.

The question of whether the arms and armour-making companies and the collaborative agreements and arrangements between them contributed to the European arms race and the outbreak of the First World War is a complex one. It is certainly true that in Britain private-sector armament firms played a greater and greater role in equipping the navy. Their percentage share of ship construction, including armour (Vote 8 of the Naval Estimates), increased from about 30% of the budget in 1890 to around 65% at the outbreak of the First World War.

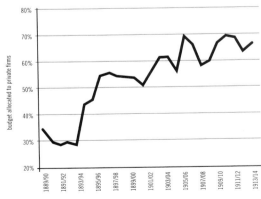

The graph shows the percentage work under Vote 8: Shipbuilding, Repairs and Maintenance, carried out under contracts with private companies. The calculation excludes fuel for the fleet.

The fastest period of growth in the budget was between 1893 and 1896, roughly coinciding with the large building programme of the Naval Defence Act of 1889 which was aimed at restoring the two-power standard with respect to the French and Russian navies. The growth in the private companies' share of naval capital expenditure dates from before the naval arms race that began in 1906 with the launch of HMS *Dreadnought*. It could be argued that this increased role in naval construction gave the armour manufactures greater influence in what President Eisenhower much later labelled the industrial–military complex.[4] The amount of investment the armaments firms needed to make in order to fulfil these contracts meant that they could not afford to keep their plant idle for any length of time. The *Engineer* magazine reported in February 1889 that in spite of recent orders 'there is much valuable plant – particularly armour plate plant – doing literally nothing.' However, their increased importance to the Admiralty is reflected in the fact that Lord George Hamilton, the First Lord of the Admiralty, was touring the Sheffield armour plants and doubtless the companies used this opportunity to make their case for contracts to keep the plant busy.[5]

The importance of maintaining this private-sector industrial capacity certainly influenced the procurement policies of both the British and American governments in the period leading up the First World War. Such a close relationship has its dangers, as Eisenhower warned the USA in 1961: 'The potential for the disastrous rise of misplaced power exists, and will persist. We must never let the weight of this combination endanger our liberties or democratic processes. We should take nothing for granted.'

INTERNATIONAL AGREEMENTS

The international Harvey patent pool arrangements

The Harvey company, which invented and patented the Harvey process for making cemented armour in the United States in 1891, were neither an armour-producing nor a steel-making company. They made their breakthrough using equipment at the Washington Naval Yard and initially using steel ingots made at Creusot by the French company, Schneider. They later bought the patents for the Tresidder method of high-pressure sprinkling of the hardened plates that was combined into the new process. The Harvey company made their money through licensing the use of their process to the armour-making companies, and in 1893 the Harvey Steel Company was set up to acquire the British patent rights for the Harvey process. Similar companies were also set up in the United States and in France.

In 1884 a second British company was set up which acquired the rights for European countries not already covered by other 'Harvey' companies and for the rest of the world. This company also acquired the patents for the making of thin armour plates from the German firm of Friedrich Krupp AG. As the existence of four 'Harvey' companies was complex and could potentially lead to conflict between the members, the four companies formed a syndicate in October 1894. This syndicate consisted of the main armour plate manufacturers of Britain (John Brown, Charles Cammell and Vickers), France (Aciéries de la Marine, Schneider and Chatillon), Germany (Dillinger, Huetten and F. Krupp) and the United States (Bethlehem and Carnegie).

The intention of the syndicate was to control prices outside the four countries involved and to divide up orders between the members. The syndicate did not cover the arrangements within the four countries themselves. However, this syndicate was not a great success and the British companies in particular were aggrieved because the number of orders they were receiving from foreign governments meant that they were paying much more into the common pool than they were getting out. As a result Albert Vickers chaired a meeting of the member companies in 1900, and new arrangements were agreed. This involved registering a new company called the Harvey United Steel Company Ltd, in which was vested the rights of the Harvey Steel Company of Great Britain and the Harvey Continental Steel Company to the patents for the Harvey and Krupp armour-making processes.[6] The two American companies withdrew from the new company in 1908.

The Harvey United Steel Company had a membership drawn from all of the world's major armour manufacturers and at the time of the 11th Annual Report in March 1912, just after the end of the Harvey and Krupp patents, the directors of the company were named as being:

	Company	
Albert Vickers	Vickers, Sons & Maxim	Chairman
William Beardmore	William Beardmore & Co.	
Rafaele Bettini	Societa degli Alti Forni Fondiere ed Acciaiene de Terni (Vickers Terni)	
John A. Clarke	Cammell, Laird & Co.	
Charles E. Ellis	John Brown & Co.	Also representing Coventry Ordinance Works & Thomas Firth & Co.
J. M. Faulkner	Sir W. G. Armstrong Whitworth & Co.	
Edwin Marshall Fox	Harvey Steel Co.	
Col. C. F. M. Houdaille	St Charmond Steel Co.	
J. W. Hughes		Possibly the accountant
Col. M Hunsiker	Carnegie Steel	
Léon Lévy	Chatillon Commentry Co.	
Fritz Saeftel	Der Dillinger Huttenwerke	
Edouard Saladin	Schneider & Cie	
Heinrich Vielhaber	Krupp AG	

The registered office was at 28 Victoria Street, Westminster, London: Vickers' London headquarters.

In 1912 Harvey United Steel reported that its annual income had dried up, as the licences it held had now expired. It reported that it held assets of £34,594 in its reserve funds and an ongoing dispute over the payment of £30,000 of royalties. This may well have referred to a dispute between the Harvey Steel Company of America and the US government over the payment of royalties on armour produced by the Midvale Steel Company. This dispute related to a contact signed in 1893 between the Harvey company and the US government which:

> Granted the right to use for the treatment of armour plate for its vessels the 'Harvey process' and any and all improvements made by the Harvey Steel Company upon such process, and to use and employ the armour plates manufactured according to said process. The United States agreed to pay the Harvey Steel Company a royalty of one-half cent per pound on the finished plate.

However, the US government argued that it had not specifically required the armour plate to be produced by the Harvey process. In their judgement of 3 February 1913 the US Supreme court ruled that royalties of £25,352 would have to be paid because, although the techniques had developed, they retained the same essential principles of carburisation.[7]

In 1906 the Vickers Board minutes recorded an agreement with the Harvey United Steel Company that the royalty for the licences paid by Vickers for 'sundry patents' under which armour plate was manufactured was set at £0.50 per ton up to the end of 1906. This royalty was to be paid when plates were 'manufactured, delivered and paid for'.[8] Between 1903 and mid-1910 when the five British companies stopped paying royalties, they paid a total of £405,725 to the Harvey United Steel Company for use of their patents on armour production valued at £10.6 million. The amount paid by each company was:[9]

	Tonnage	Value	Royalty	% of value	Royalty per ton
Armstrong Whitworth	20,935	£2,669,324	£92,888	3.5%	£4.44
William Beardmore	16,017	£1,669,701	£62,345	3.7%	£3.89
John Brown	18,374	£1,748,424	£65,386	3.7%	£3.56
Cammell Laird	19,054	£2,118,055	£81,719	3.9%	£4.29
Vickers	19,216	£2,485,866	£103,386	4.2%	£5.38
Total	93,596	£10,691,370	£405,724	3.8%	£4.33

Clearly the £0.50 agreed in 1906 did not cover all the patents and may have only applied to new developments of the processes. It is interesting to note that, although all the companies paid a similar amount of royalty per ton, Vickers seems to have paid both a higher percentage

of value and royalty per ton than the other companies. John Brown pays a lower price per ton than the other companies and it is possible that this could be because of their ownership of the Tresidder patent for chill spraying hardened plates.

The financial records of Cammell, Laird & Co.[10] show a number of payments to the Harvey United Steel Company that can be compared with the amount of royalty due. In 1905 these were:

Period	Amount of royalty paid
First Quarter	£546.54
Second Quarter	£10,951.66
Third Quarter	£5,390.00
Additional Payment	£250.00
Fourth quarter	£4,150.78
Total	£21,288.98

Records of the amount of armour plate manufactured by the company suggest that, based on the invoices they submitted during 1905, Cammell, Laird & Co. should have paid a figure of £22,344.36 royalty.[11] It may well be that the point in the manufacturing process at which royalty payment became due was not the same as the invoice date and that may account for the difference.

The foreign armour plate convention

As discussed earlier in this chapter, the Harvey syndicate set up in 1894 involved a pool arrangement by which the proceeds of orders from countries outside the syndicate were shared. In letters to both the Krupp and the Schneider companies, dated 8 April 1895, Charles Ellis, the managing director of John Brown, sets out the details of the pool payments:

> it is of course understood that 15 per cent of the net receipts by my company shall be pooled in accordance with your telegram of the 5th inst.

> In the event however of any payment for Harvey Royalty being rendered necessary we trust you will see no objection to this not being included in the amount to be pooled.[12]

The exclusion of the royalty fee was of course possible because the royalties were paid to the Harvey syndicates and shared among its members.

A book of Ellis's private letters for the period between the setting up of the Harvey syndicates and the formation of the Harvey United Steel Company show the extent of the collaboration between the major international armour plate companies in the 1890s. The book has copies of letters to Alexander Wilson at Charles Cammell & Co. and Albert Vickers at Vickers, as well as to Krupp and Dillinger in Germany, Schneider and the Compagnie des Hauts Fourneaux, Forges et Aciéries in France, and Carnegie in the USA. The main subject of these letters is arranging the price at which each of the companies will quote for orders from countries that did not have their own armour plate industry, such as Russia, Norway, Sweden, Spain and Brazil. The companies agreed between themselves which was going to win each tender and then fixed the level at which they quoted for the armour, so that the chosen company put in the lowest tender. A typical letter about these arrangements was written to Schneider's on 2 January 1896, about tenders for armour for two Brazilian monitors. Charles Ellis writes:

> This order has, we understand, been allocated to the French Group and we are quoting them [the Brazilian government] today 2,275 francs per 1,000 kilo delivered at Rio de Janeiro for Harveyised Steel.
>
> As this price leaves sufficient protection for the French Group we have not thought it necessary to obtain the various consents before giving in our quotation.[13]

It seems, however, that the same arrangements may have extended to tenders in counties that had their own armour plate industries. On 23 September 1895, Charles Ellis wrote to Vickers that they had tendered for an order for Harvey armour from Armstrong, Mitchell of Newcastle, who were not at this stage making their own armour plate. He says that 'as the prices named are so much above the standard price it was [...] unnecessary to ask you to communicate with our Continental friends'.[14]

The correspondence shows that the major international companies all collaborated to fix both the price of armour and the distribution of orders. Although the companies met up at various points, the collaboration seems not to have taken place through the Harvey syndicates; indeed it seems both Captain Lindoe of the Harvey Company of Great Britain and Edward Marshall Fox who was appointed as the European representative of the Harvey Steel Company in January 1892, were not included in the inter-company communications.

After the formation of the more formalised Harvey United Steel Company in 1900, the Cammell, Laird & Co. journals[15] show a number of payments to the company under what is called the 'Foreign Armour Plate Convention'. In 1905 to 1907 Cammell, Laird & Co. accounts show income and expenditure under this heading of the following amounts:

	Income		Expenditure	
	From	Amount	To	Amount
1905	Vickers, Sons & Maxim	£10,785.76	Schneider & Cie	£125.57
1906	Vickers, Sons & Maxim	£5,233.79		
1907	Vickers, Sons & Maxim	£6,624.70		
Total		£22,644.25		£125.57

There is also reference in the Vickers Board minutes for 1902[16] to the involvement of the Harvey United Steel Company in controlling and sharing investments in foreign armour-making works. The minute is worth recording in full:

> Memorandum of a special meeting of the Harvey United Steel Co Limited held on 18th May 1903 to discuss the question of establishing an armour plate plant in Spain for which John Brown & Co Limited had received enquiries. Having been read, the declaration by Mr Alfred Vickers therein reported was approved, viz that Vickers Sons & Maxim Limited would not establish Armour Plate Plant in Spain or any other part of the world (the countries named in the memo: where Armour Plant is already in existence excepted) without offering the other Armour Plate Manufacturing Firms who would make a similar declaration equal participation both in the Capital and profit of such Plant (for further details see memo in MB file).

This minute provides clear evidence that the Harvey United Steel Company was used as a forum in which the international armour manufacturers collaborated to share the benefits of foreign orders made in foreign plants as well as foreign orders manufactured in their home countries.

The existence of these arrangements was certainly suspected by governments. In the USA during a series of Congressional hearings in 1913 into the activities of the United States Steel Corporation (which had taken over Carnegie Steel in 1902) Mr Corey, ex-president of the company, admitted the existence of an international armour plate pool. When first questioned he had claimed to be unable to remember any details but on further questioning and the production of minutes of meetings at which he was present he admitted that the pool existed and claimed its aim was the division of business in neutral markets.

The *Engineer* magazine reported the hearings in its issue of 31 January 1913 but disputed whether its purpose was as Mr Corey had described. In view of the small size of the 'neutral' market for armour plate the magazine argued that the probable purpose of the pool was to control the price of armour plate in Britain, France, Germany and the United States. They argued that:

> Foreign patents, combined with the secrecy of manufacturing in respect of improvements made in the course of the years, controlled the production of the best classes of armour plate, and the heavy royalties paid by licensees, together with other conditions imposed on them, may possibly have led to the fixing of minimum prices in each of the countries where the patents were worked.[17]

The *Engineer* was a widely read magazine and its reports, as well as the investigations in the United States, would certainly have been known about within both the British government and the Admiralty. If the Admiralty had not been aware of the existence of the Harvey United Steel Company they certainly became aware of it when one of its directors, Mr Edward Marshall Fox, sent them a copy of the company's annual report for 1912 and accounts for the previous year.[18]

The annual report laid out clearly the membership of all the major armour plate companies and their representatives on the board, and set out how the company proposed to divide its income from patents between its members.

The Steel Manufacturers Nickel Syndicate Ltd

The Steel Manufacturers Nickel Syndicate Ltd was an organisation whose purpose was to purchase nickel cobalt and other minerals, and to distribute them among its members. The syndicate, however, convinced many people that the international armour plate firms collaborated together across national boundaries, putting their own commercial interests before those of their respective countries. The syndicate looms large in the evidence given by the Union for Democratic Control to the Royal Commission on the Private Manufacture of and Trade in Arms. They claimed that in 1914 the membership of the Syndicate was:[19]

	Shares held
Cammell Laird & Co.	125
Vickers, Sons & Maxim	125
John Brown	125
Sir W. G. Armstrong, Whitworth & Co.	125
F. Krupp AG	125
Schneider & Cie	125
Der Dillinger Huttenweke	118
Societa de Terni	125
Wikowitzer-berghau und Eisen gererkscaft	125
Compagnie des Forge de Chatillon Commentry	125
Hadfields Ltd	125
W. Beardmore	125

Sir William Jowett was a King's Council Barrister and a Liberal and then Labour politician. He was a mainstream figure who became Attorney General in the British government in 1929. In the period before the Second World War he called for rearmament and was Solicitor General from 1940 to 1944 in the wartime government led by Winston Churchill. He ended his career as Lord Chancellor in 1951. When he presented the case for the Union of Democratic Control he argued that the 'manufacturers of the heavy arms trade are very closely linked together, and closely linked together not merely nationally but internationally, indeed they have all the outward signs and symbols of what we call an arms ring'.

The previous sections have outlined three international collaborations between the armour plate manufacturers. Clearly they were closely linked together in sharing the benefits of patents through 'pools' such as the Harvey arrangements, manipulating the market for foreign orders and working together to secure the supply of the mineral resources they needed.

The more problematic question is to what extent these arrangements extended to the British armour-plate market and to what extent the five British companies operated as a cartel.

BRITISH RINGS AND CARTELS

Unlike the Harvey United Steel Company or the Steel Manufacturers Nickel Syndicate, formal organisations involving the armour companies at a national level are more difficult to find. Nevertheless there was a strongly held belief in both Britain and America that the armour plate makers in both countries had formed what were usually described as either 'rings' or 'cartels'. It was widely felt that these rings prevented competition in the armour plate market and forced both governments to pay higher prices than they should. In the United States this was clearly illegal, as the American House of Representatives hearings into price fixing by the United States Steel Corporation in 1911–12 shows. The legal position in Britain was not, however, as clear cut.

As an example of this, in March 1912 Mr James O'Grady, a Labour MP for Leeds, asked Winston Churchill, the First Lord of the Admiralty, 'whether he has any knowledge of a ring of armour plate manufacturers; if so, whether their operations are confined to Great Britain or are international'. He was told by the First Lord that 'the Admiralty are aware that certain price arrangements between armour plate firms do exist, but I am unable to say whether such arrangement constitutes a ring'.[20]

It was because questions such as this represented a commonly held view that the Parliamentary Select Committee on Estimates decided, in its review of the 1913 Naval Estimates, to enquire into armour plate prices.

The committee hearings

The Select Committee interviewed four senior Admiralty officials about the production of and the price for armour plate. The officials were:

- Right Hon. T. J. Macnamara MP LLD, Parliamentary and Financial Secretary to the Admiralty;
- Mr F. W. Black CB, Director of Navy Contracts;
- Mr W. H. Whiting, Supervisor of Contract Work;
- Rear Admiral A. G. H. W. Moore, Third Sea Lord and Controller of the Navy.

The Naval Estimates were divided into various votes, each with a number of subheadings: Vote 8 – Section D was for 'Armour for His Majesty's Ships and Vessels'. The chairman of the Select Committee, Sir Frederick Banbury, who was Conservative MP for Camberwell in London, opened the hearing with the comment that this was a very important item as 'statements have been made in public that there is a ring which is operating against the Admiralty for the price of armour plate'.[21] Mr W. H. Whiting, who had been the Superintendent of Contract Work at the Admiralty for eight years and prior to that was the Senior Assistant

---

i   The amount in the 1913/14 Naval Estimates for Armour Plate (Section D) was £2,031,861.

Director for Naval Construction, was asked if he thought there was such a ring in existence. His answer was a masterpiece of evasion: 'I think there are certain things which one can see which are quite consistent with the existence of a ring. It is quite another to say that I believe in the existence of a ring, because that would mean some positive proof.' In a follow-up question he was asked if he felt that the Admiralty could get equally good armour plate at a lower price, and he replied that he was 'quite sure they could not'. And he went on to agree with the proposition that, if the armour could not be obtained more cheaply, then the existence of a ring was not important. The committee members pressed him on whether he thought the base price paid for 'standard' armour plate was a fair one and he avoided answering this question on a number of occasions even though admitting he was the expert adviser to the board of the Admiralty on this issue.

The Superintendent of Contract Work outlined the process through which armour plate was ordered:

- The Admiralty placed the orders for armour for all ships, irrespective of whether they were built in the Royal Dockyards or built by contract with private shipyards.
- Generally the five armour firms were not invited to tender separately except for very specific bits of armour (which he did not define).
- The base price was agreed by the Admiralty with 'whole of the five firms'. It was *not* fixed at the absolute dictation of the firms. The base price did not include the costs of bending the plates or of machining them.
- The base price was subject to revision at certain times.
- Separate contracts were made with each firm for separate batches of armour and in those contracts the specific requirements for that batch of armour were taken into account and the price adjusted to reflect this.
- In placing orders the Admiralty paid constant attention to the manufacturing capacity of the firms.
- The Admiralty had 'some knowledge' of armour prices in other countries but considered it 'all but impossible' to make useful comparisons. The most recent figures were from the US where (he said, slightly disapprovingly), 'they are in the habit of publishing these things'.
- It was 'always the practice' that the government was provided with and actually tested sample plates.

The Admiralty had no members of staff who had worked in armour plate manufacturing but had a 'considerable number of men who have served for many years as Inspectors of rolling mills in those works'. They inspected plates during the whole manufacturing process, which was a condition of the armour plate contracts with the manufacturers.

Elsewhere in the proceedings of the committee the members examined Captain F. G. Eyre, who was responsible at the Admiralty for steel inspections. He told them that the main office of the Inspector of Steel was based at 7, Orchard Street in Sheffield, with a sub-office in Newcastle. The inspectors were naval officers who had naval experience. The office had recently been expanded by the addition of an analyst and three assistant analysts with the intention of making the office independent of the gun works at Woolwich.

It was put to Mr Whiting that since the government had only five firms to deal with and those five firms dealt collectively with the government, then that constituted a ring. He replied that that was 'not an unfair deduction' but would not be pushed further.

He was asked about the existence of an international armour ring, which had been raised by the Navy Budget Committee in Germany. At a meeting of this committee it had been stated that Krupp's were not allowed to sell armour plate in Britain, nor British firms in Germany, and also reported that the Italian government could only get one international firm, the American Midvale Works, to tender for armour plate. It was his personal opinion that there was no longer an international armour ring but he gave this opinion with a certain reservation. His real view on the existence of rings is, however, revealed in an internal Admiralty memo in 1914 when he wrote to a colleague that:

> It must be borne in mind that precisely the same 'Ring' complaints are made in America, that the number of Firms there is even less than in this Country (there being only three, viz Bethlehem, Carnegie & Midvale) and that **there is a good reason to believe that 'Ring' arrangements are made in the same way as is done here**. Furthermore, it is probable that if American Firms are invited to tender, an international ring will be formed [my emphasis].[22]

In view of the difficulties the committee members had in getting the Director of Contracts or the Supervisor of Contract Work to discuss anything that they classed as policy, and in view of their wide definition of what was policy, the Select Committee took evidence from the Third Sea Lord and Controller of the Navy on 5 May 1913. The controller, who was in charge of the contracts department and the relationships with the armour manufacturers, negotiated with the committee that his evidence would be treated as confidential and so we do not know what Rear Admiral A. G. H. W. Moore said to the committee. In a handwritten file note Admiral Moore commented that 'I understand the Committee has finished its investigation of the armour prices, accepting my evidence, which however was not recorded and is being treated as confidential to the Committee.'[23]

The findings of the committee

The findings of the Select Committee about the prices paid for armour plate were:

> On the question of armour plating and its cost, your Committee received valuable information from the Third Sea Lord, which the Admiralty asked should be treated as confidential. They desire to say that, after careful consideration of Admiral Moore's evidence, they are satisfied that, having regard to the particular considerations which must govern the Admiralty in dealing with this matter the money voted is efficiently administered, with due regard to economy so far as it is compatible with considerations of fighting efficiency.

The committee voted on the wording of this paragraph and the vote was evenly split, with four MPs voting for and four (including Mr Goldstone, the proposer of the amendment) voting against. The chairman then used his casting vote to include this wording in the final report. A further amendment was then proposed by Sir Herbert Roberts and was passed. This inserted the following new paragraph:

> Your Committee heard evidence with reference to the difficulties involved in obtaining competitive tenders for armour-plating and gun-mountings owing to the existence of trade rings, and are of the opinion that it is desirable that this question should be further carefully considered by His Majesty's Government.

Options for getting armour at a lower price

Mr Whiting said to the Select Committee that if the firms charged unreasonable prices, the Admiralty had three options, which were to encourage a new firm to set up an armour plant, to make the armour themselves, or to buy it from abroad.

Admiralty papers reveal that all of these three options had been studied at some point.

Option 1: Encouraging a new firm to enter the market

The option of encouraging new entrants to the market had been shown to work in the USA when the Midvale Steel Company entered the market in 1903 and undercut the two existing companies' prices by around 5%. In Britain the Admiralty were approached in 1912 by Mr Marshall Fox,[24] previously a director of the Harvey United Steel Company (see p.68), about setting up a new steel manufacturing plant capable of making 6,000 tons of armour plate every year to compete with the five existing manufacturers. Mr Fox suggested that if he were given a guarantee of a certain volume of orders he would be able to undercut the present price by around £3 per ton. The Admiralty and Mr Fox had detailed discussions during 1912 and 1913 about setting up a plant.

It is unclear from the correspondence how much direct experience of the manufacture of armour plate Mr Fox had. He assured the Admiralty that he was 'the pioneer of modern armour plate manufacture […] throughout the world' and would have no problem producing high-quality armour. The Admiralty were slightly sceptical of his current knowledge of running a manufacturing business as opposed to the collection of royalties on behalf of the Harvey United Steel Company.

On 6 February 1913 senior members of the Admiralty held a conference with Mr Marshall Fox. Present were the Additional Civil Lord (Sir F. Hopwood), the Third Sea Lord (Rear Admiral Moore), the Financial Secretary (Sir W. Graham Greene), and the Director of Contracts (Mr F. W. Black). At the meeting and in a follow-up letter the Admiralty raised queries about the potential new company's ability to produce plates of the same quality as the existing manufacturers. They were aware of improvements in the quality of armour plate that were taking place and it must have been disturbing to hear Mr Marshall Fox saying that no new development had taken place since the Harvey and Krupp processes were introduced. They noted that a large expenditure on research over a number of years had produced considerable progress and that this was continuously necessary to raise the quality of future armour plate.

The Admiralty were also concerned about the quality of the sample plates produced. Test showed how they compared to existing plates:[25]

Weight of armour	Striking velocity of shells resisted		
	Marshall Fox trial plates	Standard Krupp quality	New quality
400 lbs	1,400	1,510	1,590
240 lbs	1,285	1,180	1,320

They told Mr Marshall Fox that his sample plates 'do not afford, from the tests which the Admiralty have made on them, any material to support your confident expectation that you could produce a quality of armour equal to what the Admiralty is already able to obtain'.

They also expressed major concerns about giving any guarantee of orders until the plant was up and running, as this could cause major delays in the building of capital ships if things went wrong – the other armour plate manufacturers might not be able to step in to meet any shortfall.

Shortly after this meeting Mr Marshal Fox withdrew his offer to set up a new armour plate works. The impression given in the Admiralty file is that this was a relief to the officers, but they were concerned that Mr Fox might show up the Admiralty in a bad light. In an internal note dated 1 February 1913, to Thomas Macnamara, the Financial Secretary to the Navy, an official (possibly Mr Whiting) says that Mr Fox's 'position is that he may, of course, make it public that the Admiralty have declined to support him in his endeavour to supply armour plate at a cheaper price than at present paid to the ring'.[26] Such publicity would, of course, be most unwelcome at a period when the House of Commons was enquiring into rings and price fixing!

During the negotiations Mr Marshall Fox had become worried that the existing manufacturers knew about his proposals and he wrote from Barcelona to the Admiralty expressing his concern that they would undercut him. From his experience of working with them in the Harvey consortiums he was certainly familiar with the armour plate manufacturers' methods of operation and his suggestion that cartel-like behaviour was to be expected from the five companies may well have been based on personal knowledge of their operating practices.

Option 2: To set up a government manufacturing plant

In his evidence to the Select Committee in 1913 Dr. Macnamara said that the possibility of setting up a government armour plate works had been discussed both formally and informally on a number of occasions. In one form or another the French and Russian governments had taken this approach. In France, the state factory at Guerigny had started to produce thin armour plates in 1904, and in 1909 the decision was taken to expand the plant to make heavy cemented armour plate.

The report of the French Chamber of Deputies[27] written in 1912 by M. P. Painlove argued that setting up a plant was necessary because the state was 'confronted with a syndicate of suppliers who have fixed beforehand the prices to be submitted and which divides among it members the various parts of orders'. The French report argued that collaboration between the government and such a syndicate was no bad thing if the two parties in question 'act with moderation and sincerity'. The paper argued that the establishment of a government factory enabled the state to compete with the private trade and to have accurate information about the proper purchase price of armour plate. This knowledge of the process would form the basis of the 'highest importance when the prices asked by the tenderers were under consideration'.

In spite of heavy expenditure the heavy armour plant was not expected to be fully operational until 1914. It was described in a French report as being a place where 'millions had been sunk under the pretext of economies rendered impossible by the very enormity of the task'.

However, despite having access to the translation of the French report and, it is reasonable to assume, information about the American debate on setting up their own plant, the British Admiralty were not keen on going down that route. In 1914 Rear Admiral Moore said in a file note that he had 'no reason to change my previously expressed opinion, that it would be unwise and uneconomical to set up a government manufactory'.[28] This was also the position taken by Prince Louis of Battenberg, the First Sea Lord.

Option 3: Buying armour from abroad

Dr. Macnamara, said he had discounted the option of buying armour from abroad as a matter of policy although he accepted that ruling this out might increase the price the Admiralty paid. His reasoning was that:

> We do not rely on a foreign supply by buying in this country. In the first place, we are not under any obligation to secure it, as we might have to secure it, at a time when it would be highly inconvenient, if not impossible: and then there are is the advantage that by doing it in this country we can have it all made under our own direction and inspection. Both those matters are important; the first extremely important.[29]

His argument that the security of supply was vitally important was a critical one, and there was evidence that in times of crisis the orders from smaller countries buying armour plate were given less priority than those placed by the country in which the works was situated. It does not seem that buying from abroad was a policy adopted by any of the major pre-war naval powers.

Endnotes

1. Joseph Daniels, Secretary of the US Navy, writing to the Senate Committee on Naval Affairs 14 July 1913. 63rd Congress, 1st session, Document 129, Library of Congress V903.A5, 1913.
2. Scott, *Vickers – A History*, p. 86.
3. Report of the Special Committee on Investigation of the Munitions Industry (The Nye Report), US Congress, Senate, 74th Congress, 2nd session, 24 February 1936.
4. President Dwight D. Eisenhower, Farewell address to the nation, 17 January 1961.
5. *Engineer*, 8 February 1889, p. 127.
6. Vickers Board Minutes, 2 June 1902, Volume 5, CU1363, p. 54.
7. US Supreme Court, 227 US 165 (1913).
8. Vickers Board Minutes, Book 5, 10 May 1906, CU1363, p. 223.
9. SIMT, Armour Plate Pool ledgers, MNVK.
10. Wirrall Archive Service, Journal T 005/0109, Journal U 005/0010.
11. Calculated from the armour plate ledgers, SIMT Library, MNVK.
12. Sheffield Archives, 1988/50 ESC-SCC-0013590.
13. Ibid.
14. Ibid.
15. Wirrall Archive Service, Journal T 005/0109, Journal U 005/0010.
16. Vickers Board Minutes, Book 5, 21 November 1902, CU1363, p. 95.
17. *Engineer*, 31 January 1913, p. 124.
18. National Archive, ADM 116/3456.
19. Royal Commission on the Private Manufacture of and Trade in Arms, Evidence of the Union of Democratic Control, July 1935. Published by UDC, Victoria St, London.
20. Hansard, HC Deb 13 March 1912 (series 5), vol. 35 cc1075–6.
21. Parliamentary Select Committee on Navy Estimates 1913–14, 30 April 1913, p. 103. ©2006 ProQuest Information and Learning Co.
22. National Archive ADM116/3456.
23. Ibid.
24. Ibid.
25. Ibid., p. 97.
26. Ibid., p. 157.
27. Translation of article in the report of the French Chamber of Deputies, No 1880, 1912; National Archive ADM 116/3456,.
28. National Archive ADM 116/3456, 27 March 1914FF.
29. Parliamentary Select Committee on Navy Estimates 1913–14, 30 April 1913, p. 6. ©2006 ProQuest Information and Learning Co.

CHAPTER 9

THE BRITISH ARMOUR PLATE POOL AGREEMENT

The previous chapter looked at the allegations from many quarters that the international armour plate manufacturers operated cartels at both international and national level, and that these cartels forced up the price of armour plate. The evidence we have looked at shows that the manufacturers worked together at an international level in organisations such as the Harvey United Steel Company, the foreign armour plate convention and the Steel Manufacturers Nickel Syndicate. The difficulties that all governments had in establishing effective competitive tendering processes suggests that price-fixing arrangements were common in all the major industrial countries, although actual evidence of these collaboration is hard to find.

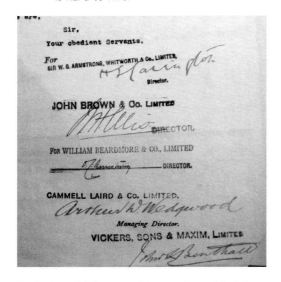

The signatures of all five armour plate companies on a letter to the Admiralty in February 1911. The letter is written on Vickers headed notepaper and signed by senior directors from each of the companies.

In Britain it seems that the Admiralty, and possibly the government more widely, had largely accepted that such cartels existed and had decided that the best strategy was to work with the armour makers. As Mr Whiting acknowledged in his evidence to the committee on the Estimates in 1913, 'for the main supply of armour the price is […] based on a definite price arrangement by the Admiralty with the whole of the five firms'[1] rather than on competitive tendering.

The schedules of prices agreed between the Admiralty and the armour makers from 1910 onwards clearly show the process of negotiation between the Admiralty and the armour makers as a collective, seemingly co-ordinated by Vickers.

The Admiralty was clearly sensitive to accusations that they were overpaying and were keen to keep the agreed schedules secret, both from their own dockyards and from the House of Commons. Although we do not know the contents of Rear Admiral Moore's confidential evidence in 1913 to the House of Commons Select Committee on the Estimates, it is possible that he shared the existence of the price agreement with them and argued that this was the best way both to get a fair price and, importantly for the Admiralty, to maintain a stable manufacturing base.

The evidence about the way in which the armour plate manufacturers collaborated together has, up until recently, been largely circumstantial. However, a series of ledgers have recently been found in the Sheffield Industrial Museums archives. These documents throw a spotlight on the extent of the collaboration between the armour plate manufacturers in the period after 1903.

This period was dominated by a naval arms race in which Britain sought to maintain its naval supremacy based on the traditional 'two-power standard' which required the British navy to be at least as strong as the next two largest navies combined. With the launching of HMS *Dreadnought* in 1906 all the world's major navies started from the same point, as the previous generation of ships were rendered obsolete, and Britain faced increased competition from Germany, which wished to establish itself as a world power with a strong navy.

The ledgers are interesting because they provide a production and financial record of the arrangements between the five armour plate manufactures based on an agreement they made on 3 February 1903. The agreement was known as the 'British Armour Plate Pool Arrangement' and was an agreement between Armstrong Whitworth, William Beardmore, John Brown, Cammell Laird and Vickers & Maxim.

There are two volumes of the ledgers covering the period 1903 to 1920 and they were clearly kept centrally by one of the companies on behalf of the five members of the pool. The ledgers have the address of a Manchester stationer and one of the loose documents has a stamp for 'Sir W. G. Armstrong Whitworth Armour Dept. 21 Feb 1912'. As well as this, the content of the some of the loose memos and notes kept inside the ledgers supports the idea that the ledgers were kept at Armstrong Whitworth's armour department at Openshaw works in Manchester.

On the right-hand page of the ledgers there is a record of the orders placed with the five firms for armour plate which shows the following information about each order:

- the date the order was placed;
- the type of armour ordered;
- the ship or ships the armour was ordered for;
- the organisation placing the order – most orders were from the Admiralty;
- the estimated weight / thickness of the armour;
- the estimated price per ton; and
- remarks on the armour.

On the left-hand page the ledgers record all the financial details about the order including the following information:

- the date of the invoices, which were generally every six months;
- the type of the invoice – mostly advance payments, final invoices and credits;
- the amount of the invoices;
- the royalty payable to the Harvey United Steel Company; and
- the amount paid into a pool, which was 20% of the income received by the companies after they had paid and royalties.

The ledgers begin in the pre-Dreadnought era and an early example from the ledger is an order for 1,527 tons of armour for the pre-Dreadnought HMS *Lord Nelson*, one of the two ships of the *Lord Nelson* class, which was built at Palmer's shipyard on the Tyne. The order for this armour plate was placed with Cammell Laird on 16 February 1905 and was for bulkheads, side (belt) armour, bow protection and the armour on the sloping middle decks. The left hand page of the ledger shows the order details:

A	B	C	D	E	F	G
Date of Order	Description	Ship	Ordered by	Estimated weight (tons) of plate and fittings	Price £sd	Remarks
16/02/1905	Bulkhead	Lord Nelson	Admiralty	114	£119/0/0	480 &320lbs
20/02/1905	Side			430¼	£135/0/0	480lbs
				62¼	£130/0/0	360lbs
				382	£121/10/0	320lbs
				196	£118/10/0	240lbs
				273¼	£115/10/0	160lbs
	Bow protection			22	£96/0/0	80lbs
	Middle Deck slopes			48	£85/0/0	80lbs
				1,527¾		

Notes on the order:

Column A shows the date of the order which appears to come in two parts, on 16 and 20 February 1905. The *Lord Nelson* was laid down on 18 May 1905 so this armour was ordered before the building of the ship was started.

Column B shows the type of armour ordered. The first two elements are for bulkhead and side (or belt) armour. It is possible that these were ordered on the 16th. The second two elements were for bow protection and middle deck slopes; again, it is possible that these were ordered on the 20th.

Column C contains the name of the ship. For some orders this has the names of more than one ship, and where this is the case they are normally ships from the same class. Where the orders are for plates to be tested by the Admiralty (usually at Shoeburyness) this is shown in this column.

Column D shows that the armour was, as one would expect, ordered by the Admiralty. If the order had been for gun shields the name of the ordinance works with whom the order for the gun mountings was placed is shown. The ordinance works placed the order with their own armour works; for example Armstrong Whitworth's, whose ordinance works at Elswick won the order for both the *Lord Nelson*'s 12-inch and 9.2-inch gun mountings, placed their orders for gun shields with their own Openshaw armour works and in this case the order would be shown as coming from Elswick.

Columns E, F and G show the estimated weight, price per ton and weight of the armour plate per square foot (One square foot of armour one inch thick weighs 40.8 lbs.). These figures can be compared to information from other sources about the armour for the *Lord Nelson*:

- The main bulkhead in the *Lord Nelson* class was the rear bulkhead, which joined the belt armour to the rear barbette. The ledger shows that this was formed from 12- and 8-inch plates, although most records give the thickness of the aft bulkhead as being 8 inches.
- The main belt of side armour was 190 feet long and 7 feet high. In the midship section it ran from the sides of the fore barbette as far back as the aft barbette and had a maximum thickness of 12 inches, which is shown in the ledger as 480 lbs. The order also shows armour of 9, 8, 6 and 4 inches thickness which is consistent with the known weight of the *Lord Nelson's* armour in the main belt, upper belt, the lower edge of the belt and the after belt armour. The total weight given for the belt armour for the *Lord Nelson* class was 1,398.3 tons[2] and the ledger shows an order weight of 1,343.75 tons.
- The bow protection armour was 2 inches thick and formed the ship's ram. The total designed weight was 22¼ tons. These designated weights compare closely to the figures given in the ledger.
- The middle deck slopes were 2 inches thick and sloped down from the middle deck to the edges of the lower deck; this thickness is the same as given in the ledger. The total designed weight of the slopes was 88 tons but only 48 tons of this is shown in this order. Generally not a great deal of deck armour is shown in the ledger and it may be that the 'missing' 40 tons may be of a type of armour not included in the Pool Agreement.

On the right-hand side of the ledger there are the financial and invoicing details of the order:

H	I	J				K	L	M	N	O
Date	Class of payment	Invoiced weight of plates				Payments received £sd	Royalty £sd	Net Amount £sd	20% to Pool £sd	Remarks
		Ton	Cwt.	Qtr.	Lbs.					
30/06/05	Advance					£8,382/17/6		£8,382/17/6	£1,676/11/6	
31/12/05	Advance					£34,099/15/2		£34,099/15/2	£6,819/19/0	
30/06/06	Advance					£67,432/6/10		£67,432/6/10	£13,486/9/4	
30/06/06	Final	217	6	3	16½	£3,407/1/0	£1,826/6/4	£1,580/14/8	£316/3/0	
30/06/06	Advance					£5,053/0/6		£5,053/0/6	£1,010/12/1	
30/06/06	Final	54	14	2	21	£736/10/6	£191/11/6	£544/10/1	£108/19/10	
31/12/06	Advance					£48,271/11/6		£48,271/11/6	£9,654/6/4	
31/12/06	Final	1,218	3	0	13	£19,792/19/10	£9,026/7/2	£10,766/12/8	£2,153/6/6	
31/12/06	Final	10	19	3	0	£171/13/8	£38/9/2	£132/14/6	£26/10/11	
30/06/07	Advance					£3,239/16/5		£3,239/16/5	£647/19/3	
30/06/07	Final	67	6	2	27½	£1,122/19/2	£382/17/7	£740/1/7	£148/0/4	

Notes on the invoicing and pool payments:

Columns H and I show the date of the invoice and the type of invoice. For the order for the *Lord Nelson* there are eleven invoices of which six are advances and five are final invoices. It is not clear in this order or in the others which part of the order the invoices relate to – or indeed whether the invoices relate to completed plates from the whole order.

Column J shows the weight of armour plate for each final invoice. The weight is shown in imperial weights, which are made up of:

	Tons	Hundredweight (cwt)	Quarters (qtrs)	Pounds (lbs)
Made up of:	20 cwt	4 qtrs	28 lbs	

The final weight of armour plate delivered for this order was 1,568 tons, 11 cwt, 0 qtrs, 22 lbs. In the decimal equivalent this represents 1,568.56 tons.

Column K shows the amount invoiced for in £.s.d. For this order for armour plate the total amount invoiced to the Admiralty was £191,710/12/1 (£191,710.65). This compares to the estimated price of the order (taken from columns E and F) of £187,134.

Column L shows the royalty payable to the Harvey United Steel Company for use of the patents it controlled for the Harvey and Krupp processes. For this order the amount payable was £11,465/11/9 (£11,465.59). This is 5.98% of the invoiced income or a payment of £7.31 per ton of armour plate.

Column M is the net income after the amount paid in royalty has been deducted.

Column N is a payment of 20% of the net income into a pool arrangement set up under the British Armour Plate Pool Agreement in 1903. For this order of armour for the *Lord Nelson* Cammell Laird paid £36,048/18/1 (£36,048.90) into the collective pool.

THE POOL ARRANGEMENTS

The figures in Column N provide hard evidence that the British armour plate manufacturers were operating a pool arrangement in which they paid a percentage of their income from armour plate into a common pool. Unfortunately no copy of the Pool Agreement has, as yet, come to light. However, from the information provided in the ledgers we do know some things about how the arrangement worked:

- The pool ledger was kept centrally, possibly by Armstrong Whitworth in Manchester.
- The pool was made up from the five companies each paying 20% of their net earnings, after the deduction of the royalties paid to the Harvey United Steel Company. This percentage was payable on naval armour plate for British ships and some armour plate ordered by the War Office.
- The calculations about the distribution of the pool were made on a half-yearly basis at the end of June and December.

How the financial arrangements for the pool worked

The distribution of the pool was based on whether a company's contribution to the pool was greater or lesser than the average of all five companies: the way that this amount was calculated is most clearly seen in the summary tables at the back of the second ledger. For the first six months of 1911 the 'General Summary' of the amount of armour each company had manufactured and how much they had paid into the pool is set out:

The pool calculation in the ledgers for the first half of 1911.

Date	Company	Invoiced weight of plates & fittings				Cash received £sd	Gross Pool 20% £sd	Net Pool	
		Tons	cwt	qtrs	lbs			To pay	To receive
	Armstrong	3,953	15	2	13	£405,011/6/7	£81,002/5/5	£18,827/0/10	
	Beardmore	2,939	1	1	7	£212,469/6/6	£42,493/17/4		£19,681/7/2
30/6/1911	Brown	3,975	10	3	8	£295,190/6/8	£59,038/1/4		£3,137/3/3
	Cammell	3,815	14	0	21	£283,775/1/7	£56,755/0/4		£5,420/4/2
	Vickers	3,555	1	3	25	£357,934/11/7	£71,586/18/4	£9,411/13/9	
	Total	18,239	3	3	18	£1.554,380/12/11	£310,876/2/9	£28,238/14/7	£28,238/14/7

From this table we can work out the calculation for any of the companies. For example the calculation for Cammell Laird is:

a	The total income received by all five companies	=	£1,554,380/12/11
b	The total amount paid into the pool	=	£310,876/2/9
c	The average amount paid into the pool (row b divided by five companies)	=	£62,175/4/6
d	Total amount paid into the pool by Cammell Laird	=	£56,755/0/4

Because Cammell Laird paid less into the pool than the average of the five companies they received a payment from the pool equivalent to the difference between their payment (d) and the average payment (c). This was £62,175/4/6 minus £56,755/0/4 = £5,420/4/2.

Similar calculations can be made for the other four companies.

Tracking the pool payments

A summary at the end of the first ledger book sets out in detail the annual amounts each company paid into or received from the pool for each half-year period. These amounts, for the period December 1903 to July 1909, are shown for all of the five companies in the following table:[3]

Date	Armstrong Whitworth		W. Beardmore		J. Brown		Cammell Laird		Vickers	
	Pay / receive	£sd	Pay / receive	£sd	Pay / receive	£sd	Pay / receive	£sd	Pay / receive	£sd
31/12/1903	pay	£1,414/15/10	receive	£1,038/19/2	pay	£662/4/8	receive	£1,038/19/2	pay	£0/17/10
30/06/1904	receive	£292/3/0	receive	£16,108/2/10	receive	£8,812/5/1	receive	£1,748/19/6	pay	£26,961/10/5
31/12/1904	pay	£16,495/8/10	receive	£13,339/2/9	receive	£188/4/5	receive	£3,580/19/1	pay	£612/17/5
30/06/1905	receive	£1,080/11/0	receive	£3,122/14/0	receive	£467/6/2	receive	£8,891/19/1	pay	£13,562/0/3
31/12/1905	pay	£3,615/11/9	pay	£1,804/2/2	receive	£927/0/11	pay	£5,462/6/5	receive	£9,954/19/5
30/06/1906	pay	£19,701/0/4	receive	£12,363/16/11	receive	£41,360/3/9	pay	£25,516/10/7	pay	£8,506,9/9
31/12/1906	pay	£29,741/11/9	receive	£5,948/10/0	receive	£10,992/18/6	receive	£10,752/14/8	receive	£2,047/8/7
30/06/1907	pay	£24,581/1/5	receive	£4,688/19/4	receive	£753/10/5	receive	£11,961/2/5	receive	£7,177/9/3
31/12/1907	receive	£4,605/15/1	receive	£9,047/5/3	receive	£4,276/17/6	receive	£1,276/0/2	pay	£19,205/18/0
30/06/1908	receive	£5,485/17/3	receive	£9,800/11/7	pay	£19,752/16/5	receive	£5,441/15/6	pay	£975/7/11
31/12/1908	receive	£15,580/1/6	receive	£3,100/16/4	pay	£13,144/8/10	receive	£4,610/18/9	pay	£10,147/7/9

The details of the figures for Cammell Laird are shown in the table below

Date	Invoiced weight				Gross invoiced income	Pool	
	Tons	Cwt	Qtrs	Lbs		To pay	To receive
31/12/03	1,800 tons free						£1,038/19/2
30/06/04	387	13	0	20	£72,585/12/4		£1,748/19/6
31/12/04	732	14	1	12	£105,428/2/8		£3,580/19/1
30/06/05	1,639	13	2	10	£183,987/1/7		£8,891/9/1
31/12/05	1,522	16	0	14	£141,977/16/6	£5,462/6/5	
30/06/06	2,861	15	0	17	£415,757/8/9	£25,516/10/7	
31/12/06	2,334	15	0	17	£172,602/0/0		£10,752/14/8
30/06/07	632	2	3	9	£173,003/4/6		£11,961/2/5
31/12/07	1,764	9	2	4	£140,339/17/0		£1,276/0/2
30/06/08	543	14	3	1	£122,305/4/11		£5,441/15/6
31/12/08	1,099	11	3	23	£106,993/12/4		£4,610/18/4

The summary table from the ledgers showing Cammell Laird's pool payments for the period 1903 to 1908.

The armour plate ledger does not, however, specify how these pool payments were made but Cammell Laird's financial records enable us to track the payment.

A number of Cammell Laird's account books are held in the Wirral Archive Service at Birkenhead. The following information is drawn from journal ledgers, which are a method of the accounts department for keeping a record of inter-company transfers between different account headings.

In the journals there are a number of references to payments relating to the British Armour Plate Pool as well as payments of royalties to the Harvey United Steel Company and to a separate pool arrangement covering 'foreign' armour plate orders. All of these entries show payment to and from Cammell Laird and the crediting or debiting of these amounts from the Cyclops West Forge Department Revenue Account into other internal accounts.

The payments relating to the British Armour Plate Pool are shown in the table below:[4]

Ledger date	Period	Credit / Debit	Received from / Paid to	Amount
30/6/1903	1903 Q1	Credit	Vickers	£308/7/8
30/6/1903	1903 Q2	Credit	Vickers	£1,334/7/54
30/9/1903	1903 Q3	Credit	Vickers	£946/10/2
30/9/1904	1904 Q1 & 2	Credit	Vickers	£1,749/19/6
31/3/1905	1904 Q3 & 4	Credit	Vickers	£612/17/5
31/3/1905	1904 Q3 & 4	Credit	Armstrong	£2,968/1/8
sub total	1904 Q3 & 4			£3,580/19/1
30/10/1905	1905 Q1 & 2	Credit	Vickers	£8,891/9/1
31/3/1906	1905 Q3 & 4	Debit	Vickers	£5,462/6/5
31/12/1906	1906 Q3 & 4	Credit	Armstrong	£10,752/14/8
30/9/1907	1907 Q1 & 2	Credit	Armstrong	£11,961/2/5
31/12/1907	1907 Q2 & 3	Credit	Vickers	£1,276/0/2

The extract from the Journals for 31 December 1904[5] shows two payments into the Cammell Laird accounts. One is from Vickers (account ref: 404) for £612/17/5 and the other is from Armstrong Whitworth (account ref: 435) for £2,968/1/8. Both amounts, totalling £3,580/19/1, were credited to the Cyclops West Forge Account (account ref: 263).

The Vickers financial records[6] also show payments made under the pool arrangements and these correspond to the amounts recorded in the Cammell Laird journals. The Vickers accounts show payments and receipts of:

Date	Amount	
	From Vickers to Cammell Laird	From Cammell Laird to Vickers
30/9/1904	£1,749/19/6	
14/4/1905	£612/17/5	
20/11/1905	£8,891/9/1	
10/4/1908	£1,276/0/2	
12/04/1906		£5,462/6/5

Cammell Laird's pool entitlements, as shown in the Armour Plate Pool ledger, match up with payments in and out of the Cammell Laird and Vickers accounts. These records clearly show that although the pool was administered centrally, the pool payments were made by inter-company transfers rather than though a central pool bank account.

Period	Armour Plate ledger		Cammell Laird journals		Vickers journals		Notes on other payments
	Credit	Debit	Credit	Debit	Credit	Debit	
1903 Q1	£1,038/19/2		£308/7/8				
1903 Q2			£1,344/7/5				
1903 Q3			£946/10/2				
sub total			£2,599/5/3				
1904 Q1 & 2	£1,748/19/6		£1,749/19/6			£1,749/19/6	
1904 Q3 & 4			£612/17/5			£612/17/5	
1904 Q3 & 4			£2,968/1/8				Received from Armstrong's
sub total	£3,580/19/1		£3,580/19/1				
1905 Q1 & 2	£8,891/9/1		£8,891/9/1			£8,891/9/1	
1905 Q3 & 4		£5,462/6/5		£5,462/6/5	£5,462/6/5		
1906 Q3 & 4	£10,752/14/8		£10,752/14/8				Received from Armstrong's
1907 Q1 & 2	£11,961/2/5		£11,961/2/5				Received from Armstrong's
1907 Q2 & 3	£1,276/0/2		£1,276/0/2			£1,276/0/2	

The extract from the Journals for December 1904[6] (see opposite) showing two payments to Cammell Laird under the pool arrangements.

The only differences between the Armour Plate ledger and the jounals are in 1903, which was the first year of operation of the pool arrangement. In this year a significant amount of production was described as 'Free Pool' and Cammell Laird received an allowance of 1,800 tons which may explain the different figures in this year. The figures from the Vickers' journal enable us to see the money being transferred out of one company's accounts into the others.

WHO DID BEST FROM THE POOL ARRANGEMENT?

An analysis of which of the five companies did the best out of the pool arrangement shows that Vickers, Sons & Maxim were by far the largest contributor to the pool, putting in a total of £433,673 between 1903 and 1920. Their Sheffield neighbour Cammell Laird, on the other hand, were the largest beneficiary receiving support worth £257,590 from the pool over the same period.

Paying more into the pool than they got out	Receiving more from the pool than they paid in
Vickers £433,673	
Armstrong Whitworth £63,698	
	£82,447 Beardmore
	£157,376 John Brown
	£257,590 Cammell Laird

In the period 1903 to 1907 Cammell Laird ranked equally with the other armour plate manufacturers, making 23% of the armour produced, equal to the share held by both Armstrong's and Vickers. However, the company's share of production fell and by 1913 to 1916 they manufactured only 13% of the armour made. In spite of their falling market share the growth in orders for armour plate meant that the amount of armour plate they made actually increased.

The workings of the pool arrangement meant that as the overall production increased, the size of the pool grew accordingly. Because Cammell Laird's share of overall production fell they became entitled to a bigger share of this larger pool. Between 1912 and 1915, when armour production was at its peak, 13% of Cammell Laird's income from armour plate came from pool payments from the other firms.

CONCLUSION

The Armour Plate Pool ledgers at SIMT clearly show the existence and the workings of the British Armour Plate Pool Agreement. They do not, however, answer the question about the reasons and motivations for setting up such an agreement. In the early stages of the agreement the pool arrangement worked relatively equally, with none of the five armour plate companies receiving large amounts of income from the pool. It is arguable that the pool arrangements provided the five companies with a degree of mutual support and bound them together in their dealings with their major customer, the British government. However, around 1910 this position changed and between 1910 and 1916 Vickers became by far the largest contributor to the pool, paying a total of £320,330 to the other four companies. William Beardmore, in whom Vickers had a majority shareholding, were also a net contributor to the pool in this period.

Once the pool became so lopsided, and Vickers became overwhelmingly the largest contributor, it seems likely that dynamics of the agreement would have changed. Vickers were renowned for the quality of their management and their commercial acumen and one wonders what the directors saw as the strategic advantage for their company of remaining in the pool. Although no discussion about the Pool Agreement appears in the formal minutes of the company's board of directors, this does not of course mean that such discussions did not take place.

There were clearly benefits for the companies whose operations were being supported by the pool but the British Admiralty also benefited, at least indirectly. The agreement supported the maintenance of a wide manufacturing base at a time when the Admiralty were placing larger orders and also trying to raise the quality of armour plate. It is possible that, without the Pool Agreement, the weaker manufacturers might not have been able to make the investments in new plant which enabled them to achieve the quality improvements that the Admiralty was demanding, and they might as a consequence have stopped making armour plate. The consequences of losing even one of the five manufacturers would have delayed the Admiralty's Dreadnought-building programme at a time when the Dreadnought arms race was being stoked by the development of heavier 'super-Dreadnought' battleships with more armour and larger guns.

Endnotes

1. Parliamentary Select Committee on Navy Estimates 1913–14, 30 April 1913, p. 103. ©2006 ProQuest Information and Learning Co.
2. Burt, *British Battleships 1889–1904*, p. 324.
3. SIMT Armour Plate Pool ledger, Vol. 1. M560A
4. Wirral Archive Service Cammell Laird & Co Ltd, Accounts Journal, 005/0108, pp. 9 and 10.
5. Ibid., 105/0109, p. 30.
6. Sheffield City Archive, SCC-0013014

CHAPTER 10

PROBLEMS AT CAMMELL LAIRD

Armour plate making at Cammell Laird's Sheffield works was carried out on two sites. The steel was forged at the Grimesthorpe Works and then transferred to the Cyclops Works, where the processes that turned it into cemented armour plate were carried out. In 1906 and the first part of 1907 Cammell Laird experienced problems with the War Office and the Admiralty over 'malpractices' at the Grimesthorpe Works.

The Board of Trade, which was not an active participant in the dispute, co-ordinated government actions in relation to contractors and was therefore kept informed by the Admiralty and the War Office.[1] The Cammell Laird board minutes are held at the Wirral Archive and give an account of all the board's activities. Unfortunately they are quite formal and much interesting information is only referred to rather than reported in detail.

PROBLEMS OF QUALITY CONTROL

It appears that problems with testing procedures were found not just at Cammell Laird but at a number of other firms as well. Mr Samson, of the Consultative Branch of the Board of Trade's Marine Department, wrote a note marked 'private' to his colleague Mr Marwood on 18 September 1907. He begins by thanking him for his note about Cammell Laird and goes on to say that:

> There is I fear a great amount of fraud being practiced at some of our steel works, and it would be in the interest of the public as well as the steel makers themselves if effective steps were taken to stop it. It would be very useful if several of the firms were treated in a similar manner to the one referred to.[2]

In a follow-up letter Mr Samson goes on to outline a number of examples where there was suspicion of fraud at four firms:

- In the case of C. W. Robinson & Co of Polmont there was suspicion that some of the test stampings on steel castings had been 'forged or otherwise manipulated'. As this occurred on two occasions, a special testing regime was put in place for this firm.[3]
- The Caledonian Steel Castings Company appeared to have forged test pieces they were making for Fairfield's Shipbuilding Company. This was the second time this had occurred at the company.[4]
- The surveyor had reasons to think that the test pieces of certain steel castings made by the Steel Company of Scotland for John Brown & Co. had been tampered with. As there was no hard evidence, the matter was allowed to drop.
- The Consett Iron Company made a parcel of steel rivets for the Rivet, Bolt & Nut Company of Glasgow that were tested and passed by the board's surveyors at the Consett factory. However, suspicions arose and the rivets were retested and completely different results were obtained, 'thereby raising a very grave suspicion of fraud'. This was not the first time incidents of this nature had occurred at the firm.

It may well be therefore that the government was experiencing a range of problems with the quality of steel forgings and that they decided that they had to make an example of Cammell Laird.

THE DISPUTE

In April 1907 the Admiralty and the War Office, which were Cammell Laird's two main customers for armour plate, held an investigation at the Grimesthorpe Works in Sheffield into allegations of malpractice. This enquiry clearly found problems and required the company to take action.

However, neither the enquiry nor the correspondence from the government relating to it were reported to the Cammell Laird board of directors. It appears that Mr F. C. Fairholme, the joint managing director of the company, tried to deal with the matter on his own, but this clearly did not satisfy the government and after six months they wrote to the company in September 1907 notifying them that they intended remove Cammell Laird from the government's list of contractors until further notice.

The board launched an investigation led by four of the directors. It was reported to the board that this investigation:

[h]ad examined a number of the officials at the Sheffield Works, with respect to alleged irregularities, and that as the result of the enquiry it was established that malpractices had been carried on in the Works, but that it appeared that these practices had been largely checked under the existing management, although not entirely discontinued.[5]

On 9 October 1907 the board wrote to the War Office and the Admiralty requesting a new enquiry as they wished to point out:

The disadvantage at which they are placed in dealing with the matter, owing to the fact that they are not at present in full possession of all the facts which led up to and were disclosed during the informal Enquiry as unfortunately no proper notes of the proceedings were taken by the officials.[6]

The letter apologised for the fact 'that representatives, through a misconception of their position, made no attempt to co-operate in the Enquiry'. The board requested that a personal meeting should be held between the chairman of the board, Mr John McGregor Laird, and the government.

The chairman subsequently held meetings with Lord Tweedmouth, the First Lord of the Admiralty, and Lord Desart who was the Solicitor General and government's senior legal adviser. No reports of these meetings are found in the board minutes or the Board of Trade file; however, at the end of the month the War Office (and probably the Admiralty as well) wrote to Cammell Laird outlining the steps they would have to take to be reinstated on the list. These were:

– The Directorate of your company being reconstructed under a new Chairman.
– The Managing Directors of the Grimesthorpe Works being removed.
– Prosecution of incriminated persons being initiated by you to the satisfaction of the Army Council.

However no orders, direct or indirect, exclusive of those for armour plates which must at present be completed at the Cyclops Works, will be given for work which the Company proposed to execute at their Grimesthorpe Works, until the Army Council are wholly satisfied that the working arrangements of that place have been thoroughly reformed. [7]

It would seem that John McGregor Laird's interviews with the senior members of the government had not convinced them of his ability to sort out the problems.

Reports of the problems at Cammell Laird clearly reached some of the shareholders and at the end of October 1907 the board drafted a letter trying to reassure them.

Both Fredrick Fairholm and Albert Longden, the joint managing directors, were asked to resign, and the board suggested that the chairman might like to consider doing the same. Mr McGregor Laird took some time to decide what to do but in the end he bowed to the inevitable and he resigned on 31 October 1907. He was replaced by Dr Francis Elgar, Professor of Naval Architecture, ex-Head of the Royal Dockyards and Managing Director of Fairfield Shipyard, a company with which Cammell Laird had close relationships and a cross-shareholding. A report appeared in *The Times* on 8 November minimising the problems at the company and praising the ex-chairman for his 'rigid regard for the historic and honourable name of his firm'.[8]

Immediately after the resignation of the chairman and managing directors, the board began to take action to restore the government's confidence in the firm. They appointed Mr G. P. Parker of Woodcock, Ryland and Parker to investigate what had been going on and he reported to the board at the beginning of November 1907. Sadly there are no details of his verbal (or later written) report in the board minutes. By November 1907 things had improved to such an extent that the government agreed a statement with Cammell Laird confirming that they were happy with the progress being made. The statement reiterated the conditions for reinstatement and continued:

We understand that the above named requirements are being actively carried out by the Company.

The Chairman and the Managing Directors as Officers responsible for the management have retired from the Board, although they were individually unacquainted with the circumstances that directly caused the present difficulties.[9]

Later that November it was reported to the board that the Admiralty had enquired about a new order for armour plate.

The extent of the problems at the Grimesthorpe Works are shown in the minutes of the Finance and General Purpose Committee in January 1908. This reported on an agreement to pay pensions to people who had been dismissed. These included:

N. Jepson	Grimesthorpe	30/- per week from 26 Jan 1908
J. Easthorpe	Blacksmith, Grimesthorpe	20/- per week
H. Baxter	Fettler, Grimesthorpe	20/- per week from 23 Dec 1907

There is also a recommendation that the salary of a Mr Barker, transferred from Grimesthorpe to Cyclops works, be reduced from £700 to £550 per annum.

In March 1908 two further members of staff, Mr L. Burrows and Mr George Bourne, were discharged by the board 'in accordance with the Admiralty requirements'. Finally, on 2 April 1908, the War Office and the Admiralty both sent letters to Cammell Laird stating that they had been restored to the list of government contractors subject to 'the severance of the connection between your firm and all the late officials of the Company who have been discharged or have received notice to leave in connection with the disclosures of improper practices is permanent and final'.[10]

According to the Armour Plate Pool ledger Cammell Laird received an order for around 2,400 tons of armour plate on 29 January 1908 for the battleships *Collingwood*, *St Vincent* and *Vanguard*. This was prior to them being officially restored to the lists in March.

THE IMPACT OF THE SUSPENSION ON CAMMELL LAIRD

The impact of being removed from the Admiralty and War Office lists for the supply of armour plate was potentially severe, particularly as the armour plate business was the most profitable of the company's activities. The report of the directors to the company's annual shareholders meeting, held on 27 March 1908, stated that they would not be able to pay a dividend for the previous year and explained the problems they had experienced:

> It was brought to the notice of the Board in September last, that serious irregularities had been going on at the Grimesthorpe Works, and that the Government Departments, with whom the Company has in the past done a large amount of business, were not satisfied with the way in which their representations had been met, and had in consequence removed the Company from their Lists of Contractors. When the late Chairman and Managing Directors, who were responsible for the organisation and control of the Company's business, realised the gravity of the position, they tendered their resignations in the interests of the Company, as it appeared that if this step were taken, and other changes made, the Government might restore the Company to its Lists of Contractors. These resignations were accepted, and Mr. Francis Elgar was appointed Chairman.[11]

This had a potential impact on the company in two ways: on new orders for armour plate and on finances.

New orders for armour plate

The SIMT Armour Plate Pool ledgers show the following orders for armour plate for the period from November 1906, when the crisis began, to March 1908 when Cammell Laird was restored to the list:

Date of order	Description	Ship	Ordered by	Weight of plate (tons)
24/02/1907	1 - KC plate 9ft x 7ft x 9in			20.61
10/12/1906	40lbs Bulkhead CNS	Swift	Laird	10.09
27/03/1907	3 Bowplates	Commonwealth	Admiralty	5.30
04/02/1907	3 - 9in plates KC		Shoebury	31.12
14/01/1907	1 - 120lbs 8ft x 6ft plate KNC		Shoebury	2.70
	1 - 120lbs 8ft x 6ft plate CNS			2.85
	1 - 120lbs 8ft x 6ft plate High per[formance?] Nickel			2.72
02/03/1907	2 - 9in plates KC			41.32
26/03/1907	2 - 9in plates KC		Shoebury	
13/04/1907	1/2in plates, CNS Torpedo destroyer	'Saracen'	J. White & Co.	7.66
09/08/1907	Not specified			6.23

An analysis of the orders placed during the suspension period shows that a total of 120.5 tons of armour plate were ordered from Cammell Laird. The breakdown of these orders is shown in the table below:

Type of order	Tons	Percentage of total
Orders from Cammell Laird's shipyard	10.09	8.11%
Orders from other private shipyards	7.66	6.16%
Unspecified armour ordered by Admiralty	26.18	21.05%
Orders for Shoeburyness for testing	75.14	60.42%
Order from Admiralty for a ship	5.30	4.26%
Total	124.37	100.00%

- The order from Laird's and the other private shipyard (J. Samuel White, based in Cowes in the Isle of Wight) were for destroyers and were not ordered through the Admiralty, and thus not covered by the exclusion.
- The order from the Admiralty for plate for a ship (HMS *Commonwealth*) was very small and may well have been a continuation of work Cammell Laird was doing prior to the ban on the same ship.
- The largest two orders are for Shoeburyness, which was a government range at which armour plate was tested. It is likely because of the size of the plates that the other unspecified orders from the Admiralty also went to testing sites.

For comparison the following table shows the total for the years 1905 to 1910 and the drastic fall in orders in 1907:

	1905	1906	1907	1908	1909	1910
Number of orders received	16	11	7	6	16	23
Total Tonnage	5,712	3,169	120	2,539	3,307	6,882
Value of orders received	£651,155	£408,453	£11,933	£253,714	£345,048	£644,088

THE IMPACT ON CAMMELL LAIRD'S FINANCES

Generally speaking large orders for armour plate took about a year to make and deliver to the shipyards. The company therefore continued to work on armour plate orders that had been placed with the company before the suspension.

The armour plate division of Cammell Laird was the most profitable in the company and the impact of the Admiralty/War Office ban on the company's armour plate income and their overall profit is shown in the following table. Invoices were generally submitted on a six-monthly basis.

	CL profit / loss (1)	Armour invoiced (tons) (2)	Net armour income (2)
Jun-05	£269,807	1,640	£169,596
Dec-05		1,523	£134,024
Jun-06	£349,280	2,859	£403,800
Dec-06		2,334	£159,692
Jun-07	£75,410	632	£174,071
Dec-07		1,764	£132,560
Jun-08	-£48,750	544	£120,022
Dec-08		1,091	£102,458
Jun-09	£128,740	1,474	£73,917
Dec-09		1,172	£170,860

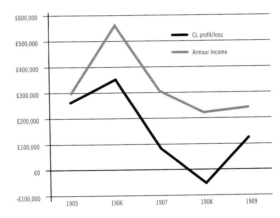

Source: 1. Warren, p. 132, from *The Economist*; 2. SIMT, Armour Plate Pool ledger.

The above table and graph clearly show how closely the company's profitability was related to the armour plate business and the impact that the exclusion had on Cammell Laird's profitability. It shows that, as the orders worked their way through the system, income and profitablity fell, reaching their lowest level in 1908 before picking up again.

The extent of these financial problems is shown in the board minutes by the number of negotiations the company had during this period to extend and secure its overdraft facilities with its bankers. The board minutes show discussions with the following banks:

- Alliance Assurance: negotiations for a £125,000 loan;
- Sheffield Banking Company Ltd: security for an overdraft of £125,000;
- York City & County Bank Ltd: security for existing overdraft plus an additional loan of £100,000; and
- Bank of Liverpool: security of £100,000 offered on the value of Tranmere Bay shipyard.

The company also took out loans from a number of companies, totalling around £50,000. To provide security for all the facilities, the company had to issue tranches of debenture stock.

THE 'WHISTLEBLOWER'

It seems that Cammell Laird's suspension from the government's list of contractors was based on information provided to the War Office by a Mr George H. Goodison about faked testing of gun forgings. He was the foreman in the testing department at the Grimesthorpe Works where the forgings were made.

George Goodison was born in Sheffield in 1865 to Henry, a labourer, and Sarah Anne, and brought up on Grimesthorpe Road[i] near to the Cammell Laird works. He had a brother, Frederick, who was three years younger than him. On starting work George became a machine driller.[12]

In 1899, aged 34, he married Rosina Maddick in her home town of Hull. They had a daughter, Rose, who was born in 1900 and they lived at 16 Bolsover Road, Sheffield. In the 1901 census George is described as being a 'Steel Testing Foreman'. In his letter to the Board of Trade he says that he was a foreman in charge of testing for fourteen years.

Mr Marwood of the Board of Trade wrote in the departmental files on the Cammell Laird suspension that 'Mr Goodison was the author of the charges against Messrs. Cammell Laird & Co which led to that firm being struck off the Admiralty and War Office lists of Contractors.' In a postscript to his note he adds that 'Goodison only made his charges against the firm after an unsuccessful attempt at blackmail'.[13]

As a result of his information, George Goodison left Cammell Laird, where presumably he was no longer welcome, and was given a job as an examiner in the War Office's inspection team in Sheffield. Shortly after he was given the job the staff were transferred to the Admiralty, when they took over the duties of the inspection of naval ordinance. Soon afterwards the Admiralty terminated Mr Goodison's employment as an examiner.

As a result of his dismissal by the Admiralty George Goodison wrote an impassioned letter to the President of the Board of Trade, who was a member of the British Cabinet. In order to make sure that officials did not block his grievance he wrote directly to the politician's home address.[14] Sir Winston Churchill (the President of the Board of Trade from April 1908 to February 1910) passed the letter on to his officials. In the letter George Goodison made the following allegations:

The envelope for the letter George Goodison wrote to Winston Churchill at his home address.

I have been discharged for what reason Major Stansfield would not state, so I draw my conclusion from his own words, some time ago he said that firm's objected to my seeing their work because I knew the trade secrets […] The firm in question has said they would ruin me some-time & it is quite evident they have had a hand in my discharge.

He then went on to threaten to expose the malpractices:

I must find means to support my wife & child […] No doubt if I let the foreigners know what has been done to this work they will find means of paying back some of the things that Sheffield manufacturers are saying about their false marking, which is trivial compared […] to what I have been ordered to do to their work. If you will use your influence Sir, in finding me employment some-where I shall be very grateful. If this cannot be done I shall be driven to the last resource & it will be the fault of the Government if the prestige of British trade suffers. I cannot help it I must have a living.

He went on to outline the extent of the malpractice he said he had witnessed at Cammell Laird, where

- many railway accidents were caused by defective steel which he said he could prove by showing false marks and the firm's memos ordering him to fake tests;
- the connecting rods for the engine of HMS *Bullfinch* were supplied '8 tons below specification limit'. He claimed he was ordered to mark 'good steel for tests which gave 10 tons higher braking strain than the actual steel supplied'. He claimed that this caused the loss of the vessel 'with all hands'.

George Goodison alleged 'false marking and general malpractices' were carried out at the Grimesthorpe Works. Mr Whiting, the Superintendent of Contract Work at the Admiralty, told the Select Committee on the Estimates in 1913 that, although the problems had occurred before his time, the malpractice centred around the 'improper substitution of inspectors stamps' so that forgings appeared to have been passed by the War Office's inspectors, when in fact they had not.[15]

---

i   The 1881 Census shows the family's address as number 740; in 1891 they had moved to 722.

HMS *Bullfinch*.

The 'Bullfinch disaster' which George Goodison refers to occurred on the Solent during the commissioning tests of HMS *Bullfinch*, a C-class 30-knot destroyer built by Earl's of Hull with two vertical triple expansion steam engines.

During trials in 1898 she broke an engine connecting rod at nearly full speed. This fractured a cylinder and the escaping steam killed eleven men. The *Bullfinch*, however, was brought back into port and served throughout the First World War. According to David K. Brown,[16] the early destroyers' designs pushed the limits of steam engine technology and there were a number of similar accidents. Interestingly there was a parliamentary question about the disaster to the First Lord of the Admiralty asking whether the 'machinery was supplied by the Admiralty to the contractor, and whether he will consider if the machinery used on board torpedo catchers and torpedo boats is sufficiently strong to meet the energy with which the engines have to be driven'.[17]

The number of incidents occurring to early destroyers when they were operating at high speed was a concern. The extreme stresses the engines were under at these speeds certainly demanded high-quality steels and engineering. If George Goodison's claims that Cammell Laird falsified the testing of the connecting rods for the engine are true, then it would appear that not only had the malpractices at the Grimesthorpe Works had been going on for a number of years, but also that the consequences of such malpractices could be fatal.

The Board of Trade communicated with the Admiralty and the War Office after they had received George Goodison's letter. They took the view that 'he may not be altogether a desirable person but he rendered service in connection with his enquiry' and that if he was dismissed because of staff reductions or a similar reason they might 'find him something to do'.[18]

The Admiralty responded that 'the officers of the Admiralty under whom he served did not consider that his work was satisfactory and that his presence on the Staff was having an undesirable effect upon the other members of the staff. No specific act of negligence or disrespect was, however brought forward.'[19] In consideration of his services in the enquiry into malpractices at Cammell Laird, Mr Goodison was awarded one hundred guineas.

The Admiralty official suggested that Mr Marwood visit him at his office where he could explain matters more fully. Such offers of off-the-record conversations imply that there was more going on than the formal record suggests, but sadly do not help us understand what it was.

On the basis of this communication the Board of Trade concluded that the Cammell Laird suspension was well known and that they should 'take no notice of this at all'.[20]

There is no evidence on the Board of Trade file that they replied to George Goodison's letter of complaint and he clearly had difficulty in finding employment in the steel industry. From what we know of the close co-operation of the three major Sheffield steel firms in the Armour Plate Pool Arrangement, as well as other co-operative arrangements, it is not unlikely that some sort of unofficial blacklisting took place. We know from the 1911 census that he had had to move from the suburban house in Woodseats, from where he wrote to Sir Winston Churchill, and had become a grocer and off-licence holder at 145 Abbeydale Road in the city. He later moved to a shop on Queens Road where he worked until the early 1930s.

Endnotes

1. National Archive BT13/44.
2. BT 13/44, letter dated 18 September 1907; the signature is unclear but probably reads Samson.
3. Refers to BT file number M 10 556/06.
4. Refers to BT file number M 23,231/07.
5. Wirrall Archive Service , CL Board Minutes, Vol. 8, p. 346.
6. Ibid., p. 348.
7. National Archive, BT13/44, 2 November 1907.
8. *The Times*, 8 November 1907, clipping in National Archive BT13/34.
9. Wirrall Archive Service, Cammell Laird Board Minutes, Book 8, 6 November 1907, p. 370.
10. National Archive, BT13/44, 2 April 1908.
11. Wirrall Archive Service, CL Board Minutes, Vol. 8, p. 425.
12. UK Census 1891.
13. National Archive, BT 13/44, File note 8 December 1909.
14. Ibid., 30 November 1909.
15. Parliamentary Select Committee on Navy Estimates 1913–14, 30 April 1913, p. 135. ©2006 ProQuest Information and Learning Co.
16. Brown, *Warrior to Dreadnought*, p. 140.
17. Question by Sir Edward Gourley (Sunderland) to First Lord Mr Goschen. Hansard HC Deb 28 July 1899, (series 4) Vol. 75 c668.
18. National Archive, BT13/44, Mr Marwood (BT) to Mr Brade (War Office), 8 December 1909.
19. Ibid., Letter from Admiralty to Mr Marwood (BT) 18 December 1909.
20. Ibid., File notes.

PART THREE

ARMOUR AND THE DREADNOUGHTS

INTRODUCTION

Britain's position as the predominant industrial power was challenged during the late nineteenth century. In 1870 Britain was making four times as much iron as Germany, and twice as much steel, but Germany overtook Britain's steel production in 1893 and its iron production in 1903. By 1910 German production of iron and steel was around twice that of Britain. Much of this growth in steel production was initially absorbed by German industries but by 1910 Germany was exporting more steel than Britain, which had previously been the world's largest steel supplier.[1]

A similar trend occurred in the chemical industries. Statistics for the industry are less readily available than for the steel industry but Landes (*Unbound Prometheus*)[2] uses the production of sulphuric acid, which is a precursor of many industrial chemical processes such as fertilizers, explosives, petroleum refining and textiles and dye making. Using production of sulphuric acid as a yardstick for the relative performance of Britain and Germany:

1. In 1900 Britain produced around 1,000,000 tons compared to Germany's 550,000 tons.
2. By 1913 Britain produced around 1,100,000 tons compared to Germany's 1,700,000 tons.

In overall terms Germany's industrial growth meant that by 1913 its share of world manufacturing output was 14.8% compared to Britain's 13.6%. Only thirty years earlier Britain's share had been about three times as large as Germany's.[3] The reverse was, however, true of Britain's foreign investments, which in 1913 were £793 million compared to Germany's £230 million.

The rapid growth of Germany as a major continental and world industrial power almost inevitably led to international tensions and during the first years of the twentieth century there was a marked deterioration in the relationship between Britain and Germany. In 1896 Kaiser Wilhelm II had sent a telegram to Kruger, the leader of the Transvaal Republic, congratulating him on repelling a raid by British irregular forces, which the British saw as unwarranted interference in the running of their empire. When the British and the Boers went to war from 1899 to 1902, both the German government and public opinion were very much on the side of the Boers. British public opinion was inflamed by the German attitude.

The German Naval Law of 1898 legislated for a fleet of nineteen first-class battleships, eight armoured costal defence ships and twelve large and thirty small cruisers. The Naval Law of 1900 proposed a much larger battle fleet of two fleet flagships, four battleship squadrons each of eight ships, eight large cruisers and twenty-four small cruisers. It also planned a fleet of cruisers for international operations and a reserve fleet. This building programme meant that Germany would have the second biggest navy (after Britain) by 1906, overtaking both France and Russia and changing the British view of which navies it traditionally measured its strength against.

In 1901 there were talks between representatives of the British and German governments about the possibility of an alliance. These were mostly conducted outside the formal diplomatic channels and seem to have been full of misunderstandings, on both sides, about the other's intentions. The talks did not heal the growing breach between the two countries and the British government became increasingly concerned about the rise in German naval power. In November 1901 Lord Selborne, the First Lord of the Admiralty, circulated a Cabinet Paper to his colleagues. He said:

> The naval policy of Germany is definite and persistent. The Emperor seems determined that the power of Germany shall be used all the world over to push German commerce, possessions and interests.[4]

A year later he wrote:

> The more the composition of the new German fleet is examined the clearer it becomes that it is designed for a possible conflict with the British fleet.

A leaked letter from the Kaiser to the Tsar of Russia, written in October 1902, in which he signed himself as 'Admiral of the Atlantic', confirmed British suspicions of Germany's ambitions. This hostility towards each other was felt in both countries and was reflected in popular bestsellers. In Germany the novel *Der Weltkreig: Deutsche Träume* (the English edition was translated as *The Coming Conquest of England*) sold 25,000 copies, and in England *The Riddle of the Sands* by Erskine Childers stoked fears of a German invasion.

The response of Britain and France to the growing power of Germany was a series of agreements known as the *Entente Cordiale*, which were signed in April 1904. The agreements settled a series of long-standing disputes between the two countries in Madagascar, Egypt, Newfoundland, Siam and West Africa. The agreements lowered the level of tension and although they did not constitute an alliance it meant that the British navy could focus on the growing threat from Germany.

Improved relations with the French were, however, hampered by the Russo-Japanese war in which the British supported and helped their Japanese ally and the French similarly supported their Russian ally. Germany sought to exploit these differences and during the Moroccan Crisis of 1905 the Kaiser visited Morocco and spoke in favour of Moroccan independence against French colonisation. The British government was concerned that the Germans were seeking coaling stations on the Atlantic coast of Morocco, which they wanted to prevent. An international conference, which was held in Algeciras in 1906, temporarily defused the crisis.

The Moroccan Crisis did not in fact lead to splits in the *Entente Cordiale* and in 1905 unofficial non-binding discussions were begun between the British and French armies and similar naval discussions also took place. The assumption underlying these discussions was that the enemy would be Germany.

THE DREADNOUGHT ERA BEGINS

It was in this tense international context that Britain embarked on its building programme of Dreadnought battleships. The 1905 Naval Estimates programme of Dreadnought building involved four ships: the *Dreadnought* herself, which was classed as a battleship; and three battlecruisers, *Invincible*, *Indomitable* and *Inflexible*. The new class of battlecruisers, which were originally called heavy cruisers, were designed to replace the heavy cruisers of the pre-Dreadnought era and they carried an armament of eight 12-inch guns, but were designed to be faster and less heavily armoured than the Dreadnought battleships. Admiral Jackie Fisher had pushed hard for the development of these ships, which he believed were the ships of the future, able to pick and choose when to engage the enemy and powerful enough to engage them at long range.

From 1909 onwards a new class of heavier battleships, the super-Dreadnoughts, replaced the early Dreadnought battleships and battlecruisers. These ships carried larger calibre 13½-inch guns and their thickest armour was 480 lb (12-inch) rather than the 440 lb (11-inch) plate carried by the early Dreadnoughts. These battleships of the *Orion* class were complemented by a new *Lion* class of battlecruiser which also carried 13½-inch guns and whose thickest armour had been increased from 6 inches to 9 inches.

The last class of battleships to see service in the First World War were an even heavier class of super-Dreadnought. These ships, of the *Queen Elizabeth* and *Royal Sovereign* classes, carried eight 15-inch guns and were more heavily armoured with the maximum thickness of armour increased to 520 lb or 13 inches, and with approximately 1,400 additional tons of armour added. The *Queen Elizabeth* class were oil-fired and were designed to be faster than previous Dreadnoughts and, with a speed of 23 knots, could keep pace with the fleet's battlecruisers.

Endnotes

1. Landes, *The Unbound Prometheus*, p. 269.
2. Ibid., p. 273.
3. Niall Ferguson, *The Pity of War* (Penguin Books, 1999), p. 35.
4. A. J. Marder, *From Dreadnought to Scapa Flow: Vol. 1, The Road to War* (Seaforth, 2013), p. 107.

CHAPTER 11

ARMOURING THE EARLY DREADNOUGHTS

HMS *Dreadnought*.

The first Dreadnoughts

Work on HMS *Dreadnought* formally began at Portsmouth dockyard at 7 a.m. on 2 October 1905. In an effort to gain advantage over naval rivals, over 700 tons of the ship had already been built and, due to the stock of pre-prepared materials, 2,000 tons of the ship were built in the first two days.[1] The *Engineer* reported that 'accumulations of material for building the *Dreadnought* increase at Portsmouth, and by the time she is laid down there will be nothing to do but put the ship together. The odds are, therefore, that a "record" will be achieved'.[2] They did, however, question the real worth of a record set in this way. The *Dreadnought* was launched on 10 February 1906, just over four months after she was laid down.

The total weight of armour fitted to HMS *Dreadnought* was 5,000 tons, of which Cammell Laird received the order for the side armour, estimated at 1,829 tons. The Cammell Laird order was recorded as being for:

Order details from ledger[3]		As fitted[4]
11-inch (440 lb) tapered armour	687 tons	641 tons of 11-inch tapered to 7-inch side armour 47 tons of 11-inch magazine screens
9-inch (360 lb) tapered armour	62 tons	63 tons of 8-inch screen
8-inch (320 lb) side armour	523 tons	510 tons
6-inch (240 lb) forward side armour	396 tons	427 tons
4-inch (160 lb) aft side armour	185 tons	184 tons

Cammell Laird actually invoiced for 1,956 tons of armour, but an estimated 98 tons of this was for the conning and signal towers.

The other firm to provide most of the remaining armour was Armstrong Whitworth, which made the aft bulkhead, the barbettes, the main deck slopes and the gunshields.

The three battlecruisers were around the same displacement as the *Dreadnought* but had eight 12-inch guns instead of the *Dreadnought's* ten and were also more lightly armoured as they were intended to rely on their speed to avoid being hit. The Admiralty requirement for the armour was that it should protect against 'flat trajectory fire at about 9,000 yards range.'[5]

The final design for the battlecruisers gave them a total weight of armour of 3,460 tons, which was around 20% of their displacement compared to 28% for the *Dreadnought*. In compensation 19% of their displacement was taken up with their machinery compared to only 11% in the *Dreadnought*.

Thickness of armour protection[6]	
Main belt armour	6 inches amidships, 4 inches forward
Barbettes	7 inches reducing to 2 inches
Fore bulkhead	7 inches
Aft bulkhead	6 inches
Conning tower	10-inch face, 7-inch rear, 3-inch sides, 2-inch roof
Main deck	1 to 1 ½ inches
Lower deck	1½ to 2½ inches
Turrets	Faces and backs 7 inches, sides and roof 2½ to 3 inches

The two midship 12-inch turrets of the battlecruiser HMS *Indomitable*.

The side armour for the three ships appears to have been divided between Armstrong Whitworth and John Brown's,[7] which were each given orders for the side armour for the ships being built in their own yards. The order for side armour for *Indomitable*, which was built by Fairfield's, was split between the two companies.

Ship	Shipyard	Side armour orders			
		Armstrong		J. Brown	
		Tons	Cost	Tons	Cost
Invincible	Armstrong	2,180	£230,749		
Indomitable	Fairfield	1,080	£117,486	1,038	£112,665
Inflexible	J. Brown			2,133	£229,275

Both Armstong Whitworth and John Brown charged £108 per ton for the armour for *Indomitable*. Armstrong's armour for the *Invincible* cost £106 per ton and John Brown's charge for the *Inflexible* was £107.

THE REFORMING LIBERAL GOVERNMENT AND THE NAVY

The 1905 programme had been introduced by the Conservative and Unionist government, which had been in power since 1895. In 1902 Arthur Balfour had become the Conservative Prime Minister. The First Lord of the Admiralty was Lord Selbourne, who was replaced by Lord Cawdor in March 1905. However, in the general election of early 1906 the Liberal party won an overall majority with a programme of home rule for Ireland and social reforms, which included old-age pensions, unemployment insurance and rights for trade unions. The Liberals were supported by a thirty-strong group of Labour MPs, who benefited from an electoral pact negotiated between Herbert Gladstone from the Liberal party and Ramsey MacDonald from the Labour Representation Committee, in which they agreed not to put up candidates against each other in selected seats.[8] The Liberal leader, Sir Henry Campbell-Bannerman, became Prime Minister and was succeeded by his Chancellor of the Exchequer, H. H. Asquith, in 1908.

Prior to leaving power the Conservative government had set out the Cawdor Memorandum of naval building, named after the First Lord. This proposed a building programme of four large armoured ships a year. The incoming Liberal government initially accepted this but later sought to reduce naval expenditure in order to finance their programme of social reforms.

As there was no evidence of any other country laying down any Dreadnought ships, it was agreed with Lord Fisher at the Admiralty that the 1906/07 programme could be reduced from four ships to three and a further two ships could be dropped from the 1907/08 year's programme if the forthcoming international conference due to be held in 1907 at the Hague was successful. The conference was intended to build on the earlier Hague Convention of 1899 on the rules of war and the British government hoped that it could be extended to include a reduction in arms expenditure.[9]

Under this reduced programme the 1906 Naval Estimates were for three battleships of the *Bellerophon* class. They were HMS *Bellerophon*, *Temeraire* and *Superb*. The design requirement was for an improved Dreadnought and the final agreed design was for ships some 700 tons heavier than the *Dreadnought* with an addition of a 4-inch secondary armament to strengthen their anti-torpedo defences.

Thickness of armour protection[10]	
Main belt armour	10 to 8 inches, 7 and 6 inches forward, 5 inches aft
Upper belt	8 inches
Centreline barbettes	9 inches, 5 inches below main deck except aft barbette rear face which was 9 inches below the deck
Beam barbettes	10 inches on outer face, 9 inches on inner face, 5 inches below main deck
Aft bulkhead	8 inches
Anti-torpedo bulkhead	1 to 3 inches
Conning tower	11-inch face, 8-inch rear, 3-inch roof, 2-inch floor
Main deck	¾ to 1½ inches
Middle deck	1 ¾ inches, 3 inches around after barbette
Turrets	11-inch faces, 12-inch backs, 3-inch roofs

The orders for the armour plate were placed with the companies in November 1906 and the *Bellerophon* was laid down on 3 December. Three companies received orders for 4,906 tons of armour for the *Bellerophon*:[11]

Area of armour	Armstrong Whitworth		
	Date of order	Tons	Cost
Conning Towers	27/11/07	153.80	£2,136.42
TOTAL		153.80	£2,136.42

Area of armour	Cammell Laird		
	Date of order	Tons	Cost
Barbettes	02/11/06	1,151.42	£160,370.71
TOTAL		1,151.42	£160,370.71

Area of armour	Vickers & Maxim		
	Date of order	Tons	Cost
Side belt			
Deck armour	02/11/06	2,110.22	£243,226.51
Bulkheads			
Gun shields	01/12/06	1,490.52	£219,307.93
TOTAL		3,600.74	£462,534.44

The analysis of the orders recorded in the armour plate ledger shows that the Sheffield companies, Cammell Laird and Vickers, Sons & Maxim, made most of the armour plate for the *Bellerophon* while two of the armour plate manufacturers, W. Beardmore and John Brown's, did not receive any orders for this ship although John Brown did receive a large order for armour plate for the *Superb*, which was built at Armstrong's Elswick yard.

This order for the *Superb*'s side armour consisted of:

lbs weight per sq ft.	Thickness (inches)	Tons of armour ordered
400	10	765
360	9	81
320	8	388
280	7	232
240	6	214
Total		1,680

In total John Brown's received orders for 3,269 tons of armour for the *Superb*, worth a total of £377,451.

THE FAILURE OF ARMS CONTROL AND THE 1907 ESTIMATES

The first Hague Conference had been held in 1899 and, although it had made major progress on codifying the rules of war, it did not achieve another of its objectives, which was an agreement on disarmament. In 1905 the Russian government, whose forces had been recently heavily defeated by Japan, proposed holding a second conference to discuss some of the issues left unresolved at the first meeting. Their proposed agenda did not include the issue of arms reduction and Campbell-Bannerman's British government, supported by the Italians, proposed that this issue should be included. The Americans were in favour of discussing the issue but were dubious about the idea itself and the Russians and the French were lukewarm. Germany and Austria–Hungary were opposed to any discussion of arms limitation, arguing that Britain was trying to fix its position of superiority and that they were entitled to increase their naval strength. By the time of the launch of HMS *Superb*, the third of the *Bellerophon* class, the Hague Conference had finished, without arms limitations or reductions being discussed at all.

In August 1907 Britain and Russia signed the Anglo-Russian Convention, settling many of their differences. Britain now had understandings with both France and Russia, the two historic naval rivals against whom the two-power standard had traditionally been measured.

The naval arms race between Britain and Germany now began in earnest and in February 1908 Germany amended its Naval Law of 1900, which shortened the service life of naval ships and thus enabled the construction of modern Dreadnoughts as replacements for the older ships. Dr Macnamara, the Parliamentary and Financial Secretary to the Admiralty, explained in the House of Commons that this meant that between 1908 and 1911 the number of large armoured ships built in Germany each year would increase from three to four.[12]

Increases in Dreadnought construction

In view of the failure of the Hague Conference to discuss armament reduction the government reluctantly authorised the building of a further three battleships as part of the 1907 programme. The ships of the *St Vincent* class were slightly enlarged and improved versions of the *Bellerophon* and were named the *St Vincent*, *Collingwood* and the *Vanguard* and were equipped with a new, more powerful, 12-inch Mark XI guns. The armour plate layout was very similar to the previous design except that the main 10-inch belt armour was extended in length and stretched from the fore barbette to the aft barbette. The thickness of the fore and aft belt was reduced.

	Thickness of armour protection[13]
Main belt armour	10 to 8 inches, 7 and 2 inches forward, 2 inches aft
Upper belt	8 inches
Centreline barbettes	9 inches, 5 inches below main deck
Beam barbettes	9 to 10 inches on outer face, 9 inches on inner face, 5 inches below main deck
Bulkhead	Forward 4 and 5 inches, aft 8 inches
Anti-torpedo bulkhead	1½ to 3 inches
Conning tower	11-inch face, 8-inch rear, 3-inch roof, 2-inch floor
Main deck	¾ to 1½ inches
Middle deck	1¾ inches
Lower deck	1½ inches forward, 3 inches aft
Turrets	11-inch faces, 12-inch backs, 3-inch roofs

John Brown's received orders for 1,525 tons of side armour and 1,230 tons of barbette armour for the *St Vincent* worth in total £293,732. The order for the side armour was

lbs weight per sq. ft.	Thickness (inches)	Tons of armour ordered	Price quoted per ton
400	10	950	£117.50 – 10%
320	8	425	£115.5 – 10%
280	7	150	£115.5 – 10%
Total		1,525	

The prices quoted for the armour was the same as for the previous *Bellerophon* class but they included a 10% discount that had been negotiated between the Admiralty and the armour firms. This discount is referred to in Admiralty internal correspondence as coming into operation sometime before December 1909 but gives no exact date.[14]

The 1908 Naval Estimates were the cause of conflict between the Admiralty and the radical or 'economic' wing of the Liberal Cabinet. The 'economists' argued for continuing reductions in expenditure and in November 1907 the Cabinet refused to accept the proposals for a £2 million increase put forward by Lord Tweedmouth, the First Lord. After a period of negotiation, a programme of two Dreadnoughts was agreed accompanied by savings elsewhere in the Admiralty's budget. The ships in this programme were a battleship, HMS *Neptune*, and a battlecruiser, HMS *Indefatigable*.

The *Neptune* was an enlarged and modified version of the *St Vincent* class but with a superfiring 'X' turret mounted above the 'Y' turret at the stern of the ship. This development, which had been adopted by other navies, enabled the *Neptune* to fire a full 10-gun broadside although the siting hoods for aiming, which were placed on the roofs of the turrets, meant that the X turret could not fire over the Y turret without stunning the observer. The armour protection was very similar to the *St Vincent* class except that the 10-inch main belt did not extend as far

A view of the aft superfiring 12-inch guns of HMS *Neptune*.

and the forward belt was increased from 2 inches to 2½ inches. Splinter protection was also provided to the funnel uptakes for the first time. The total weight of armour was 5,706 tons, which was distributed as follows:

Thickness of armour protection[15]	
Main belt armour	10 to 8 inches, 7 and 2½ inches forward, 2 inches aft
Upper belt	8 inches
Centreline barbettes	9 inches, 5 inches below main deck
Beam barbettes	10 inches on outer face, 9 inches on inner face, 5 inches below main deck
Bulkhead	Forward 5 inches, aft 8 inches
Anti-torpedo bulkhead	1½ to 3 inches
Conning tower	11-inch face, 8-inch rear, 3-inch roof, 2-inch floor
Main deck	1¼ inches
Middle deck	1¾ inches
Lower deck	1½ inches forward, 3 inches aft
Turrets	11 inch faces, 12 inch backs, 3 inch roofs

Armstrong Whitworth received the order for the barbette armour for HMS *Neptune* worth in total £137,176. The order was for:

lbs weight per sq. ft	Thickness (inches)	Tons of armour ordered
360	9	1,075
200	5	240
Total		1,311

The side armour was manufactured by John Brown's, which made 1,529 tons at a cost of £159,898. Vickers also made 234 tons at a cost of £40,332. The prices quoted for the side and barbette armour were the same as for the previous *St Vincent* class and also included 10% discount.

Vickers, Sons & Maxim made the fronts of the turret shields for the 12-inch guns (558 tons of 11-inch armour at a cost of £79,357) but subcontracted the remainder of the shield armour to Cammell Laird. Normally the firm making the gun mountings made all the armour for the turrets in their own armour works. Cammell Laird manufactured 245 tons of shield armour at a cost of £29,675 but this price included a discount of 25%, perhaps because Vickers were aware of the profit margin on armour plate and were not willing to give all of this profit to their sub-contractor.

The battlecruiser which was ordered as part of the 1908 programme was the *Indefatigable*, a development of the *Indomitable* class. The *Indefatigable* carried 3,735 tons of armour, compared to the 5,706 tons of armour on the battleship HMS *Neptune* and the 3,460 tons carried by the earlier battlecruisers. The *Indefatigable* was laid down in February 1909 at Devonport Royal Dockyard (Plymouth) and was launched in October of the same year.

The government was now led by H. H. Asquith after Campbell-Bannerman had retired following a serious heart attack. David Lloyd George, a leading radical (also known as 'economists') within the Liberal party, was appointed as Chancellor of the Exchequer and Reginald McKenna, a Liberal Imperialist – and therefore more supportive of naval expenditure – as First Lord of the Admiralty. Although the more extreme navalists had protested strongly about the reductions in the naval building programme prior to 1908, they did not gain widespread support because of an improved relationship with France and the decimation of the Russian fleet by the Japanese navy. However, by the end of 1908 Germany had laid down nine Dreadnought battleships or battlecruisers and in 1909 had ordered a further four ships. By comparison Britain had ten ships completed or under construction; two other ships had been ordered but not laid down and the Admiralty was proposing a further six ships in 1909. Although none of the German ships had yet entered service, compared to the four British ships in service the German construction programmes could result in Germany having thirteen capital ships in 1912 compared to a British total of eighteen.[16] This ratio was certainly not compatible with a two-power standard, if Dreadnoughts alone were considered, but the balance improved in Britain's favour if pre-Dreadnoughts were also considered.

The German government protested that their building programme was constrained by their Naval Laws, but in a memo from McKenna to the Foreign Secretary, Sir Edward Grey,[17] McKenna explained that although the money for building ships remained in the budget year specified in the Naval Laws, what was happening in practice was that the companies building the ships were being paid in arrears:

> On receipt of an order from the Government (the shipbuilder) would be able to borrow from their bankers up to the amount covered by the inspector's certificate for work completed. I am informed that the banks concerned, having been appraised of the heavy drain in cash which would be made upon them, in financing the firms, have held a meeting and have made a joint representation to the Government, who have undertaken to assist them, if required, out of funds from the Savings Banks.

There was concern that the Germans were accelerating their building programme through faster construction times and also by investing in extra capacity at Krupp's gun mounting factory, which reduced one of the main bottlenecks in warship construction and could potentially enable the Germans to build up to eight ships per year. Britain had previously been able to build battleships in two years, compared to the three years it took in Germany, but now it seemed that the German shipyard would be able to build as quickly and the Admiralty calculated that this could mean that Germany would have seventeen battleships and battlecruisers by 1912, rather than the thirteen they had announced.

In March 1908, Herbert Asquith, standing in for the Prime Minister, who was ill, made the government's position on maintaining naval superiority clear. He said:[18]

> We must maintain the unassailable supremacy of this country at sea; and that for that purpose the two-Power standard, as it is commonly called — whether a scientific formula or not — is a good practical and workable one.

This alarmed the First Lord of the Admiralty, Reginald McKenna, who laid out his concerns the Prime Minister in a memo dated 3 January 1909:

> I am anxious to avoid alarmist language, but I cannot resist the following conclusions which it is my duty to submit to you:
>
> 1. Germany is anticipating the shipbuilding programmes laid down by the Naval Laws of 1907.
> 2. She is doing so secretly.
> 3. She will certainly have 13 big ships in commission in the spring of 1911.
> 4. She will probably have 21 ships in commission in the spring of 1912.
> 5. German capacity to build Dreadnoughts is at this moment equal to ours.

He believed that the German capacity would 'give the public a rude awakening should it become known'.[19]

In a subsequent memo to Sir Edward Grey, McKenna set out the anticipated production of ships under the accelerated German programme and the graph shows how this acceleration in building would alter the number of German Dreadnoughts in their fleet.

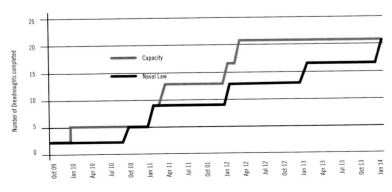

The graph of German shipbuilding shows how much sooner they would reach a total of twenty-one ships if they used their maximum capacity rather than sticking to the programme set out in the Naval Law.

In the event, as McKenna admitted to the House of Commons in February 1911,[20] the German building programme did not achieve the forecast levels of production. Only one vessel from the 1909/10 programme had been launched. The ships of the 1910/11 programme were not expected to be completed in April 1912 as forecast and were not expected to be completed until the spring of 1914.

The Naval Lords wanted to order eight Dreadnoughts in the 1909 Estimates and in Cabinet discussions McKenna argued hard for a programme of six ships while his radical colleagues, led by Lloyd George and Churchill, argued for a programme of only four ships. The Cabinet eventually reached an agreement for four ships, plus four additional ships in the following year, if the situation required it. As Winston Churchill put it in *The World Crisis 1911–1918*: 'In the end a characteristic and curious decision was reached. The Admiralty had demanded six ships: the economists [of which Churchill was, at the time a prominent member] offered four: and we finally compromised on eight.'[21]

In the March 1909 Estimates no financial allowance was made for building the second group of four ships and this led to them being described as 'phantom ships'[22] by those wishing to see a larger programme; however, McKenna eventually persuaded the Naval Lords to support the programme.

The government's position was eased somewhat because in the spring of 1909 the governments of Australia and New Zealand, which were self-governing dominions within the British Empire, agreed to pay for a Dreadnought each. The Australian government also agreed to pay for the supporting cruisers and destroyers to make up a balanced unit within the fleet. It was agreed that these additional ships would be battlecruisers and two additional ships of the *Indefatigable* class were ordered.

The armour protection provided for the *Indefatigable, Australia* and *New Zealand,* as the new ships were named, was:

	Thickness of armour protection	Difference in Australia and New Zealand
Main belt armour	2½ inches stern, 4 to 6 inches amidships, 2½ inches forward The 6-inch belt was reduced in length but 2½-inch armour was extended to the bow and stern	Belt ended short of the bow and stern. 4-inch section forward increased to 5-inch & 2½-inch section aft increased to 4 inches
Barbettes	7 inches reducing to 2 inches (3 inches on Y barbette)	
Fore bulkhead	3 to 4 inches	Reduced to 1½ inches
Aft bulkhead	4½ inches	Reduced to 4 inches
Conning tower	10-inch face, 3-inch sides, 2-inch roof	
Main deck	1 to 2 inches	Extended aft
Lower deck	1½ to 2 inches	Increased from 2 to 2½ inches
Turrets	Faces and backs 7 inches, sides and roof 3 inches	

The two ships ordered by the dominion governments were laid down in June 1910. John Brown's, which built the *Australia* at their Clydeside yard, received no orders for her armour; but on 18 August 1910 Armstrong Whitworth's, which had not received any shipbuilding orders for ships in the 1908 Estimates, received orders for the side armour for *Australia* and for side and barbette armour for the *New Zealand*.[23]

	Order	Weight ordered	Invoiced cost	Average price per ton
New Zealand	Sides and barbettes	1,769	£168,695	£95.36
Australia	Sides	1,766	£167,736	£94.98

By the time the orders for the armour for *Australia* and *New Zealand* had been placed, the Admiralty had reached an agreement with the five armour plate companies that applied to all armour orders placed by the Admiralty after 16 June 1910. The prices quoted in the armour plate ledger for the orders for side armour for the two ships are:

	Thickness	Price quoted	Price schedule[24]
240 lb	6 inch	£98.55	£93
200 lb	5 inch	£98.10	£93
160 lb	4 inch	£98.10	£93

The price schedule was for standard armour before it had been shaped so the prices quoted are likely to be higher than the standard price. The average price of £94.98 which was actually charged for the side armour for the *Australia* is closer to the new price schedule than the original quoted price and may reflect the benefits to the Admiralty of the new agreement in reducing armour costs.

NAVAL SCARES AND SOCIAL EXPENDITURE

Even though the offer from Australia and New Zealand had increased the building programme, the government's compromise of four ships now and four ships later was met with a storm of protest from Conservative and Unionist politicians, the navalist press and the Navy League, who campaigned for eight ships under the slogan 'We want eight and we won't wait'. The argument for these ships was expressed by the *Standard* newspaper, which said that 'the progress Germany is making is most serious and it can no longer be contended that the German programmes are failing to materialise.'[25]

The Liberal government faced a motion of censure in the House of Commons on 29 May 1909 which stated: 'That in the opinion of this House the declared policy of His Majesty's Government respecting the immediate provision of battleships of the newest type does not sufficiently secure the safety of the Empire.' The leader of the Conservative opposition argued that the Liberal government's policies of the last three years and the Cabinet arguments about the current naval programme meant that they could not be trusted with ensuring the Empire's security.[26]

Although the government won this vote overwhelmingly by 353 votes to 135, they put forward a motion in parliament to approve an advance budget of £3,148,200 for the following year in advance in order to build the second group of four ships.

Funding new social and naval programmes

Churchill later commented that, although he and Lloyd George were correct that the concern about an accelerated German building programme was exaggerated, and they were therefore right in the narrow sense, they were absolutely wrong, in what he described in a very Churchillian phrase, in 'relation to the deep tides of destiny'. He praised McKenna for the 'resolute and courageous manner in which he fought his case and withstood his party'.[27]

This increased programme of naval expenditure meant that the Liberal government now had a problem of how to afford both the increase in naval expenditure and their social programme, which included the Old Age Pensions Act, which they had passed in 1908 and which came into effect in 1909/10. By December 1908 nearly 600,000 pensions had been agreed at a potential annual cost of around £7.5 million.[28] This compared to the net naval expenditure on 'Shipbuilding, Repairs and Maintenance' (Vote 8) in 1908/09 of £7.2 million.[29]

To pay for the government's programme, Lloyd George's budget proposed sharp increases in taxation, including income tax, death duties, stamp duty on sales and share transactions, taxes on alcohol and tobacco, increased road tax and on capital gains made from property. In spite of resistance by the opposition parties this was passed, with a large majority, in November 1909. The unelected House of Lords then rejected the budget on the grounds that its radical character required the 'judgement of the country', in other words a new general election. In the consequent general election held between 15 January and 10 February 1910 the Liberal government was returned to power, but with a reduced number of seats and dependent on the votes of the Irish Parliamentary party to gain a majority. The Labour party increased its representation from twenty-nine to forty seats. A second election in December 1910, called to try and solve the Parliamentary deadlock, produced a similar result to the January election.

Eventually the House of Lords passed the budget as well as the Parliament Act (1911), which reduced their ability to block legislation put forward by the elected House of Commons.

Responding to the naval scare

The Colossus and Hercules, which were ordered as part of the 1909 Estimates, were based on the design of the Neptune but a combination of developments in naval armaments and the information that Germany was building larger and more powerful ships led the Admiralty to look at major improvements in the later ships ordered in the 1909 Estimates.

Compared to the Neptune, the Colossus and Hercules had thicker waterline protection but the belt did not extend to the bow or stern. The thicker barbette armour was also increased by 1 inch but was correspondingly reduced in less vulnerable areas. The main deck armour was also increased by ¼ inch in thickness while the side screens were reduced in length to protect only the magazine spaces:

Thickness of armour protection[30]	
Main belt armour	10 to 8 inches, 7 and 2½ inches forward & aft
Upper belt	8 inches
A barbette	10 inches on outer face reduced to 7 inches below upper deck and 5 inches below main deck. Inner faces 9, 7 & 4 inches respectively
Beam barbettes	11 inches on outer face, 9 inches elsewhere, reducing to 6 & 4 inches below main deck
X barbette	10 inches on exposed face, remainder 9 inches. 4 inches below main deck
Y barbette	10 inches above main deck, 4 inches below
Main bulkheads	Forward 4 inches, aft 8 inches
Forward bulkheads	Inner 5 inches, outer 2 inches
Magazine screens	1¼ to 3 inches
Conning tower	11-inch face and sides, 8-inch rear, 3-inch roof, 2-inch floor
Main deck	1½ inches
Middle deck	1¾ inches
Lower deck	Forward 1¾ to 2½ inches, aft 3 to 4 inches
Turrets	11-inch faces, 12-inch backs, 3-inch roofs

The total weight of armour was 5,474 tons which was made up as follows:

	Tons
11-inch belt	1,026
8-inch belt	434
7-inch belt	150
A barbette	352
P & Q barbettes	451
X barbette	341
Y barbette	200
Bulkheads	241
Bolts	32
Decks	1,770
Torpedo protection	210
Uptakes	57
Towers	145
Backing	65
Total	5,474

The orders for the two ships shown in the armour plate ledger are:

		Colossus			Hercules	
	Company	Weight (tons)	Cost	Company	Weight (tons)	Cost
Belt	Beardmore	1,659.92	£174,299	J. Brown	1,642	£171,410
Bulkhead and side				Cammell Laird	120	£10,194
Conning towers	Cammell Laird	77.60	£7,441	J. Brown	77	£7,396
Bulkheads and barbettes	Armstrong	778.45	£78,537	Cammell Laird	1,621	£161,896
	Cammell Laird	125.78	£10,511			
Barbettes	Vickers	810.47	£81,847			
Shields	Vickers	899.89	£111,572	Armstrong	897	£111,664
Totals		4,352	£464,207		4,357	£553,560

ARMOUR PRODUCTION FOR THE EARLY DREADNOUGHTS

The armour plate ledgers allow us to explore the production of British armour plate in more detail by looking at annual production and income for each of the companies in the pool. The table shows the total amount of armour plate produced for the early Dreadnoughts, covered in this chapter, over the period 1905 to 1910:

Year	Annual production of armour plate									
	Armstrong Whitworth		W. Beardmore		John Brown		Cammell Laird		Vickers	
	Tons	Income	Tons	Income	Tons	Income	Tons	Income	Tons	Income
1905	1,516	£184,133	0	£0	0	£0	2,071	£248,140	36	£5,193
1906	3,228	£350,672	2,130	£244,309	7,006	£757,079	2,316	£320,741	4,364	£583,148
1907	2,263	£276,704	76	£9,086	0	£0	0	£0	2	£124
1908	2,241	£282,457	2,763	£295,814	2,968	£311,244	2,525	£252,610	2,459	£281,115
1909	3,326	£362,260	2,637	£275,351	3,249	£338,705	3,172	£334,966	2,655	£319,354
1910	4,193	£533,833	0	£0	69	£6,121	545	£45,463	492	£57,587
1911	0	£0	0	£0	69	£6,633	679	£6,733	0	£0
Total	16,767	£1,990,059	7,607	£824,560	13,361	£1,419,782	11,308	£1,208,653	10,008	£1,246,521

	% of production
Armstrong	28.8%
Beardmore	13.0%
J Brown	22.8%
Cammell	18.2%
Vickers	17.2%

The table shows the share of the armour plate for the early Dreadnoughts produced by each of the five armour makers.

MAKING ARMOUR PLATE FOR THE EARLY DREADNOUGHTS

In August 1905 the Engineer reported a rumour that the armour plate orders for the 1905 Estimates had been divided up between the armour plate manufacturers with equal shares going to Armstrong Whitworth, John Brown and Cammell Laird. Vickers and Beardmore were to share a larger part of the order between them. According to the Engineer 'this would give a welcome help to the industry, especially in Sheffield, where new work is much needed in the armour plate mills'.[31] However, the armour of the new Dreadnought was not the radical feature of its design and was made in the same way as the preceding generation of ships such as the Agamemnon and Lord Nelson. In a 1903 publication John Brown & Co. gave a very detailed account both of the Krupp armour-making process and of the machines that were used at the Atlas Works in the early years of the twentieth century. This method of making Krupp armour was consistent from 1897 to around 1910 and is therefore a good description of the processes by which the armour for the early Dreadnoughts was manufactured.

The open hearth furnace

John Brown had six acid-lined Siemens open hearth furnaces of different sizes in their foundry at the Atlas Works. They were housed in a building 480 feet long and 78 feet wide. The larger furnaces had a capacity of 40 tons and were used exclusively for making steel for armour, while the smaller furnaces were used for general steel making.

Pressing and rolling the ingot

When the steel was ready it was poured into large ladles that ran on rails. These ladles were raised on a hydraulic lift and run over the casting pit where the steel was poured via a trough into 40- or 50-ton moulds. This method was considered to be much safer than transporting the ladles with a crane and John Brown's reported that they had had no accidents since the system of transporting the rails had been installed. During this process the liquid steel was continually stirred with long rods, as the melting point of the steel is so high that it starts to solidify the moment it loses temperature. The furnaces were able to produce about nine ingots per week for the armour plate works.

As the steel ingot needed to be transferred to the hydraulic press before the steel was completely solidified, only a short period of time was allowed for the steel to cool in the mould before the mould was removed and the ingot transferred to the reheating furnace. The length of the cooling period was determined by the thickness of the ingot.

The reheating furnaces were of the 'bogie' type with the bottom of the furnaces being withdrawn on rails. Each furnace could take an ingot of 20 feet by 12 feet and was fired by either gas or coal, as John Brown's had found that the fuel used made no difference in the effectiveness of the process. The ingot was lifted on to the bogie with a crane and run into the furnace and the entrance was bricked up. The ingot stayed in the reheating furnace for a short time until it was at the required temperature. The reheating furnace was then opened and the ingot was lifted off the furnace bogie with a 150-ton travelling crane and transferred, via rollers, to the hydraulic press, which had been installed in 1895 and at the time was one of the two most powerful in the world, the other being in the United States.

The ingot rested on a horizontal table and was put in the correct position with horizontal rams, which both adjusted the position of the ingot during the process and provide lateral pressure on it. The hydraulic press was driven by steam from a marine boiler generating up to 3,000 horsepower for short periods of time. The press could exert a pressure of 10,000 tons over an area of 4,000 square inches (2½ tons per square inch). The ingots started at around 42 inches thick and were reduced to 12 to 18 inches during which they were reheated three times. At periods of maximum demand the pressing shop was able to deal with two 30- to 50-ton ingots every twenty-four hours.

When the ingot had been reduced to a slab of 18 inches maximum thickness, it was taken from the press shop to the rolling mill shop where it was placed in one of the two furnaces alongside the rolling mill, which were able to take slabs 11 feet wide. When the slab was at the required heat the bogie was withdrawn from the furnace and taken down an incline to the train of rollers, which were 36 inches in diameter and could take a slab 11 feet wide and up to 22 inches thick.

The slab was then rolled back and forth through the rolls until it was a little thicker than the final thickness required.

LEFT: The 10,000-ton hydraulic press. The ingot was held in place by the horizontal hydraulic rams, which can be seen in the foreground.

ABOVE: The rolling mill shop. The engine which drove the rollers was on the left.

TOP: Furnaces for carburising the plates. The movable bogie on its rails can be seen at the base of the nearest furnace.

CENTRE: The armour chilling process in action. Captain T. J. Tresidder first introduced this method at the Atlas Works in the 1870s.

ABOVE: One of the machine shops with a travelling crane at the far end.

Hardening the plate

The plate was then passed to the hardening department where it underwent the first phase of the hardening process, which was designed to increase the hardness of the plate's surface but maintain the toughness throughout the rest of the plate so that it did not shatter or crack. The plate was first placed on a bogie, which could take a plate up to 37 feet long and 11 feet wide, and was rolled into one of the four furnaces.

The furnaces were similar to the Siemens furnaces with regenerative chambers on either side admitting a mixture of gas and air into the furnace alternately from each side. After the plate had been in the furnace for a length of time which depended on its thickness, it was withdrawn from the furnace and chilled by a water sprinkler which had been invented by John Tresidder, one of John Brown's directors.

For the chilling process the plate was placed over a grid of perforated water pipes on a base of spiral springs, which were designed to support plates of different shapes. A movable grid of perforated water pipes was then placed over the plate. While the plate was still hot, water was sprayed on both sides from the thousands of perforations in the pipes at a pressure of 30 lbs per square inch (psi) from four pumps. This spraying continued for between thirty minutes and an hour depending on how thick the armour plate was.

Scaling and machining

The plate was then removed from the sprinkler and was scaled by pneumatic tools at a pressure of 80 psi. The high frequency of the pneumatic tools and the deafening noise apparently led to the machine becoming known as 'the Missus's tongue'. When this process was finished the plate then passed to one of the six armour plate shops where the planing and machining of the plates was carried out. These workshops were up to 600 feet in length and were 60 feet wide. Each bay in the workshop was equipped with a 50- to 60-ton electrically driven gantry crane.

The workshops contained eighty-three powerful machine tools able to work on large armour plates. The first machining operation was planing the plates, described by John Brown's as 'a most important and tedious operation'. It was insisted on by the Admiralty because it was considered that the rough surface affected the speed of the ship.[32]

The workshops contained forty-one screw planing machines, which were electrically driven and fitted with magnetic clutches for reversing the direction of the machines. The largest planer was able to work on plates 15 feet long and 10 feet high.

After the plate had been planed and had its edges trimmed with a slotting machine, the surface of the plate was shot-blasted with cast iron powder at 80 psi pressure before being passed to the cementation or carburisation workshops.

The cementation process

The cementation furnaces were 22 feet long and 12 feet wide and the plate was put into the furnace on a bogie running on rails. Generally speaking two plates were placed on the bogie with one of their faces in contact with carbon. The front of the furnace was bricked up and the plates were left in the furnace for a number of days at a constant temperature. The temperature was maintained at a level at which the required amount of carbon would be absorbed by the face of the plates. The cementation process was a critical one in making the hard face of the armour and the temperature was taken every half hour throughout the day and night. The temperature was measured by placing a hollow metal cylinder of a known weight in the furnace until it was at the same temperature as the furnace. The cylinder was then withdrawn and put in a standard volume of water and the increase in the temperature of the water was measured with a thermometer. This enabled the furnace attendant to maintain the furnace at a standard temperature.

Bending the plates to shape

After the plate had been carburised for the required amount of time it was withdrawn from the furnace and bent to the required shape. The templates for each individual plate were produced at the shipyards, based on the drawings prepared by the Admiralty's Department of Naval Construction.

The plate-bending press was located in its own workshop and was supported by two cranes and two sets of pumps for creating the hydraulic pressure for the bending machine's rams. The press itself had side plates made from 7-inch armour and was 26 feet high and 9 feet wide. The armour plate to be bent was first placed in one of two reheating furnaces and heated to the required temperature. It was then placed on the press and supported by packing, and three hydraulic rams capable of exerting 6,000 tons of pressure were used to bend it into shape. There was also a smaller, 2,000-ton bending press which was used for thinner armour up to 6 inches thick.

After the plate was bent to the required shape it was sent to the machine shop where edge planers, slotters and surface planing machines were used to give the plate its approximate final shape. The plate was then returned to the hardening shop for the completion of the hardening process. Here it was placed in the bogie furnace, which has been described previously, and reheated to a uniform temperature. It was then removed from the furnace and dipped vertically into one of two tanks of oil. Each tank contained 40 tons of oil and was surrounded by a jacket in which cold water was circulated to keep the oil from

TOP: Screw planers working on the surface of armour plates.

CENTRE: A slotting machine trimming plates. The plate may be a casement for the secondary armament of a pre-Dreadnought.

ABOVE: Bending armour in the bending press.

Belt armour being assembled on the shop floor to test if it fitted together.

An electrically powered edge grinding machine.

A machine for drilling and putting screw threads in the back of armour plates.

becoming too hot. The plate was then removed from the oil bath and underwent further heat treatments in the furnace. During this process the plate became warped and this had to be corrected by the 6,000-ton bending press. After the final heat treatment the plate could only be bent in one direction, as it was impossible to stretch the hard face of the plate without breaking it. To overcome this problem the bending process aimed to make the plate a bit too convex. Thus in the final straightening the hard surface of the plate was compressed rather than stretched.

The finished plate was then tested for carbon content at different depths by drilling test holes for analysis. It was then taken to the erecting shop where it was fitted to its neighbours to make sure that the whole assembly fitted together. The shop floor was made of planed iron plate and was 217 feet long and 48 feet wide. The plates were lifted by a 50-ton travelling crane.

If any of the plates needed correcting this had to be done on an edge grinding machine, as the plate was at that stage too hard for machine tools such as the planers used earlier in the process.

Drilling holes into the plate

After the plates had been checked to ensure they fit together they were then drilled on both sides. These holes served two purposes:

- Holes were drilled and tapped (the process of cutting the screw thread) in the back of the plate to take the bolts that fastened the armour plate to the ship. In the case of the side armour belt the bolts passed through the steel plates of the hull of the ship, the wood backing of the plate and screwed into the tapped holes on the back of the armour plate.

- Holes also needed to be drilled into the front of some of the plates. For example the side belt armour had to have attachments for the torpedo booms supporting the anti-torpedo netting. To drill holes in the hardened face of the armour the face had to be softened using an electric annealing machine that heated the plate and created a small soft spot that could be drilled. When the plate cooled the annealing had made the area around the hole even harder.

Endnotes

1. *Engineer*, 6 October 1905.
2. Ibid., 22 September 1905, p. 287.
3. SIMT, Armour Plate Pool ledger, Vol 1, M560.
4. Burt, *British Battleships of World War One*, p. 29.
5. Ibid., p. 46.
6. Ibid., p. 45.
7. SIMT, Armour Plate Pool ledger, Vol. 1, M560.
8. A. K. Russell, *Liberal Landslide: The General Election of 1906* (David & Charles, 1973), p. 28.
9. N. A. Lambert, *Sir John Fisher's Naval Revolution* (University of Carolina Press, 1999), p. 134.
10. Burt, *British Battleships of World War One*, p. 45.
11. SIMT, Armour Plate Pool ledger, Vol. 1, M560.
12. Hansard, HC Deb, 27 March 1911, (series 5) Vol .23 cc886-7.
13. Burt, *British Battleships of World War One*, p. 69.
14. National Archive ADM116/3456.
15. Burt, *British Battleships of World War One*, p. 69.
16. Marder, *From Dreadnought to Scapa Flow: Vol. 1, The Road to War*, p. 152.
17. S. McKenna, *Reginald McKenna 1863–1943* (Eyre & Spottiswoode, 1948), p. 78.
18. Hansard, HC Deb, 10 March 1908, (series 4) Vol. 185 cc1335-94.
19. McKenna, *Reginald McKenna 1863–1943*, p. 73.
20. Hansard, HC Deb, 8 February 1911, (series 5) Vol. 21, cc266-8.
21. W. Churchill, *The World Crisis, 1911–1918* (Oldhams Press, 1938), Vol. 1, p. 24.
22. Hansard, HC Deb, 26 July 1909, (series 5) Vol. 8, c855.
23. SIMT, Armour Plate Pool ledger, Vol. 1, M560.
24. National Archive ADM116/3456, p. 51.
25. Quoted in Burt, *British Battleships of World War One*, p. 134.
26. Hansard, HC Deb 29 March 1909, (series 5) Vol. 3, cc145-146.
27. Churchill, *The World Crisis, 1911–1918*, Vol. 1, p. 30.
28. Calculated from figures given in *The Times*, 21 January 1909.
29. T. A. Brassey (ed.), *The Naval Annual 1909* (J. Griffen & Co.), p. 366.
30. Burt, *British Battleships of World War One*, p. 69.
31. *Engineer*, 25 August 1905.
32. John Brown and Company Limited, Atlas Works Sheffield, p. 29.

CHAPTER 12

MODIFIED KRUPP ARMOUR AND THE SUPER-DREADNOUGHTS

The Admiralty had initially approved a battlecruiser of a similar design to the *Indefatigable* as part of the 1909 Estimates. This was based on information from the Naval Intelligence Department that the planned German battlecruisers would not be larger than this design. However, Admiral Jellicoe, the Third Sea Lord, learned through private sources that the planned German ships would be substantially larger than previously thought. Coupled with the concern that the Germans were now capable of matching the British shipbuilding industry in the speed of building Dreadnoughts, this caused the Admiralty to rethink their programme. The Admiralty had already decided in October 1908 to develop a new 13½-inch gun to replace the 12-inch gun on the early Dreadnoughts and, as a result of the information about German intentions, it was decided to order larger ships equipped with the new guns, which fired shells 50% heavier than the older main guns.

Captain Edmund Slade, the Director of Naval Intelligence, reported that Admiral Fisher, the First Sea Lord, was typically enthusiastic, seeing the larger ships as springing a surprise on Germany in the same way as the Dreadnought had done, and forcing them to spend extra money on top of their ordinary naval estimates.[1] In November 1909 Fisher wrote that 'the ships we have just laid down are as far beyond the *Dreadnought* as the *Dreadnought* was beyond all before her!'

As had been the case following the introduction of the *Dreadnought* in 1905, the larger ships reignited the debate about the relative merits of the battleship and the battlecruiser and which design should predominate. In March 1910 Admiral Reginald Bacon, a close associate of Fisher at the Admiralty, read a paper to the Institution of Naval Architects entitled 'The Battleship of the Future'. In this paper he argued that the future lay in not in more heavily armoured battleships but in larger, faster battlecruisers as the 'race between gun and armour which had been going on for over half a century is being decided, for the moment, in favour of the gun'.

THE DEVELOPMENT OF THE KRUPP PROCESS

Admiral Reginald Bacon had taken the position of Managing Director of the Coventry Ordinance Works in 1909, having previously been the Director of Naval Ordnance, an example of the close relationship between the Admiralty and the armament firms in practice. The Sheffield firms of John Brown and Cammell Laird and the Glasgow shipbuilders Fairfield had set up the company so that they could compete with Vickers and with Armstrong in the manufacture of heavy guns and gun mountings. As Director of Naval Ordnance, Bacon was, of course, familiar with the development of the new 13½-inch gun, and he argued in his paper that it was 'perfectly hopeless to think of attempting to supply armour which would be impenetrable to any guns which may be constructed in the reasonable future'. However at another talk to the Institution of Naval Architects in July 1911,[2] Charles Ellis, the managing director of John Brown & Co., argued that that the development of armour plate was ongoing and that 'it should not be assumed that finality had been reached' and that 'particularly in connection with capped projectiles of large diameters, as compared with the thickness of armour attacked improvements will be made' and that the armour manufacturers were keen to take advantage of any new discoveries. The discussion included a contribution from Sir William White, the Director of Naval Construction between 1885 and 1902, who commented on the efforts that the armour firms had put into improving Krupp armour and that this development been supported by an Admiralty research fund for experimental purposes.

The developments in armour plate to which Charles Ellis referred were based on advances in the heat treatment process and in particular the modification of the original Krupp method. The new techniques involved a double hardening of the steel plate first on one side and then on the reverse side. This description of the process is based on a patent which Vickers, Sons & Maxim applied for on 14 October 1910 and which was accepted in June 1911.[3] This modification of the Krupp process improved the structure of the back of the plate and increased its resistance to capped armour-piercing projectiles.

Only slight changes in the actual composition of the steel were made during this period. The carbon content, which had previously been at a level of about 0.3%, was increased to between 0.4% and 0.5%, which gave higher tensile strength, while the steel alloy remained much the same as before with 0.3% to 0.4% manganese, 3.7% to 3.95% nickel and 1.7% to 2% chromium added to the steel.

The process of making 'modified Krupp armour' was described in the Vickers patent:

1. After being rolled and annealed to increase its ductility, the plate was cemented in the normal manner except that it was cemented on the face and the back simultaneously, instead of only on the face.

2. The cementation time varied with the thickness of the plate – it was around fifteen days for a 6-inch plate and eighteen days for a 12-inch plate.

3. The cemented plate was then heated to 815 °C and bent to shape while hot.

4. It was then heated to between 787 °C and 843 °C and oil hardened.

5. The plate was then heated to between 649 °C to 732 °C and cooled in air on supports.

6. The plate was then heated to between 593 °C and 677 °C (depending on its carbon content) and was then sprinkled and cooled to air temperature.

7. The plate was then machined and drilled in a similar way to the previous process.

8. For the first hardening, the plate was placed on a sand bed with the back upwards and differentially hardened at a temperature of between 1,010 °C and 1,121 °C (depending on the thickness of the plate) to a depth of about two thirds of the plate.

9. The plate was then sprinkled in the normal way, after which the face was concave.

10. The plate was placed on a sand bed for a second time, this time with the face upwards, and it was differentially hardened again, at a temperature of between 1,010 °C and 1,121 °C (depending on the thickness of the plate), to a depth of about 1⅝ inches to 1¾ inches for a 6-inch plate and 2 to 3 inches for thicker plates.

11. The second differential hardening process drew out the previous hardness on the back of the plate.

As a result of the double hardening, the structure of the back of the plate was described as being a fine fibrous state with a tensile strength very much greater than in the basic Krupp process. The improvements in the manufacturing processes meant that armour of all thicknesses was able to resist tests by shot, fired at an extra 80 to 150 feet per second. This represented an increase of between 5% to 10% in ballistic resistance and an improved resistance to cracking and general disintegration under attack.[4]

Sample plate specification of Vickers modified Krupp armour

Vickers produced a range of sample plate specifications for each weight of armour. These specifications provided a standard 'recipe' which could then be followed exactly in making other plates of that weight. The sample plate no. 5138 was for 240 lb (6-inch) armour and was approved on 13 July 1911. It is quoted by A. D. Stacey as a good example of the modified armour of this period.[5]

The steel plate contained the following elements:

Carbon	:	0.465%
Silicon	:	0.126%
Manganese	:	0.350%
Sulphur	:	0.037%
Phosphorous	:	0.027%
Nickel	:	3.770%
Chromium	:	2.070%

The heat treatment process for the 6-inch cemented plate was:

Process	Treatment
Cogging & rolling	1,065°C to 1,093°C
Softening after first rolling	Heat to 621°C and cooled in air
Softening after second rolling	Heat to 621°C and straightened
Cementation	Heat for 3 days to raise the temperature to 954 °C and kept at that temperature for 10 days
Hardening	Heat to 815 °C and dip in oil
Softening	Heat to 662 °C and water sprinkle
Re-softening	Heat to 662 °C and water sprinkle
Hardening	Heat to 726 °C and dip in oil
Softening	Heat to 660 °C and cool in air
Re-softening	Heat to 660 °C and water sprinkle
Final harden	Place on sand bed heated to 816 °C Plate heated to 862 °C for 145 minutes
Re-soften	Heat to 682 °C and water sprinkle
Final harden	Place on sand bed heated to 812 °C Plate heated to 861 °C for 140 minutes

The hardened face of the plate was 16% of the thickness of the plate and the percentage of carbon in the steel at different depths from the face was:

⅛ inch	⅜ inch	⅝ inch	1 inch	1½ inch	2 inch
1.12%	0.95%	0.70%	0.53%	0.50%	0.50%

This specification was approved by the Admiralty after tests of its mechanical properties and resistance in firing trials. The firing trials were carried out on 18 November 1910 and consisted of five shots with a 9-inch armour-piercing projectile weighing 380 lb. The limits of the plate were reached at a projectile velocity of 1,380 feet per second, 60 feet per second faster that the agreed standard.

When the Admiralty placed a contract with a company, the reference number of the sample plate was quoted in the contract. The company were allowed to modify the methods of rolling and heat treatment temperatures, if these changes were agreed with the Admiralty inspectors, but the plate had to match the analyses, mechanical test results and ballistic performance set out for the sample plate. The sample 6-inch plate therefore represents the standard which all armour of similar weight was expected to achieve.

THE SUPER-DREADNOUGHTS

As we saw in Chapter 11, the first two ships of the 1909 estimates were the Dreadnoughts *Colossus* and *Hercules* which were developments of previous designs.

The second pair of ships ordered as part of the first half of the two-part 1909 Estimates represented major developments on the basic Dreadnought design and were known as the super-Dreadnoughts. The battleship HMS *Orion* and the battlecruiser HMS *Lion* were ordered as two of the first four ships of the 1909 order. The second group of four ships was made up of three further battleships of the *Orion* class and another battlecruiser, HMS *Princess Royal*.

The final 1909 programme was therefore made up of six battleships and two battlecruisers ordered in two groups. The orders in the first group were staggered to allow for the development of the design for the new larger ships. The second group were all ordered at the beginning of the 1910/11 financial year.

Ship	Type	Builder	Laid down
First part of the 1909 programme			
Colossus	Dreadnought battleship	Scott	08/07/09
Hercules	Dreadnought battleship	Palmer	30/07/09
Orion	Super-Dreadnought battleship	Portsmouth	29/11/09
Lion	Super-Dreadnought battlecruiser	Devonport	29/11/09
Second part of the 1909 programme			
Monarch	Super-Dreadnought battleship	Armstrong	01/04/10
Conqueror	Super-Dreadnought battleship	Beardmore	05/04/10
Thunderer	Super-Dreadnought battleship	Thames Iron Works	13/04/10
Princess Royal	Super-Dreadnought battlecruiser	Vickers	02/05/10

The lead ships of the *Orion* and *Lion* classes were built in the Royal Dockyards and the remaining six were built in private yards.

THE *ORION* AND *LION* CLASS

The *Orion* class were larger, more heavily armed and better protected that their predecessors of the *Colossus* class.

	Displacement	Length	Armament	Broadside weight	Armour
Colossus class	20,030 tons	510 ft	10 x 12 inch 16 x 4 inch	8,500 lbs	5,474 tons
Orion class	21,922 tons	545 ft	10 x 13½ inch 16 x 4 inch	12,500 lbs	6,460 tons

The main differences in the armour layout were that the vertical side armour was improved to withstand attack by the anticipated larger guns of the new German battleships. The main belt was 12 inches (480 lbs) thick compared to 11 inches (440 lbs) in the *Colossus*. It extended almost to the fore and aft barbettes. The top of the belt was at the height of the middle deck and in the bottom was 3 feet 4 inches below the waterline. In total the main belt was 20½ feet deep. The belt was extended fore and aft compared to the *Colossus* class with a 6-inch section reducing to 4 inches at the extremities. The fore and aft belt was the same height as the main belt. The 520 lb side armour in the *Orion* class was the thickest armour fitted to any British ship since the 230 tons of the same thickness of armour was used on the turrets of the *Lord Nelson* class.

	Thickness of armour protection[6]
Main belt armour	12 inches, 6 and 4 inches forward and aft. Lower belt 9 inches reducing to 6, 4 and 2½ inches
Upper belt	8 inches
A + B barbettes	10 inches on outer face reduced to 6 inches below main deck. Inner faces 9 reducing to 7 and 3 inches below main deck
Q + X barbettes	9- and 7-inch faces, 10-inch sides reducing to 3 inches below main deck
Y barbette	10 inches outer face and sides, inner face 9 and 7 inches. 3 inches below main deck
Main bulkheads	Forward 6 inches, aft 10 inches
Conning tower	11-inch face and sides, 3-inch roof, 4-inch floor
Upper deck	1½ inches
Middle deck	1 inch
Lower deck	Forward 1 to 2½ inches. Aft 3 to 4 inches
Turrets	11-inch faces, 8-inch sides, 3- to 4-inch roofs

The armour for HMS *Monarch*, which was built at Armstrong Whitworth's shipyard at Elswick, was made by Armstrong Whitworth themselves as well by Cammell Laird. The orders were:

Armour	Order date:	Last invoice date	Company	Tonnage produced	Cost
Side armour	16/6/1910	31/12/1911	Armstrong	2,648.61	£255,129.50
Side armour (80 lbs Krupp non-cemented)	6/9/1910	31/12/1911	Armstrong	56.05	£13,540.43
Bulkheads and barbettes	18/1/1910	30/6/1911	Armstrong	607.93	£62,379.17
Barbettes	16/6/1910	31/12/1911	Cammell Laird	992.90	£98,275.40
Bulkheads (80 lbs Krupp non-cemented)	25/5/1910	31/12/1910	Cammell Laird	18.85	£2,890.27
Conning tower	25/5/1910	31/12/1911	Cammell Laird	77.45	£7,434.45
13½ inch gun shields	20/12/1909	31/12/1911	Armstrong	953.71	£119,178.93
			Totals	5,355.50	£558,828.15

The battlecruiser HMS *Princess Royal*, built at the Vickers' shipyard at Barrow.

The orders shown in the Armour Plate Pool Ledger show that Armstrong, Beardmore and John Brown each got between 20% and 25% of the armour plate orders for the *Orion* class with Cammell Laird and Vickers sharing the other quarter between them.

The battlecruisers of the 1909 Estimates, the *Lion* and *Princess Royal*, were also armed with the new 13½-inch guns which were housed in four turrets. They were less heavily armoured than the *Orion* class battleships but, unlike previous battlecruisers, they were longer and heavier that the battleships.[7]

	Displacement	Length	Horsepower	Speed	Armour
Lion class	26,350 tons	660 ft	70,000 HP	28 knots	5,140 tons
Orion class	21,922 tons	545 ft	27,000 HP	21 knots	6,460 tons

The main armour belt was 9 inches thick and extended from abreast the conning tower to the Y barbette. The lower edge was 3 feet below the waterline and the upper edge was 8½ feet above it. This thickness of armour was less than in the equivalent German battlecruisers of the *Seydlitz* class whose belt was 300mm (12 inches) at the thickest point. The inadequacy of the protection was demonstrated at the Battle of Dogger Bank in January 1915, when HMS *Lion* was hit twice below the waterline and seven times about it. The damage was extensive, driving the armour well into the hull structure and damaging internal compartments and putting the port engine out of action. The flooding that resulted caused the ship to list 10°. At the Battle of Jutland the more heavily protected *Seydlitz* took an enormous amount of damage, but was able to return to Kiel under her own power.

	Thickness of armour protection[8]
Main belt armour	9 inches, 6, 5 and 4 inches forward, 5 and 4 inches aft
Upper belt	6 inches, 5 and 4 inches forward and aft
A, B & Q barbettes	9 inches on outer face, reduced to 3 inches below main deck. Inner faces 8 inches reducing to 3 inches below main deck
Y barbette	9 inches outer face and sides reducing to 3 inches below main deck. Inner face 8 inches reducing to 3 inches below main deck
Main bulkheads	4 inches
Conning tower	10-inch face and sides, 3-inch roof
Forecastle deck	1½ to 1¼ inches
Upper deck	1 inch
Lower deck	1 to 2 inches
Turrets	9-inch faces, 9-inch sides, 8-inch rear, 2½- to 2¼-inch roofs

The armour orders shown in the armour plate pool ledger for HMS *Lion* and HMS *Princess Royal* are:

Armour	Order date:	Last invoice date	Company	Tonnage produced	Cost
Lion					
Shields	21/9/1909	31/12/1911	Armstrong	642.61	£78,608.62
Barbettes (note 1)	10/3/1910	30/6/1911	J. Brown	913.50	£89,968.55
Side	9/3/1910	30/6/1911	Cammell Laird	2667.40	£249,201.51
Bulkheads	18/1/1910	31/12/1910	Vickers	212.57	£18,710.93
			Total	4436.08	£436,489.61
Princess Royal					
Barbettes (note 2)	1/6/1910	31/12/1911	Vickers	3,433.44	£326,516.63
Barbette	1/6/1910	30/6/1912	Vickers	15.09	£803.40
Shields	1/5/1910	31/12/1911	Vickers	661.86	81,178.6
Bulkheads	18/1/1910	31/12/1910	Vickers	212.57	£18,710.93
Conning tower	1/5/1910	31/12/1911	Vickers	73.56	£7,073.87
			Total	4,396.52	£434,283.43

Note 1: Split between *Orion* and *Lion*.

Note 2: Described as barbette but presumably including side armour due to the quantity.

R. A. Burt[9] gives a total weight of armour for the class of 5,140 tons but the armour orders in the ledger exclude some elements such as deck plating.

THE 1910/11 PROGRAMME

The 1910/11 Estimates included proposals for four battleships and one battlecruiser. The battlecruiser, *Queen Mary*, was almost identical to the *Lion* class with few alterations in her armour layout. The four battleships of the *King George V* class were improved versions of the *Orion* class. The 1910/11 programme was the first set of orders for capital ships since the retirement of Admiral Jackie Fisher in January 1910 on his 70th birthday. His final period at the Admiralty had been soured by a major conflict with Charles Beresford, the admiral and politician who was Commander-in-Chief of the Channel fleet, and had publicly disagreed with Fisher's plans for the organisation and distribution of the fleet. Admiral Sir Arthur Wilson took over as the First Sea Lord.

The *King George V* class

The four members of the *King George V* class were all ordered in January 1911. The two ships built at the Navy's Royal Dockyards were laid down on 16 January:

	Shipyard	Machinery
King George V	Portsmouth	Parsons
Centurion	Devonport	Hawthorne, Leslie

The ships that were built in the private yards were laid down slightly later with the company building the ship also making the machinery:

	Shipyard	Machinery
Ajax	Scott	Scott
Audacious	Cammell Laird	Cammell Laird

The four *King George V* class ships had armour protection which was of a similar layout to the previous *Orion* class, the principal differences being:

- The forward main bulkhead was increased in thickness from 6 inches to 10 inches.
- The upper side bulkhead was increased in thickness from 8 inches to 10 inches.
- The after bulkhead was reduced in thickness from 2½ inches to 2 inches.
- The upper deck around 'Q' barbette was increased in thickness from 1½ inches to 1¾ inches.
- The forward 4-inch secondary armament was given 3- to 3½-inch armour protection.
- Longitudinal screens 1 inch thick protected the engine rooms (except in *Orion* where they only protected the magazines).

Like the *Orion* class, the *King George V* class did not have longitudinal anti-torpedo bulkheads. The lack of this feature was felt when HMS *Audacious*, the only Dreadnought build by Cammell Laird at Birkenhead, hit a mine and sank in 1914.

Armstrong Whitworth received the order for the bulkheads and barbettes for HMS *Centurion*, which was built at Devonport dockyard. The breakdown of this order is shown in the Armour Plate Pool Ledger. The two orders have been split into those for the barbettes and the bulkheads:

Armour specification:		Bulkheads (Tons Ordered)		Barbettes (Tons Ordered)
Weight (lbs)	Thickness (inches)			
400	10	220	185	295
360	9		90	180
320	8	95		
280	7			25
240	6	100		
160	4	15		
120	3		150	
80	2	20		
Tapers				
400/120	10/3		25	85
360/120	9/3		30	80
280/120	7/3		15	
240/120	6/3		140	
Total (tons)		450	635	665
			1,300	
			1,750	

The size of this order is in line with the armour weights in the Final Legend for the ship, which gave a weight of armour for the bulkheads and barbettes as follows:

	Weight (tons)	
Forward bulkhead	183	
Aft bulkhead	230	
'A' barbette		236
'B' barbette		401
'Q' barbette		193
'X' barbette		286
'Y' barbette		192
Totals	413	1,308
	1,721	

The order was in two parts and the actual amount of armour invoiced was slightly smaller:

Armour	Order date:	Last invoice date	Company	Tonnage produced	Cost
Bulkheads and barbettes	12/11/1910	31/12/1912	Armstrong	1,035.51	£104,321.44
Barbettes	27/1/1911	31/12/1912	Armstrong	625.34	£62,086.23
			Total	1,660.85	£166,407.67

The *Queen Mary*

The armour protection for the *Queen Mary* was very similar to that of the *Lion* and the *Princess Royal*. The main differences were:

- The forward upper belt extended further forward and not as far aft.
- The protection of the funnel uptakes was reduced.
- Light armour protection was provided for the forward secondary 4-inch guns.
- The after torpedo control tower was strengthened.

The armour orders for the *Queen Mary* recorded in the armour plate pool ledger are:

Armour	Order date:	Last invoice date	Company	Tonnage produced	Cost
Belt	29/1/1911	30/6/1913	J. Brown	2,647.04	£248,406.79
Barbettes	17/1/1911	30/6/1912	J. Brown	835.98	£81,303.64
Bulkheads	23/12/1910	30/6/1912	Armstrong	89.41	£8,298.45
Ring bulkhead	2/9/1911	30/6/1913	Armstrong	27.50	£2,471.84
Shields	24/12/1910	30/6/1913	Armstrong	637.43	£75,612.92
Sighting hoods	27/4/1912	31/12/1912	Cammell Laird	12.33	£1,441.75
Protection to hoists	29/12/1910	31/12/1911	J. Brown	121.56	£10,211.36
Conning tower	28/7/1911	30/6/1913	J. Brown	86.22	£8,553.56
			Total	4,457.47	£436,300.31

Of the total of 21,205 tons of armour plate recorded for the 1910/11 programme in the armour plate pool ledger, Armstrong Whitworth made 13%, William Beardmore 28%, John Brown 18%, Cammell Laird 3% and Vickers 38%. As Vickers had a majority stakeholding in Beardmore's, between them they were responsible for manufacturing 56% of the armour plate.

THE 1911/12 PROGRAMME

The four battleships ordered as part of the 1911/12 programme were those of the *Iron Duke* class. A singe battlecruiser, HMS *Tiger*, was also ordered and she was the last battlecruiser ordered before the First World War broke out.

The *Iron Duke* class were improved versions of the *King George V* class but had a secondary armament of 6-inch guns instead of the 4-inch guns of the previous ships. The ships had improved protection for the secondary guns and they also carried more fuel and had a slightly higher speed. The armour protection was much the same as the *King George V* class with the following variations:

- The main belt extended further forward and the armour was spread more evenly throughout the belt.
- The maximum thickness of the main bulkheads was reduced from 10 inches to 8 inches.
- An additional aft bulkhead was fitted.
- The after lower deck was thickened.
- The barbette armour was redistributed.

The *Emperor of India* or the *Benbow* in 1915 with other ships of the 4th Battle Squadron of the Grand Fleet.

HMS Tiger on the slipway at John Brown's Yard. The teak planking which will act as a backing for the side armour can be seen and shows the smaller size of the side armour protection in a battlecruiser.

As with the King George V class, two of the ships were built in the Royal Dockyards and two were built in private yards

	Shipyard	Laid down
Iron Duke	Portsmouth	15/1/1912
Marlborough	Devonport	25/1/1912
Benbow	Beardmore	30/5/1912
Emperor of India	Vickers	31/5/1912

Of the total of 23,465 tons of armour plate recorded for the 1911/12 programme in the Armour Plate Pool Ledger, Armstrong Whitworth made 20%, William Beardmore 42%, John Brown 12%, Cammell Laird again made only 3% and Vickers made 23%. The Vickers–Beardmore combination was responsible for manufacturing 65% of the armour plate as well as building two of the four ships in their own dockyards.

Armstrong Vickers, however, made the gun mountings and turrets for two of the ships, the *Iron Duke* and *Marlborough*. The order for the armour for the five gunshields for each ship was for 940 tons made up as follows:

	Weight (tons)	Cost per ton
Vertical armour	600	£130
Roof armour	220	£112
Floor protection	30	£101
Floor, high tensile steel	85	£73
Splinter protection	3	£104
Gunport protection	2	£104
Total	940	

The actual amount of armour invoiced for was

	Order date	Last invoice date	Tonnage produced	Cost invoiced
Iron Duke	18/1/1912	30/6/1913	969.55	£110,210.54
Marlborough	18/1/1912	30/6/1914	991.50	£112,837.40

HMS *Tiger* was originally conceived as a development of the *Queen Mary* design but Sir Phillip Watts, the Director of Naval Construction, proposed a number of new designs. The design that was selected had the 'X' turret behind the third funnel rather than in front, as was the case in previous battlecruisers. This gave the turret a greater field of fire. The armour layout of the *Tiger* varied from the *Queen Mary* in the following way:

- The armour belt was extended further forward and aft;
- The 9-inch main belt was not as deep and a lower belt of 3-inch armour was added;
- The secondary battery was protected by 6-inch side armour and a 5-inch forward bulkhead;
- The length of the main armour deck was increased;
- The lower deck armour was increased from 2½ inches to 3 inches.

The order for the side armour for HMS *Tiger* was given to Vickers, Sons & Maxim. The amount ordered was 2,657 tons made up of the following weights of plate:

Armour		Tons ordered	Price per ton
Weight (lbs)	Thickness (inches)		
360	9	1,124	£95
240	6	528	£93
200	5	487	£93
160	4	398	£93
120	3	124	£95

ARMOUR PLATE PRODUCTION FOR THE 13.5 INCH ARMED SUPER-DREADNOUGHTS

As was the case with the early Dreadnoughts, the armour plate ledgers allow us to explore the production of British armour plate in more detail by looking at annual production and income for each of the companies in the pool. The total amount of armour plate produced for the eighteen super-Dreadnoughts fitted with 13.5-inch guns is shown in the following table:

	Annual production of armour plate									
Year	Armstrong Whitworth		W. Beardmore		John Brown		Cammell Laird		Vickers	
	Tons	Income	Tons	Income	Tons	Income	Tons	Income	Tons	Income
1909	3,551	£413,617	2,113	£221,320	3,465	£363,534	1,698	£169,337	2,693	£316,116
1910	6,558	£683,674	13,747	£1,564,415	6,204	£634,479	6,663	£633,216	13,036	£1,290,774
1911	3,667	£353,699	131	£6,828	7,390	£711,106	5,325	£632,947	1,928	£230,510
1912	2,320	£267,222	5,153	£519,156	1,059	£112,740	818	£95,415	6,667	£672,513
1913	0	£0	0	£0	0	£0	66	£6,734	640	£12,094
Total	16,096	£1,718,213	21,144	£2,311,719	18,117	£1,821,858	14,569	£1,537,649	24,964	£2,522,007

The table shows the share of the armour plate produced by each of the five armour makers:

	% of production
Armstrong	17.1%
Beardmore	22.5%
J Brown	19.3%
Cammell	15.5%
Vickers	25.6%

Endnotes

1. Sumida, *In Defence of Naval Strategy*, p. 161.
2. *Engineer*, 21 July 1911, p. 79.
3. Patent Application 6664, Improvements in the Manufacture of Armour Plates, 16 June1911.
4. Stacey, 'An Historical Survey of the Manufacture of Naval Armour' p. 10.
5. Ibid., Appendix B, Index No. 1.
6. Burt, *British Battleships of World War One*, p. 69.
7. T. A. Brassey (ed.), *Naval Annual 1911* (J. Griffin & Co.).
8. Burt, *British Battleships of World War One*, p. 176.
9. Ibid., p. 178.

CHAPTER 13

MORE POWERFUL GUNS AND 'NEW QUALITY ARMOUR'

Winston Churchill was moved from the Board of Trade to become First Lord of the Admiralty in October 1911. Soon after he arrived he advocated a new class of fast battleships armed with bigger guns. He was looking for a ship which combined the speed of a battlecruiser with the protection and hitting power of a battleship. His view was that he did not see the benefits of the battlecruiser type, arguing that:

A drawing of the interior of a turret on HMS *Revenge* showing the breech of one of her 15-inch guns.

> If it is worthwhile to spend far more than the price of your best battleship on a fast heavily gunned vessel, it is better at the same time to give it the heaviest armour as well […] to put the value of a first class battleship into a vessel which cannot withstand the pounding of a heavy action is false policy. It is far better to spend the extra money and have what you really want.[1]

The search therefore began for a suitable gun, for heavier armour able to defend the new ships, and for a design which would bring all these aspirations together. Armstrong Whitworth were asked to work on a new 15-inch gun which was codenamed the '14-inch experimental gun' and the armour companies were asked to manufacture thicker 13-inch (520 lbs) armour and to improve the quality of existing weights.

NEW QUALITY ARMOUR

Setting new standards

The Admiralty pressed the armour manufacturers for heavier armour plate of 600 and 520 lbs weight per square foot (15 inches and 13 inches thick respectively) and for improvements in the resistance of other armour plate. To encourage the manufacturers to improve the quality of their armour plate the Admiralty developed new testing standards and introduced a flexible pricing structure for plates that met this standard. The increase in the severity of the tests is shown in the table:

Weight of plate per sq. ft	Nominal thickness of plate	Nature of projectile		Velocity – feet per second				
				1908[2]	1912–1914[3]		Issued December 1914	
		Calibre (inches)	Type (note 1)	Standard	Standard	Minimum	Standard	Minimum
600	15	15	APC				1,875	1,625
520	13	13.5	APC		1,250	1,170		
480	12	12	APC	1,690	1,770	1,690	1,950	1,690
480	12	12	APC					
440	11	12	APC	1,650	1,730	1,650		
400	10	12	APC	1,510	1,590	1,510	1,740	1,510
360	9	12	APC		1,460	1,340		
360	9	9.2	APC	1,340			1,950	1,600
320	8	12	APC		1,360	1,180		
320	8	9.2	APC	1,640				
280	7	9.2	APC	1,350	1,470	1,350		
280	7	7.5	APC				1,950	1,650
240	6	9.2	APC	1,180	1,320	1,180		
240	6	7.5	CPC				1,825	1,600
200	5	7.5	CPC		1,625	1,460		
200	5	7.5	APC	1,460				
200	5	6	CPC					
160	4	6	CPC	1,150	1,260	1,150	1,550	1,150
120	3	6	CPC		1,890	1,720		
80	2	6	CPC		1,420	1,270		

Note 1: APC – Armour Piercing Capped shell, CPC – Common Projectile Capped.

Direct comparisons with pre-1908 tests are not easy as prior to this date the standard target was backed with oak. The tests introduced in 1908 did away with this backing and this gave them different qualities of resistance.

When the Tresidder formula (see Chapter 3) is applied, for measuring the resistance of armour to the increasing specifications for armour plate using a standard weight of shot, the increase in the testing standards can be seen more clearly:

Weight of plate per sq. ft	Year				
	1908	1912–1914		1914	
		Standard	Minimum	Standard	Minimum
600				35.05	28.28
520		17.09	15.48		
480	22.20	23.80	22.20	27.52	22.20
440	21.42	23.00	21.42		
400	18.75	20.26	18.75	23.20	18.75
360	11.97	17.83	15.68	21.02	15.62
320	16.21	16.03	12.96		
280	12.11	13.76	12.11	16.89	13.14
240	9.89	11.70	9.89	15.29	12.55
200	10.94	12.85	10.94		
160	6.05	6.93	6.05	9.46	6.05

The table shows that the heaviest armour plate tested increased in weight from 520 lbs (13-inch) to 600 lbs (15-inch), although there is no record of armour this thick being fitted to any of the Grand Fleet. The resistance required from the heaviest armour plate rose from the equivalent of 17.09 to 35.05 inches of wrought-iron, an increase of 105%, though it does seem on this comparison that the test for 520 lb armour in the 1912/13 specification was very low – in fact lower than the test for 480 lb armour.

Where a direct comparison of the three periods is possible the figures show that:

- The minimum requirement does not alter for the heavier armour above 400 lbs (10-inch) but the standard level rises around 23%.
- For armour between 360 lbs (9-inch) and 240 lbs (6-inch) the standard rises by between 40% and 75% and the minimum rises between 8% and 30%.
- For 160 lbs (4-inch) armour the standard specification rises by 56% but the minimum required does not increase.

Perfecting the quality of the new armour

Unlike the development of the modified Krupp process, which involved an additional stage of hardening, the development of 'new quality' armour seems to have been one of gradually increasing the quality through improvements in the ability to measure and control each stage of the process, supported by improved analysis of the structure of the armour. However, although the process of armour making was becoming more scientific there was still a great deal of practical experience involved in producing the best plates.

The only company which managed to produce plates that passed the standard at all thicknesses was Vickers, which were probably at this stage the leading manufacturer. In a letter to the Admiralty the company said that 'in regard to our new quality armour generally […] now that our new plant is in working order we hope to be able to retain and perhaps improve on the present excellence of production'.[4] In a similar letter in the same month Armstrong Whitworth told the Admiralty that they had had to invest £450,000 in new equipment.

Writing to the Admiralty in 1914 about the difficulties they were experiencing in producing 520 lbs (13-inch) armour plate to a new, higher specification Charles Ellis, the managing director of John Brown, wrote:

> We have produced one very good sample, but we admit we have so far been unable to repeat it, or to discover exactly the reason of its superiority to subsequent plates which differed in the smallest percentages in analysis and tests, and which went through exactly the same treatment. We should like to assure their Lordships that the problem is having our unremitting attention, and further plates will shortly be ready for dispatch to Shoeburyness.[i] […] In addition to the actual manufacture of experimental plates, we have given great attention to the more accurate determination of temperature in our treatment furnaces, and

---

i   The main government ordinance and armour-testing facility on the south Essex coast.

have installed a complete system of modern electrical pyrometers. We are devoting the sum of £100,000 to replace some of our older carburising furnaces by modern ones of the latest design.[5]

John Brown were not alone in experiencing these problems. Cammell Laird were experiencing similar problems with plates above 12 inches. They wrote:

We have been making the most exhaustive experiments in regard to thicker plates and have concentrate our efforts mainly on the production of a successful 13 inch (520 lb) plate because we believe this presents the most serious difficulty. In the course of our investigations over the last 20 months we have manufactured 9 experimental plates.

They said that the results of the experiments had been disappointing but that they 'had gained valuable experience from them which will, we believe, enable us to solve the problem with which we have been confronted'.[6] William Beardmore's also wrote a similar letter pointing out that the their experiments and trials 'involved the expenditure of large sums'.

Rather than reject all the armour plates which did not met the new specifications for 1912 to 1914, the Admiralty introduced a differential scale for payments for plates which did not meet the standard they required but were higher than the minimum standard. A 520 lb (13-inch) plate was expected to resist being hit by a 13½-inch armour piercing projectile travelling at 1,250 feet per second. If the trial plate was able only to resist the same projectile travelling 15 feet per second slower (1,235 ft sec.) the company were paid £0.50 less per ton for the whole batch of plates from which that sample had been taken. For every 15 ft sec. after that there was a price penalty of an additional £1.00 down to the minimum standard of 1,170 ft sec. In 1913 this meant that for 520 lb plate, where the difference between the standard and the minimum was 80 ft sec., the companies could be penalised by £4.50 and the plate would still be accepted. This meant they received £93.50 rather than £98 per ton.

These deductions were listed by the Admiralty in a memo dated April 1914:[7]

Ship	Firm	Weight (lbs per sq. ft)	Approx. total weight affected (tons)	Deduction per ton	Total deduction
Queen Elizabeth /Warspite	Vickers	520	1,230	£1	£1,230
Queen Elizabeth /Warspite	Vickers	240	1,250	£4	£5,000
Barham / Valiant	Brown	520	1,350	£3¼	£4,300
Barham	Brown	240 / 160	170	£1	£170
Valiant	Beardmore	160	350	5	£1,750
Queen Elizabeth / Valiant	Beardmore	240	700	4	£2,800
				Total	£15,250

As well as the plates for which price reductions were made, four firms were reported to have had plates that failed to reach the minimum standard in the tests. These included:

• 360 lb and 160 lb plates from Armstrong Whitworth;
• 240 lb and 160 lb plates from William Beardmore;
• a 160 lb plate from John Brown; and
• a 520 lb plate from Vickers.

When the memo was written selections for test plates had not yet been made from all the armour orders. At that stage Cammell Laird, who were making armour for the *Warspite*, the *Barham* and the *Valiant*, were not recorded as having had any plates below the standard.

Sample plate specification 'new quality' armour from Vickers

Vickers wrote to the Admiralty in July 1914 that:

In regard to our new quality armour generally, we have not only been able to keep up to the high standard that we originally gave their Lordships but in most of the trials we have improved on the original results, and now that our new plant is in working order we hope to be able to retain and perhaps improve upon the present excellence of production.

They wrote that they had demonstrated at Eskmeals[i] that they were able to reproduce a 520 lb plate 'as good as our original plate No. 7061'.[8]

---

i   Vickers' gun and plate testing facility north of Barrow.

The sample plate no. 7061, which was referred to by Vickers in their letter, was approved on 24 January 1913 and the detailed specification for the plate was:[9]

Carbon	:	0.51%
Silicon	:	0.060%
Manganese	:	0.36%
Sulphur	:	0.031%
Phosphorous	:	0.026%
Nickel	:	3.83%
Chromium	:	2.01%

The heat treatment process for the 13-inch cemented plate was:

Process	Treatment
Cogging	1,065°C to 1,093°C
Rolling	1,065°C to 1,093°C
Softening after first rolling	Heat to 621°C and cooled in air
Softening after second rolling	Heat to 621°C and cooled in air, straightened and surfaced
Cementation	Data not available. The specification for 600lb plates required heating for 3 days to raise the temperature to 937°C to 951°C and kept at that temperature for 12 days
Hardening	Heat to 815°C and dip in oil
Softening	Heat to 660°C and water sprinkle
Re-softening	Heat to 660°C and water sprinkle
	Sent to machine shop
Hardening	Heat to 815°C and dip in oil
Softening	Heat to 682°C and cool in air
Re-softening	Heat to 682°C and water sprinkle
Final harden	Place on sand bed heated for 382 minutes (no temperature given)

The hardened face of the plate was 15.5% of the thickness of the plate and the percentage of carbon in the steel at different depths from the face was:

1/8 inch	3/8 inch	5/8 inch	1 inch	1½ inch	2 inch
1.01% to 1.09%	0.72% to 0.77%	0.55% to 0.44%	0.49% to 0.51%	0.49 to 0.5%%	0.49 to 0.5%%

This specification was approved by the Admiralty after tests of its mechanical properties and resistance in firing trials. The firing trials were carried out on 24 January 1913 and 11 February 1913 and consisted of the plates being fired at with 13½-inch armour-piercing shells weighing 1,250 lbs. The limits of the plate were reached at a projectile velocity of 1,280 feet per second, 30 feet per second faster that the agreed standard as set out by the Admiralty (see previous table).

THE NEW BATTLESHIPS

The *Queen Elizabeth* class

The final design agreed for the new fast battleships of the *Queen Elizabeth* class ordered as part of the 1912/13 Estimates was for ships with eight 15-inch guns in four turrets. In order to achieve the speeds required they were the first battleships to be fuelled entirely by oil, which gave them a speed of 23 to 24 knots. They were the last battleships designed by Sir Phillip Watts who had been the Director of Naval Construction at the Admiralty since 1902 and responsible for the design of all the British Dreadnought fleet to date.

Invitations to tender for the ships was sent out in June 1912. The ships were awarded to two Royal Dockyards and two private yards, and were laid down in February 1913. The Federation of Malay States offered to fund a fifth ship and this was laid down in October of the same year.

	Dockyard	Launched	Completed
Queen Elizabeth	Portsmouth Dockyard	16 October 1913	January 1914
Warspite	Devonport Dockyard	26 November 1913	April 1915
Valiant	Fairfield	4 November 1913	February 1916
Barham	John Brown	31 December 1913	October 1915
Malaya	Armstrong	18 March 1915	February 1916

HMS *Barham* being fitted out at John Brown's shipyard. On the left the forward armoured barbettes can be seen with the runners to support the gun housing already in place in forward 'B' barbette. On the right the revolving gun housing is being lowered into the rear 'X' barbette.

The armour plate for the *Queen Elizabeth* class was essentially a development of the *Iron Duke* class that had preceded it. In summary the class carried the following armour protection (excluding deck armour):[10]

	Armour element	Weight	Thickness
Main belt	Upper strake	240 lbs	6 inch
	Upper stake ends	180 lbs	4 inch
	Main strake top	520 lbs	13 inch
	Main strake lower edge	300 lbs	8 inch
	Main strake ends	80 lbs	2 inch
Bulkheads	Main bulkheads	240 lbs	6 inch
	Aft bulkhead (above lower deck)	180 lbs	4 inch
	Aft bulkhead (below lower deck)	60lbs	1½ inch
	Anti-torpedo bulkhead		
Barbettes	A barbette – face and sides (above main deck)	400 lbs	10 inch
	A barbette – face and sides (below main deck)	240 lbs	6 inch
	B barbette – face and sides (above main deck)	460 lbs	9 inch
	B barbette – face and sides (below main deck)	180 lbs	4 inch
	Y barbette – face (above main deck)	400 lbs	10 inch
	Y barbette – face (below main deck)	180 lbs	4 inch
	Y barbette – side and rear (above main deck)	460 lbs	9 inch
	Y barbette – side and rear (below main deck)	280 lbs	7 inch
	X barbette – face (above main deck)	400 lbs	10 inch
	X barbette – face (below main deck)	180 lbs	4 inch
	X barbette – side and rear (above main deck)	460 lbs	9 inch
	X barbette – side and rear (upper to main deck)	180 lbs	4 inch
	X barbette – side and rear (below main deck)	180 lbs	4 inch
Gunshields	Faces	520 lbs	13 inch
	Sides	440 lbs	11 inch
	Crowns	180 lbs	4½ inch
Secondary battery	Side plates	240 lbs	6 inch
	Rear bulkhead	240 lbs	6 inch
		180 lbs	4 inch
	Internal bulkheads	80 lbs	2 inch
	Internal transverses	60 lbs	1½ inch
	Gunshields	120 lbs	3 inch
	Casements	240 lbs	6 inch
Conning towers	Sides	400 lbs	11 inch
	Roof	240 lbs	6 inch
		120 lbs	3 inch
	Base sides	240 lbs	6 inch
	Base face and rear	120 lbs	3 inch
	CT Hood face and sides	240 lbs	6 inch
	CT Hood roof	120 lbs	3 inch
	CT Hood rear	80 lbs	2 inch
Torpedo control tower	Sides	240 lbs	6 inch
	Floor	120 lbs	3 inch
	Roof	80 lbs	2 inch

The armour plate ledgers recode a total of 6,889 tons of armour ordered for the *Warspite*:

Armour	Order date	Last invoice date	Company	Tonnage produced	Cost
4 Shields for main armament	19/10/1912	30/6/1917	Armstrong	1,080.35	£124,069.34
Armour under conning tower	26/5/1913	30/6/1914	Beardmore	113.76	£10,518.15
Conning towers	13/10/1913	31/12/1915	Beardmore	75.81	£10,733.82
Side	3/1/1913	31/12/1914	John Brown	458.91	£41,839.60
Bulkheads and barbettes	14/11/1914	30/6/1914	Cammell Laird	647.12	£65,762.03
Barbettes	6/1/1913	31/12/1914	Cammell Laird	835.76	£80,534.00
Torpedo control towers	26/7/1913	31/12/1914	Cammell Laird	34.77	£2,305.21
Battery	3/7/1913	31/12/1915	Cammell Laird	949.74	£99,703.20
Sides	1/3/1913	31/12/1915	Vickers	2,692.84	£280,024.20
			Total	6,889.06	£715,489.55

HMS *Revenge* on the slipway at Vickers' yard in Barrow. The place where the heavy armour belt will be fitted after launch can be seen on the side of the ship but the teak backing has not yet been fitted.

The total weight of armour carried by the *Warspite* was 8,600 tons. Some of the discrepancy with the volume of orders recorded in the ledgers is due to the fact that deck armour is not recorded and part may be due to the fact that a number of the orders are split with other sister ships. The calculations assume that these orders are split equally but this may not be the case.

The *Royal Sovereign* class

The five ships of the *Royal Sovereign* Class were ordered as part of the 1913 Estimates. They were designed to have a speed of 21 knots and were not as fast as the oil-fueled *Queen Elizabeth* Class.

The 'Statement of Dimensions' of HMS *Revenge* shows the thickness of the armour fitted to the ship:[11]

Side armour; upper edge above load line	15 inches to 9 inches
Side armour; lower edge below load line	5 inches to zero
Armour on side, amidships	13 inches and 6 inches
Armour on side, forward	4 inches and 6 inches
Armour on side, aft	6 inches and 4 inches
Armour on bulkhead, forward	4 inches and 6 inches
Armour on bulkhead, aft	6 inches and 4 inches
Armour on barbettes	10 inches and 4 inches
Armour on gunhouses	11 inches
Armour on conning tower, forward	11 inches
Armour on conning tower, aft	6 inches
Armour on signal tower	none
Armour on communications tube, forward	6 inches and 4 inches
Armour on communications tube, aft	4 inches
Backing behind side armour (minimum)	2 inches
Protective plating (vertical) in wake of magazine, machinery, boilers and shell rooms	1½ inches to 1 inch
Protective plating (vertical) in wake of funnel uptakes	1½ inches
Protective deck plating, forecastle deck	1 inch
Protective deck plating, upper deck	1¼ inches to 1½ inches
Protective deck plating, main deck	1 inch, 1½ inches and 2 inches
Protective deck plating, slope middle to main deck	2 inches
Protective deck plating, lower deck forward	2½ inches to 1 inch
Protective deck plating, lower deck aft	2½ inches, 4 inches and 3 inches
Armour on 6-inch gun battery	6 inches

The total weight of armour for the *Royal Sovereign* class was 8,250 tons. At her launch on 26 May 1915 the *Revenge* carried 1,487 tons, 7 hundredweight and 84 lbs of armour, the majority of which was in the bulkheads and barbettes. As was normal, the side armour was not fitted until after launch.

Records from the Vickers armour shop[12] for 1914 and 1915 show that they made 11,995 tons of armour for the ships of the *Royal Sovereign* class, with the largest amount being made for HMS *Revenge*:

	Tons of armour made
Royal Sovereign	3,023
Royal Oak	2,508
Revenge	5,256
Ramillies	1,057
Resolution	none

The weight and type of armour made for the *Revenge* was:

	Belt Tons	Barbettes Tons	Shields Tons
February 1914	279.23		
March 1914	1180.03	122.15	
April 1914	432.12	109.27	
May 1914	511.07	355.92	
June 1914	496.42	95.63	
July 1914		200.90	
August 1914		200.29	
September 1914			21.97
October 1914	97.78		22.43
November 1914	8.68		
December 1914			
January 1915	7.38		
February 1915			
March 1915	30.34		12.65
April 1915			
May 1915			
June 1915			211.00
July 1915	31.27		258.26
August 1915			261.83
September 1915	26.79		252.15
Total	3,101.11	1,084.15	1,040.29

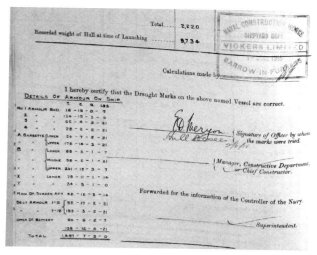

An extract from the Ship's Book for HMS *Revenge* (ADM 136) showing the amount of armour fitted to the ship when she was launched. The certificate is stamped by the Vickers shipyard at Barrow where she was built.

The main 13-inch armour belt stretched from the A barbette to the X barbette; forward of this was a thinner belt of 6 inches which reduced to 4 inches. This thinner belt was 42 feet long and it ran to within 34 feet of the bows where it reduced further to 1 inch. The aft belt was 6 inches thick and ran for 50 feet before reducing to 4 inches. The belt armour made by Vickers was split into the following weights:

Thickness of armour		
lbs	inches	Tons made
160	4	143.41
240	6	860.29
400	10	49.22
520	13	2,048.19
Total		3,101.11

ARMOUR PLATE PRODUCTION FOR THE 15 INCH ARMED SUPER-DREADNOUGHTS

As was the case with the previous Dreadnoughts, the armour plate ledgers allow us to explore the production of British armour plate in more detail by looking at annual production and income for each of the companies in the pool. The total amount of armour plate produced for the eighteen super-Dreadnoughts fitted with 15-inch guns is shown in the following table:

Annual production of armour plate

Year	Armstrong Whitworth		W. Beardmore		John Brown		Cammell Laird		Vickers	
	Tons	Income	Tons	Income	Tons	Income	Tons	Income	Tons	Income
1912	2,871	£324,083	0	£0	0	£0	0	£0	0	£0
1913	2,578	£232,807	6,252	£598,471	7,237	£726,816	4,894	£481,028	14,607	£1,493,846
1914	2,839	£347,975	6,005	£741,143	3,818	£404,427	2,608	£252,108	7,755	£802,708
1915	0	£0	241	£24,082	0	£0	27	£2,540	38	£3,397
Total	8,288	£904,865	12,498	£1,363,696	11,056	£1,131,243	7,529	£735,675	22,400	£2,299,951

The table shows the share of the armour plate produced by each of the five armour makers:

	% of production
Armstrong	13.4%
Beardmore	20.2%
J Brown	17.9%
Cammell	12.2%
Vickers	36.3%

Endnotes

1. Churchill, *The World Crisis 1911–1918*, Vol. 1, p. 99.
2. Stacey, 'An Historical Survey of the Manufacture of Naval Armour', p. 93.
3. National Archive ADM 116/3456 for 1912–1914 and December 1914
4. Ibid., Letter from Vickers to the Admiralty, 7 July 1914.
5. Ibid., Letter from John Brown to the Admiralty, 1 July 1914.
6. Ibid., Letter from Cammell Laird to Admiralty, 3 July 1914.
7. Ibid..
8. Letter from Vickers to Admiralty 7 July 1914, Ibid. p. 244.
9. Stacey, 'An Historical Survey of the Manufacture of Naval Armour' p. 105.
10. Burt, *British Battleships of World War One*, p. 281.
11. National Archive, ADM 136.
12. SIMT, Armour Plate Pool ledgers, M560.

CHAPTER 14

THE GRAND FLEET AT JUTLAND

By 1914 relationships between the Triple Entente of Russia, France and Britain and the Triple Alliance of Germany, Austria–Hungary and Italy had deteriorated. As the great German statesman Otto von Bismarck had predicted in 1888, it was events in the Balkans that triggered the conflict. On 28 June 1914 a Serbian nationalist assassinated the Austro-Hungarian Archduke Franz Ferdinand. Austria–Hungary, which was concerned by the growing strength of Serbia and its ambitions to create a greater Slavic union, sought support from its German ally and issued an ultimatum to Serbia who in turn appealed to Russia for support. Russia decided on a partial mobilisation of its army and on 28 July Austria-Hungary declared war on Serbia. The next day Sir John Grey, the British Foreign Secretary, appealed to Germany not to become involved, and they in turn asked the British to remain neutral should they invade France via Belgian territory. All the major powers then began to mobilise their armies. On 3 August the German government declared war on France and at midnight on 4 August 1914, after the deadline passed for receiving a guarantee from Germany that they would respect Belgian neutrality, Britain declared war on Germany.

In anticipation of these momentous events Britain's home fleet was mobilised and on 28 July it transferred to its war station at the naval base at Scapa Flow in the Orkney Islands because of the threat from German submarines and mine-laying in the North Sea. Now renamed the Grand Fleet, its orders were to 'bring the enemy to battle on a good occasion, and to frustrate any efforts on his part, whether they are directed towards the landing of an invading or raiding force, or to the break-up of the patrol lines at the entrances to the North Sea'.[1]

At the start of the war, the fleet included the eight pre-Dreadnought battleships of the *King Edward VII* class as Britain did not have a sufficient superiority in Dreadnoughts to do without these older ships. The pre-Dreadnoughts formed the 3rd Battle Squadron but their role in the fleet was made difficult by the fact that they were around 3 knots slower than the other battleships and had to be deployed at the rear of the fleet, where it was accepted they would probably join any action later than the faster Dreadnought battleships.[2] In April 1916 they were transferred to Sheerness as more modern super-Dreadnoughts were commissioned, and from then onwards the Grand Fleet no longer included any pre-Dreadnoughts. In comparison the German High Seas Fleet, which was based in Kiel, had two squadrons of pre-Dreadnoughts in 1914 and retained a number of the older ships throughout the war.

In August 1914 Admiral Sir John Jellicoe, who had been the Second Sea Lord, was appointed Commander-in-Chief of the Grand Fleet, replacing Admiral Sir George Callaghan. His role was twofold: to blockade German shipping and to engage the High Seas Fleet if it emerged from its harbours. However, as Winston Churchill pointed out, although the navy and the public generally looked forward to a decisive engagement, the Grand Fleet could not be sent 'into the minefields and submarine infested areas of the Heligoland Bight. But had battle been offered by the enemy under any conditions which did not put us under a serious disadvantage, it would have been at once accepted.'[3]

Admiral von Pohl, the commander of the High Seas Fleet in the early years of the war, recognised that he could not take on the more powerful Grand Fleet in a set-piece engagement. Kaiser Wilhelm II was also reluctant to risk the fleet and encouraged this cautious approach. The strength of the two fleets varied in the early years of the war and Jellicoe gave the comparative strengths of the fleets capital ships as follows:[4]

Date	British ships			German ships		
	Dreadnoughts	Pre-Dreadnoughts	Battlecruisers	Dreadnoughts	Pre-Dreadnoughts	Battlecruisers
August 1914	20	8	4	13	16	3
October 1914	20	12	6	15	16	3
January 1915	21	8	6	16	16	4
April 1915	23	8	9	16	16	4
October 1915	25	10	10	17	16	4

The High Seas Fleet, however, had superiority in destroyers having eighty-eight in 1914 compared to the Grand Fleet's forty-two. By 1915 the number of British destroyers attached to the fleet had in increased to sixty-six.

The comparative strength of the British fleet led to the Germans developing a strategy of conducting raids into the North Sea and attempting to isolate and attack smaller groups of British ships and thus reduce their superiority in numbers. As Scapa Flow was so far north, the battlecruiser squadrons under Admiral David Beatty were based further south at Rosyth so that they could respond quickly. The Admiralty had the further advantage that the Director of Naval Intelligence, Admiral Henry Oliver, had set up a unit, known as Room 40, at the Admiralty, which was able to intercept and decode the German radio transmissions. According to Jellicoe, this 'led to our being able to obtain more reliable knowledge of the movements of enemy vessels.'[5]

EARLY SKIRMISHES IN THE NORTH SEA

The German fleet made a number of sorties into the North Sea seeking small-scale engagements in which they could gain an advantage. At Heligoland Bight in December 1914 and Dogger Bank in January 1915 the battlecruisers of both fleets clashed but at the raid on the east coast in December 1914 the British fleet were not able to engage the German ships. It is not the purpose of the book to cover the details of these naval actions but there follows a brief description of each action.

The first Battle of Heligoland Bight

The first Battle of Heligoland Bight took place in August 1914 and was initiated by the British who sought to ambush patrolling German destroyers with a force of two cruisers and thirty-one destroyers. Admiral Jellicoe sent the battlecruisers under Admiral Beatty to support these, and in the ensuing action two German light cruisers were sunk by the British battlecruisers and another by the British cruisers; a German destroyer was also sunk and three cruisers badly damaged. Although the action was a minor success there were problems with radio communications between the two British forces, highlighting a problem that was to reoccur at Jutland.

The raid on the east coast

In December 1914 the Germans planned a raid on Scarborough in the hope of drawing out some of the Grand Fleet and surprising them with a larger force. The British had advance warning that a raid was planned but did not know the size of the German force. Admiral Hipper, the commander of the German battlecruisers, took a force of four ships, supported by the armoured cruiser *Blücher* and four light cruisers, to raid Scarborough and Hartlepool. Unknown to the British they were supported by the whole High Seas Fleet which was positioned east of the Dogger Bank.

The British sent a force of four battlecruisers and six battleships, supported by light cruisers, to intercept Admiral Hipper. The possibility of the High Seas Fleet engaging the smaller British force of ten Dreadnoughts was exactly the sort of situation which the Germans had been seeking but the High Seas Fleet, mindful of the orders it had been given not to endanger the fleet, returned to port and Hipper set off for home at high speed. Although the British fleet sighted Hipper's Squadron they were not able to engage them and the Grand Fleet, which had left Scapa Flow, failed to find any ships of the German fleet.

The action at Dogger Bank

On 23 January 1915 Admiral Hipper again set sail with three battlecruisers, the armoured cruiser *Blücher* and four light cruisers to patrol in the Dogger Bank area of the North Sea. Alerted by Room 40, the British battlecruiser squadrons were ordered to sail along with light cruisers from Harwich. The telegram read: 'Four German battlecruisers, six light cruisers and twenty two destroyers will sail this evening to scout on Dogger Bank, probably returning tomorrow evening',[6] thus demonstrating the extent to which German wireless communications had been compromised.

At 7.15 p.m. the light cruisers signalled to Admiral Beatty that they had sighted the enemy. After first turning towards the Harwich force, the Germans spotted the British battlecruisers and turned for home with the British ships giving chase. At 9.30 p.m. the *Lion* sent a signal to Jellicoe reporting that she was engaging the enemy ships. In the ensuing action the *Blücher* was hit and eventually sunk by torpedoes and the battlecruiser *Seydlitz* was hit by the *Lion's* 13½-inch shells, causing serious damage to two of her turrets and resulting in the crew flooding the magazines to prevent fires spreading into them. The *Lion* was hit fourteen times, including by an 11-inch shell which hit the 8-inch armour of A turret and started a small fire. Although the fire was quickly put out, the magazine was flooded in the mistaken belief that the damage was more serious. Another shell burst on the 9-inch side armour and drove one of the plates 2 feet inwards. This damaged the feed-water tank for the port engine, which had to be shut down. The damage resulted in 3,000 tons of seawater flooding the ship causing a list of 10°.

The British ships thought they had spotted a submarine and, fearing they had been drawn into a trap, turned 90° to port. This turn enabled the German squadron to break off the action and escape back to Kiel.

After temporary repairs at Rosyth, the *Lion* went to Palmers' shipyard on the Tyne. Replacement armour plate for the repairs was ordered from John Brown and Vickers. John Brown made 9.5 tons of side armour and Vickers 51 tons. Vickers also made two replacement gun shields.

THE BATTLE OF JUTLAND: THE EARLY STAGES

The major naval battle between the British Grand Fleet and the German High Seas Fleet occurred at the end of May 1916 in the North Sea off the west coast of Denmark. Admiral Scheer, who had replaced Admiral von Pohl as the commander of the High Seas Fleet in January 1916, felt that the German strategy had been too passive and devised a plan to draw the Grand Fleet out by an attack on Sunderland. A screen of German submarines would attack the fleet, and the High Seas Fleet, which would be positioned off Flamborough Head, would attack the British battlecruisers before the Grand Fleet arrived. The German fleet was not ready in time to implement the original plan and the delay meant that bad weather prevented the Zeppelins, which were essential to co-ordinate the movements of the fleet in the original plan, from being used. In Scheer's revised plan the coastal attack was replaced with a show of force by the German battlecruisers in the Skagerrak off the north coast of Denmark.[7] The advantage of this revised plan was that it was easier to co-ordinate and also that the German fleet would be nearer its ports.

The Admiralty were alerted to German activity on 17 May when Room 40 reported that nine submarines had put to sea and were stationed in the northern North Sea. On 30 May radio signals were intercepted which read '31 Gg 2490' which meant 'Carry out top secret instructions 2490 on 31 May'. The Admiralty could not interpret the meaning of the message but from its wide distribution and method of transmission, they surmised that an important operation by the whole German fleet might be planned.[8] Admiral Jellicoe was warned that the German fleet might sail and the next day the Admiralty ordered the Grand Fleet to sea. However, a misunderstanding about German signal procedures, which transferred the flagship's signal number to a shore station when the fleet sailed, led the Admiralty to believe that the German flagship was still in port, leading to uncertainty about whether the whole of the German fleet had in fact sailed.

The Grand Fleet passed through the German submarine screen outside their ports without mishap although the battlecruisers were seen by U32, which fired a torpedo at them and reported their position; U66, posted off the Firth of Forth, also reported the sailing of the main fleet. However, both submarines were wrong about the direction in which the fleet was heading. By 11.00 a.m. the Grand Fleet and the battlecruiser squadrons were making their way to their rendezvous 240 miles from Scapa Flow and 90 miles west of the entrance to the Skagerrak (the channel between Denmark and Norway).

The German battlecruisers had passed the minefields around the coast at 9.00 a.m. on 31 May and were followed by the battleships some 50 miles behind. The German fleet proceeded north while Admiral Beatty, commanding the 1st Battlecruiser Squadron and the powerful 5th Battle Squadron, made up of four fast battleships of the new *Queen Elizabeth* class equipped with 15-inch guns, steamed south-east towards the Heligoland Bight. Admiral Beatty was around 65 miles ahead of the Grand Fleet, but had orders to turn back towards it at 2.00 p.m. and was in the process of making this turn when at 2.20 p.m. HMS *Galatea*, a light cruiser sailing ahead of the battlecruisers, spotted the screening German ships and the smoke from larger ships.

HMS *Galatea*'s opening shots marked the beginning of the Battle of Jutland, the engagement for which Britain had been building and training its navy for many years. An enormous industrial commitment had provided twenty-eight Dreadnoughts, of which thirteen powerful ships had been added to the fleet since the start of the war. The battle fleet was equipped[i] with 272 heavy guns

A map of the North Sea showing the initial movements of the British and German fleets at the Battle of Jutland.

---

i   This figure excludes guns that could not be brought to bear on the broadside; for example, on the ships with wing turrets only one wing turret is counted.

including forty-eight 15-inch guns, ten 14-inch guns, 110 13½-inch guns and 128 12-inch guns representing an advantage in broadside weight of 332,360 lbs against 134,216 lbs for the German fleet.[9]

THE ENGAGEMENT

The Battle of Jutland is normally divided into a number of phases. The first of these is the battlecruiser action, made up of two parts. The 'run to the south' occurred when the British ships chased the German battlecruisers towards the High Seas Fleet. On sighting the High Seas Fleet, the British ships turned north and were pursued by the German fleet in the 'run to the north'. The second phase of the action was the engagement between the Grand Fleet and the High Seas Fleet. After the German admiral broke off the fleet action, the High Seas Fleet sought to return to port and there were a number of individual skirmishes during the night known as the 'night action'.

The battlecruiser action

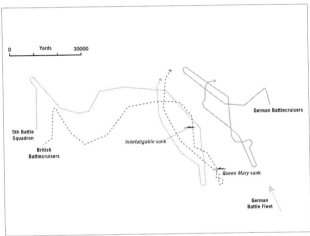

The battlecruiser action showing the run to the south and the run to the north.

The battlecruiser action began with Admiral Beatty ordering a turn to the south-east, but the signal flag for this was not picked up by the fast battleships of the 5th Battle Squadron, which were under his command. The two battlecruiser fleets were now steaming towards each other at a combined speed of around 45 knots. At this stage Beatty was not aware of the presence of the German battlecruisers and his force was split as the 5th Battle Squadron's delayed turn meant that they were 10 miles behind the battlecruisers, a distance they managed to reduce to about 6 miles. Due to favourable weather conditions the German battlecruisers spotted Beatty's ship at a range of about 10 miles at 3.25 p.m. Korvettenkapitän Georg von Hasse, the gunnery officer of the battlecruiser *Derfflinger*, reported 'they were still a long way off, but they showed up clearly on the horizon, and even at this great distance they looked powerful, massive.'[10]

The British spotted the Germans 8 minutes later at 3.30 p.m.

The run to the south

At 3.40 p.m. Admiral Hipper gave his position to Admiral Scheer and reported that he was 'in action with six battlecruisers. Request position of own battlefleet'.[11] Shortly afterwards he turned his ships towards the High Seas Fleet, which was 46 miles to the south-east. Even though the British 13½-inch guns had a longer range than the German guns, the British ships did not take advantage of this; Admiral Hipper commented that the British concept of a fast, heavily armed but lightly armoured ship 'proved, as once before during the Dogger Bank action, that the theoretical requirements of British gunnery tactics, namely to open an engagement at the longest possible range, just beyond the reach of the German guns, were not so easily met in practice'.[12] As Admiral Beatty's ships held their fire, it was the *Lützlow*, Admiral Hipper's flagship, which opened fire at 3.48 p.m., at a range of 15,000 yards, closely followed by the other ships of both squadrons.

The two battlecruiser squadrons were now travelling on parallel courses. The German fire proved to be extremely accurate, aided by their range-finding equipment and the better visibility from their position to the east, which silhouetted the British ships against the setting sun. Within three minutes of their opening fire they had hit the *Lion* and *Princess Royal* twice and the *Tiger* four times. The *Queen Mary*, which proved to have the best gunnery of the British battlecruisers, scored the first British hits at 3.55 p.m., hitting the *Seydlitz* twice, piercing a barbette and disabling the turret. Although the two battlecruiser squadrons moved slightly apart the *Lion* was hit on her midship turret, putting her out of action. Only heroic action by Major Harvey, the Royal Marine commanding the turret, who ordered the magazine to be flooded even though he was fatally wounded, saved the ship from disaster. The *Princess Royal* also had her after turret put out of action while at the rear of the line the *Von der Tann* hit the *Indefatigable* with three shells that knocked her out of action. A further salvo caused a major explosion which sank the *Indefatigable* with the loss all but two of her crew of 1,017. The German official history records that the 'good effect of their firing was unmistakable and the observed results of hits clearly showed the great penetration and bursting power of the German projectiles. At times the enemy's fire ceased altogether and the tactical cohesion of the British line appeared to be seriously shaken.'[13]

Admiral Beatty now disengaged to repair the damage to his remaining ships, ordering his destroyers to mount a torpedo attack on the German battlecruisers. However, before this could be launched the ships of the 5th Battle Squadron at last emerged through the smoke and opened fire with their 15-inch guns, causing serious damage to the *Von der Tann* and hitting the *Moltke*. The British battlecruisers now re-engaged the enemy and, had the fuses in the British armour-piercing shells not caused the them to explode on impact rather than behind the armour plate, the German ships would have been in a very difficult position. As it was the concentrated fire of *Seydlitz* and *Dirfflinger* on the *Queen Mary* caused her magazine to explode and the ship to sink with the loss of 1,266 lives.

The British squadron had lost two battlecruisers with all hands. Many of the German battlecruisers had received heavy damage, with the *Von Der Tann* having only two guns left in operation; she also had problems with her steering gear which was overheating. However, a complete breakdown was prevented by the damage control parties otherwise 'the *Von der Tann* would have been delivered into the hands of the oncoming battleships.'[14] To relieve the situation both sides ordered torpedo attacks by their destroyer flotillas. The attacks began at 4.20 p.m. and although the heavier British destroyers managed to break up the German attack it caused the 5th Battle Squadron to take the standard evasive action in these circumstances and turn away from the attacking destroyers which gave the German ships a break from their heavy and effective fire. Having repelled the German torpedo attack, the British destroyers attacked in turn and the *Seydlitz* was hit by a torpedo from HMS *Petard*, but although she took on water she did not lose any speed.

Meanwhile the British light cruisers, whose function was to provide a scouting screen for the larger ships, tried hard to gain a position ahead of the battlecruisers. At 4.33 p.m. HMS *Southampton*, the leader of the 2nd Cruiser Squadron, which was 2 miles ahead of the *Lion*, sighted the German High Seas Fleet steaming north. Commodore Goodenough immediately sent a radio signal[15] 'have sighted enemy battle fleet bearing S.E. Enemy's course North.

Shortly after receiving the signal HMS *Lion* also sighted the German battlefleet and Beatty ordered an immediate turn to the north.

The run to the north

As Beatty's battlecruisers headed north, they passed the 5th Battle Squadron heading south, still providing covering fire for the battlecruisers. Beatty ordered the battleships to follow him and the ships turned in succession, receiving heavy fire from the leading ships of the High Seas Fleet as they did so. As the British ships continued northwards to rejoin the Grand Fleet, the battlecruisers used their speed to draw out of range but not before the *Lion* had received four more hits and the *Tiger* one. The *Valiant* and the *Barham*, the front two ships of the 5th Battle Squadron, continued to engage the German battlecruisers while the *Warspite* and *Malaya* at the rear engaged the leading battleships of the High Seas Fleet. The 15-inch guns of the four British ships scored fifteen hits on the German battlecruisers and five on the battleships. In return *Warspite* received thirteen hits and the *Malaya* six, but their heavy armour, made as we have seen to an improved quality, was able to prevent any damage to their fighting ability or speed. Captain Godfrey Jollye, a Royal Marine serving on HMS *Malaya*, reported that:

> At this time the roof of 'X' turret was struck by a 12 inch shell, this shell struck almost exactly in the centre of the roof. [...] Owing to an exceptional piece of plating, only 4 ½ inches thick, the projectile did not penetrate. [...] The effect on the roof was to bulge it downwards at the point of impact, which caused all the holding down bolts, 1½ inches in diameter, on the right side of the roof to be sheared, and the whole of the centre plate of the roof to lift on that side.[16]

The original plates for the turrets were made by Armstrong Whitworth and a replacement roof weighing 23.25 tons was ordered from them on 4 June 1916, 3 days after the battle ended.[17]

The battlefleet action

The Grand Fleet was sailing south at high speed but, as neither Admiral Beatty nor other scouting ships had communicated effectively with their commander, Jellicoe was not clear about the exact position and course of the German fleet. Indeed he was not aware of the loss of the *Indefatigable* and *Queen Mary* and did not find out about this until the next day. Because of this lack of awareness of the situation the Grand Fleet was therefore sailing in compact cruising formation, unaware of how close the High Seas Fleet was.

At 5.50 p.m. the confusion began to clear slightly when *Marlborough*, the leading battleship in the starboard (easterly) column of the Grand Fleet, reported seeing gun flashes and was asked what she could see. She replied 'Our battlecruisers bearing south-south-west, steering east, *Lion* leading ship' and shortly afterwards 'Fifth Battle Squadron bearing south-west'.[18] Shortly afterwards Beatty's battlecruisers were sighted passing directly in front of the battle fleet and engaging with an enemy that was out of sight. This appearance of the battlecruisers 11 miles north-west of where they were expected made Admiral Jellicoe realise that the High Seas Fleet was likely to appear to starboard rather than straight ahead as he had expected. After signalling to the *Lion* Jellicoe eventually extracted the information that they had 'sighted enemy battle fleet bearing south west'. At 6.15 p.m., based on this information, Jellicoe ordered a deployment of the fleet into battle formation on a south-east course.

Meanwhile Admiral Hood's 3rd Battlecruiser Squadron, which was attached to the Grand Fleet, had earlier been dispatched to help Admiral Beatty's battlecruisers. Owing to signal errors, he was sailing too far to the east. HMS *Chester*, which had been built by Cammell Laird for the Greek navy, and was posted 5 miles to starboard of the battlecruisers of the 3rd Squadron, heard firing to the south-west. *Chester* turned to investigate and at 3.56 p.m. ran into four German light cruisers whose fire inflicted heavy damage on her. A young crew member, sixteen-year-old Jack Cornwell from Walthamstow in London, was awarded a posthumous Victoria Cross for continuing to man his gun even though he was mortally wounded and the rest of the gun-crew were killed. The British squadron of three battlecruisers turned to relieve the *Chester* and inflicted heavy damage on her attackers. At 6.16 p.m. they were able to take up station ahead of Admiral Beatty's remaining battlecruisers, which had by then taken station in front of the main line of British battleships.

At 6.20 p.m. the German battlecruisers were sighted leading the High Seas Fleet towards the British ships, and the two sets of battlecruisers engaged each other again at a range which reduced to around 9,000 yards. The critical moment of the battle seemed to have arrived and the gunnery officer of HMS *Lion* said of the ships of Hood's squadron that 'we felt like cheering them on as we were certain that the decisive moment of the battle had arrived'. However at 6.32 p.m. the *Lützow*, which had been hit by eight shells in the previous eight minutes, fired a salvo at *Invincible*, which hit her on the midship deck, igniting the magazine. The gunnery officer's account continued:

> Just when the defeat of the enemy seemed certain, the *Invincible* was hit by an enemy salvo, blew up by her midship turret, and split in two. It happened literally speaking in a flash: one moment she was the flagship leading her squadron, full of life, to close and it seemed likely to annihilate the enemy battle cruisers; the next moment she was merely two sections of twisted metal, the fore and the aft end of her floating apart on the water.[19]

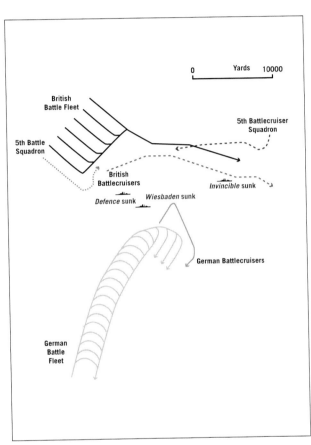

The early stage of the battlefleet action with the British fleet 'crossing the T'.

While the main fleet was deploying into its line of battle, the 5th Battle Squadron was manoeuvring to take its place in the line. At 6.19 p.m. it made a turn to the north at what became known as Windy Corner, but while the rudder of the *Warspite* was hard over to make the turn, her steering jammed and she was forced to make one and a half high-speed circles to starboard between 6.20 and 6.35 p.m. These brought her within 10,000 yards of the German battleships and she was hit twenty times, nine of them with heavy-calibre 11- and 12-inch shells.

According to V. E. Tarrant's analysis of the shells which hit *Warspite* during the battle, she was hit by a total of twenty-nine shells: nine heavy-calibre shells during the battlecruiser action and the run to the north, and twenty during her circles, of which nine were confirmed as being by heavy-calibre shells.

Of the eighteen heavy-calibre hits:

- Two hit the main belt 13-inch armour, both of which failed to pierce the armour.
- Three hit and pierced the 6-inch armour of the upper belt. One caused damage and flooding on the middle deck, the second created a hole 2 feet by 1½ feet and damaged the structures around the explosion. The third shell did not explode.
- One hit the tapered 9- to 6-inch plate between the upper and lower belts. It made a hole 2 feet by 1½ feet. The

damage caused water to pour into the port wing engine room. The *Warspite*'s executive officer, who was in charge of the repair parties, reported of this hit that 'it looked very bad, as a large triangular piece had blown out of the top corner of the main belt about a foot above the water. The fresh water and oil fuel tanks had been blown to pieces, and everything was in an awful state of dust, oil fuel and mess. Men tried to plug the hole, but tons of water were coming in and washing them back all the time.'[20] They tried to block the hole with hammocks but found that did not work and in the end they decided to fill the whole compartment with 600 hammocks, which took late into the night.

In spite of the loss of the *Invincible* and *Warspite*'s withdrawal from the action and return to Rosyth, the situation that now emerged was extremely favourable to the British fleet. Although lacking in information about the position of the fleets, Admiral Jellicoe had placed the Grand Fleet in line astern right across the path of the approaching battleships of Admiral Scheer's unsuspecting fleet. This was the perfect tactical position, known as 'crossing the T' where all the twenty-four British battleships were able to concentrate their fire on the leading enemy ships that were approaching in line astern. Unaware up to this point of the presence of the Grand Fleet in the area, the German fleet found themselves in the position they had sought to avoid at all costs.

The first flurry of the battleship action started at 6.30 p.m. and lasted only a few minutes, during which ten of the British battleships opened fire. The German official history records that:

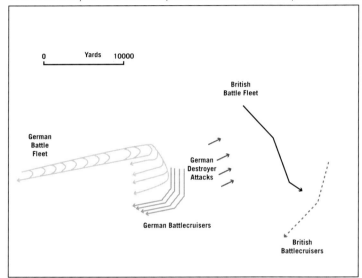

The second engagement of the battle fleet action and the German destroyer attack.

> Suddenly the German van was faced with the belching guns of an interminable line of heavy ships extending from the north-west to the north-east, while salvo followed salvo almost without intermission, an impression which gained in power from the almost complete inability of the German ships to reply to this fire.[21]

The *Lützow* and *König* at the front of the German line were hit heavily and, realising the gravity of the situation, Scheer ordered his fleet to perform a 180° turn in unison and disengage from the enemy. Jellicoe ordered his ships on a course that kept the High Seas Fleet to their west while Scheer decided to turn back to the east as he thought the British would not expect that move.

Unfortunately for him this sent his ships straight towards the British line for a second time and by 7.17 p.m. Jellicoe had 'crossed the T' again, but this time the British battleships were more concentrated and poured fire on to the leading German battleships, damaging SMS *König*, *Grosser Kurfürst*, *Markgraf*, *Kaiser* and *Helgoland*. Scheer ordered his fleet to disengage again and turn west. To cover his fleet's retreat, and to prevent the British from following, he ordered his four remaining battlecruisers to attack the British line supported by a torpedo attack from his destroyers. This almost suicidal attack became known as the 'death ride' as the battlecruisers received a total of thirty-seven hits from heavy shells, fourteen of which were on the *Defflinger*. Her gunnery officer, Georg von Hase, reported that the ship 'now came under a particularly deadly fire. Several ships were engaging us at the same time [...] We were steaming at full speed into this inferno, offering a splendid target to the enemy.'[22] One of the *Defflinger*'s rear turrets was hit by a 15-inch shell which exploded inside the turret, igniting a chain of gun cartridges and killing all but five of the seventy-eight men inside the turret. However, unlike the situation in the British battlecruisers, the charges burned rather than exploded, so the damage did not lead to a catastrophic explosion in the magazine. They had a similar escape when the other rear turret was hit, killing all eighty of the crew.

The German destroyers attacked in two waves and managed to launch thirty-one torpedoes. Admiral Jellicoe ordered the fleet to turn away from the oncoming torpedo attack. Although this was the standard manoeuvre in these circumstances, it was criticised after the battle for being too conservative because, although it meant that the torpedoes hit none of British ships, it gave the German fleet time to disengage and make their getaway. Captain Kiddle of the *Revenge*, which was two ships from the rear of the British line, reported afterwards that 'a flotilla of destroyers passed through the [German] line and made the most effective smoke screen. At this point the enemy's fleet turned eight points [180°] to starboard and withdrew rapidly out of sight.'[23]

The battlecruisers now set off south in an attempt to head off the German fleet. As they passed the wreck of the *Invincible* they were cheered by a small number of survivors on a raft.[24] At 8.19 p.m. they caught up with the German battlecruisers supported on this occasion by the German 2nd Squadron made up of their six pre-Dreadnought battleships. The British ships hit the *Seydlitz* five times as well as scoring three other hits, the *Princess Royal* receiving one shell hit in return. This action ended at 8.35 p.m. as the falling night reduced visibility.

The night action

Jellicoe decided to head south to try and block the Germans' expected escape route. At 9.00 p.m. he ordered the battleships to form four lines one mile apart and sailing at 17 knots. The battlecruisers were sailing to the west of the main fleet and the destroyers were ordered to take station 5 miles astern of the battleships to try and prevent the German ships from cutting behind them. To prevent the German fleet returning west via Horn's Reef, he ordered the laying of a minefield to block that escape route.

To the rear of the British fleet there were a series of fierce engagements throughout the night as the German fleet, which had turned to the south-west, crossed the rear of the Grand Fleet and fought its way though the screen of cruisers and destroyers that Jellicoe had posted behind him. At around midnight a flotilla of British destroyers led by HMS *Tipperary* were surprised by what they thought were three German cruisers which turned out to be the three early German Dreadnoughts of the *Nassau* class: *Nassau, Westfalen* and *Rheinland,* who opened fire at the flotilla at close range. The *Tipperary* was disabled by a hail of gunfire from the German cruisers' heavier guns and other ships were damaged. One of the flotilla members, HMS *Spitfire*, closed on the *Tipperary* to see if she could help. The *Nassau*[25] tried to ram her and the two ships hit each other on their respective port bows at high speed. After the two ships had cleared each other the smaller British destroyer found that the collision had torn off 60 feet of her side plating from a total length of 267 feet, and that 'in exchange the enemy had left 20 feet of her upper deck inside our mess hall'.[26] The blast from the *Nassau's* 11-inch guns had destroyed the *Spitfire's* bridge, although the shells had passed overhead.

As the *Spitfire's* crew recovered from the collision, what appeared to be a burning battlecruiser approached them at speed.

The *Black Prince*, launched in 1904 and one of the four member of the 1st Cruiser Squadron, had at this point become detached from the main body of British ships, probably because of the damage she had received earlier when the squadron had come under heavy fire at Windy Corner. In this isolated position she was found by a group of German battleships and the *Thuringen, Ostfriesland, Nassau* and *Friedrich der Grosse* fired at her at close range as they passed.

The damaged destroyer HMS *Spitfire* limping into the River Tyne after the Battle of Jutland.

Albert G. Williams, Boy 1st Class, J 35239 of HMS *Black Prince*. He had joined the ship only six days before the action and died alongside the rest of the crew, aged only seventeen. His death was memorialised in the plaque sent to his family. Similar medals were sent to the families of all 6,097 British sailors who lost their lives in the Battle of Jutland.

At 1.00 p.m. the cruiser *Active*, which was astern of the 2nd Battle Squadron, saw a ship behind her illuminated with searchlights and under heavy fire. The ship appeared to be heavily hit and to sink.[27] This was presumably the *Black Prince,* which was also spotted by the damaged destroyer *Spitfire*. An eyewitness on the ship reported that 'she tore past us with a roar […] and the very crackling and heat of the flames could be heard and felt. She was a mass of fire from her foremast to mainmast, on deck and between decks. Flames were issuing out of her from every corner.'[28] Although the crew of the *Spitfire* thought that she was a battleship because her funnels were widely spaced, the blazing ship turned out to be HMS *Black Prince* with two of the four funnels shot away.

The Grand Fleet saw little of the night action apart from searchlights, bursting star shells lighting up the sky, and the sound of firing to the north. However, at 11.30 p.m. Jellicoe did receive information of the whereabouts of the German fleet in a message from the Admiralty, which had intercepted and decoded a German signal at 9.14 p.m. The Admiralty's message read 'German Battle Fleet ordered home at 9.14 pm. Battlecruisers in rear. Course SSE ¾ east. Speed 16 knots.' If this information was correct it meant that the High Seas Fleet was cutting behind the Grand Fleet and heading for home via Horn Reef. However, Jellicoe decided that he could not rely on the accuracy of the message he had received as it contradicted information he had just received from HMS *Southampton* which (wrongly) suggested that the enemy was to the west of him. It is possible that the Admiralty's earlier error, that of not realising that the High Seas Fleet had sailed because the call sign for the flagship was still in Kiel, influenced his decision.

Captain Stirling, in the destroyer HMS *Faulknor,* was one of several ships that tried to report contact with enemy battleships during the night. He sent three such messages to the flagship between 1.56 a.m. and 3.13 a.m. but they failed to get through, possibly due to the radio transmissions being jammed. However, by that time they could have made little difference to the outcome as by then the German fleet had smashed through the screen of light ships behind Jellicoe's battleships and the moment had passed when it was possible for the Grand Fleet to change its course and intercept the High Seas Feet. The battle of Jutland was effectively over and the German fleet returned to their harbours, abandoning the battlecruiser *Lützow* and the light cruisers *Elbing* and *Rostock* on the way, but successfully nursing the crippled *Seydlitz* back home.

The badly damaged battlecruiser SMS *Seydlitz* showing her damaged side armour belt. Interestingly, the plates seem to be fitted vertically, unlike in British ships where they were fitted horizontally.

Endnotes

1. National Archive, ADM 137/818.
2. J. Jellicoe, *The Grand Fleet* (Cassell, 1919), p. 187.
3. Churchill, *The World Crisis 1911–1918*, Vol. 1, p. 198.
4. Jellicoe, *The Grand Fleet*, p. 33.
5. Ibid., p. 187.
6. Churchill, *The World Crisis 1911–1918*, Vol. 1, p. 560.
7. V. E. Tarrant, *Jutland: The German Perspective* (Brockhampton Press, 1999), p. 54.
8. D. MacIntyre, *Jutland* (Evans Brothers, 1957), p. 88.
9. A. Marder, *From Dreadnought to Scapa Flow: Vol. 2, To the Eve of Jutland* (Oxford University Press, 1965), p. 438; also Churchill, *The World Crisis 1911–1918*, Vol. 2, p. 1022.
10. Tarrant, *Jutland: The German Perspective*, p. 69.
11. Ibid., p. 75.
12. *Der Krieg in der Nordsee, Band V*, p. 235, quoted in Tarrant, *Jutland: The German Perspective*, p. 80.
13. Ibid., p. 141, quoted in Tarrant, *Jutland: The German Perspective*, p. 85.
14. Ibid., p. 245, quoted in Tarrant, *Jutland: The German Perspective*, p. 88.
15. MacIntyre, *Jutland*, p. 104.
16. SM Holloway, *From Trench and Turret*, Constable, London, 2006, p. 48.
17. SIMT, Armour Plate Pool ledger, Vol 2, M560.
18. MacIntyre, *Jutland*, p. 104.
19. H. W. Fawcett and G. W. W. Hooper, *The Fighting at Jutland* (Chatham Publishing, 2001; first published 1921), p. 385.
20. Fawcett and Hooper, *The Fighting at Jutland*, p. 146.
21. *Der Krieg in der Nordsee, Band V*, p. 295, quoted in Tarrant, *Jutland: The German Perspective*, p. 132.
22. Von Hase, *Kiel and Jutland*, pp. 196–200, quoted in Tarrant, *Jutland: The German Perspective*, p. 161.
23. Jellicoe, *The Grand Fleet*, p. 363.
24. Fawcett and Hooper, *The Fighting at Jutland*, p. 386.
25. Tarrant, *Jutland: The German Perspective*, p. 198.
26. Fawcett and Hooper, *The Fighting at Jutland*, p. 324.
27. Jellicoe, *The Grand Fleet*, p. 380.
28. Fawcett and Hooper, *The Fighting at Jutland*, p. 326.

CHAPTER 15

THE AFTERMATH

The Battle of Jutland was the largest set-piece naval action of the First World War. Both the British and German navies had been preparing for many years and had spent a huge amount of money on building the ships, the guns and the armour to create the two most powerful fleets the worlds had seen. The fleets that met on 31 May and 1 June 1916 were made up of:

	British	German
Dreadnought battleships	28	16
Pre-Dreadnought battleships	0	6
Battlecruisers	9	5
Armoured cruisers	8	0
Light cruisers	26	11
Destroyers / torpedo boats	79	61
Totals	150	99
	249	

MAINTAINING NAVAL SUPERIORITY

For much of the later part of the nineteenth century the Admiralty had been trying to maintain Britain's superiority as the world's predominant naval power. The Naval Defence Act of 1889 formalised the required size of the British fleet as being at least equal to the combined strength of the next two largest navies as defined by battleships 'of the most modern type'. The advent of the *Dreadnought* in 1906 meant the end of the superiority in numbers enjoyed by the British fleet up to that point because all countries were starting from the same base of building a modern battlefleet from scratch. Historically, Britain had in practice measured the strength of its fleet against a combination of the navies of France and Russia, its two traditional foes and the biggest threats to its colonial empire. However, the rise of Germany first as a unified continental power and later as an aspiring world power transformed that situation. The destruction of the Russian fleets in the Russo-Japanese war of 1904–05 and the building of alliances with Japan, France and lastly Russia meant that Britain's traditional naval rivals were now allies and therefore measuring British naval strength against them became relatively meaningless. Although the two-power standard remained the formal position of the government through the naval scares of the early twentieth century, in practical terms Britain's naval superiority needed to be measured against the growing power of the German fleet.

If naval strength is measured by battleships of the most modern type alone then the number of ships in the fleet is the proper measure of naval strength. However, not all battleships are equal. The 18,000-ton *Dreadnought* with 12-inch guns cannot be considered the same as the 27,500-ton *Queen Elizabeth* with 15-inch guns. Comparing the five most powerful navies in 1916, and taking the size and power of the ships into consideration, as well as their numbers, we can measure how Britain did in maintaining naval supremacy.

	Number of ships launched	Tonnage of ships launched	Combined weight of broadside (lbs)
Britain	50	1,162,592	258,018
Germany	26	615,888	102,655
France	7	165,789	37,770
USA	14	345,270	72,295
Japan	9	282,707	55,052

By 1916 Britain had built a Dreadnought fleet which was 125% stronger than the number of ships in the next two most powerful navies, 121% more powerful in terms of tonnage and 147% more powerful in terms of the weight of shell they could fire. Since Britain had been allied with Japan since 1902 and with France since 1904, this alliance of navies had 2.5 times the number of Dreadnoughts as Germany with 3.5 times the combined weight of broadside.

JUTLAND AND THE ARMOUR MAKERS

The huge industrial effort to build this Dreadnought fleet and equip the ships with their powerful guns was matched by the effort to clad them in armour. The British Dreadnought fleet at the Battle of Jutland carried more than 160,000 tons of armour plate. The armour for these ships cost over £12.5 million, equivalent to around £1.3 billion at 2016 prices.[1] All five of the major armour-making firms contributed to this huge undertaking, and how widely spread their armour was across the British fleet can be seen in the following table, which shows the Order of Battle of the Grand Fleet at Jutland and the armour-making firms whose armour was present on each ship.

Order of Battle	Armour made by				
	Armstrong Whitworth	William Beardmore	John Brown	Cammell Laird	Vickers, Sons & Maxim
2nd Battle Squadron					
1st Division					
King George V	✓	✓	✓	✓	✓
Ajax	✓	✓	✓	✓	✓
Centurion	✓		✓	✓	
Erin (see note)					✓
2nd Division					
Orion	✓	✓	✓	✓	✓
Monarch	✓		✓		
Conqueror	✓	✓	✓	✓	✓
Thunderer	✓		✓	✓	✓
4th Battle Squadron					
3rd Division					
Iron Duke	✓	✓	✓	✓	
Royal Oak	✓	✓	✓	✓	✓
Superb	✓	✓	✓		P
Canada (see note)	✓	✓			P
4th Division					
Benbow		✓	✓	✓	✓
Bellerophon	✓			✓	✓
Temeraire		✓		✓	✓
Vanguard		✓	✓	✓	✓
1st Battle Squadron					
6th Division					
Marlborough	✓		✓	✓	✓
Revenge		✓			✓
Hercules	✓		✓	✓	
Agincourt (see note)	✓				
5th Division					
Colossus	✓	✓		✓	✓
Collingwood	✓	✓	✓	✓	
Neptune	✓		✓	✓	✓
St Vincent	✓		✓	✓	
3rd Battlecruiser Squadron					
Invincible	✓				✓
Inflexible	✓		✓		✓
Indomitable	✓		✓		
1st Battlecruiser Squadron					
Lion	✓	✓	✓	✓	✓
Princess Royal	✓	✓			✓
Queen Mary	✓	✓	✓	✓	✓
Tiger	✓	✓	✓	✓	✓
2nd Battlecruiser Squadron					
New Zealand	✓	✓		✓	✓
Indefatigable	✓	✓		✓	✓
5th Battle Squadron					
Barham	✓	✓	✓	✓	✓
Valiant		✓	✓	✓	✓
Warspite	✓	✓	✓	✓	✓
Malaya	✓	✓			

Note: Built for foreign navies and purchased at the outbreak of war.

Three of the battleships in the British fleet at Jutland had been commissioned by foreign governments and were purchased by the British navy on the outbreak of war in 1914. These ships do not appear in the British Armour Plate Pool ledgers as presumably this was, as its name implies, reserved for British ships. It is possible that the armour for the three ships was included in the foreign armour plate convention discussed in Chapter 8. These three ships all had their armour made exclusively by the company who held the contracts. They were:

- HMS *Erin*, built by Vickers for the Turkish government as the *Reshadieh*;
- HMS *Canada*, built by Armstrong Whitworth for the Brazilian government as the *Rio de Janeiro*. After the British purchase, Beardmore made 157 tons of armour for the control towers as part of the modifications ordered by the Admiralty; and
- HMS *Agincourt*, was also built by Armstrong's for the Chilean government as the *Admiral Latorre*. Because of Chile's financial difficulties she was then put up for sale and was bought by the Turkish government as the *Sultan Osman I*.

The Sheffield armour makers

As the table shows, most of the British Dreadnoughts at Jutland carried armour from a number of companies.

	Number of ships	Percentage of ships
Armstrong Whitworth	30	84%
William Beardmore	24	65%
John Brown	24	68%
Cammell Laird	25	70%
Vickers, Sons & Maxim	27	73%

Over half (55.6%) of the British Dreadnoughts at Jutland had armour from all three of the Sheffield armour makers and 94% of the ships had armour made by at least one of the Sheffield companies.

The following table shows the orders for, and the income from, armour plate for the British armoured ships that took part in the Battle of Jutland. The table is divided into two. The first part includes all the battleships and battlecruisers, with the exception of the three ships (see above) that were ordered by foreign governments. The second table shows the armour manufactured for the older armoured cruisers that took part in the action:

Year	Armstrong Whitworth		W. Beardmore		John Brown		Cammell Laird		Vickers	
	Tons	Income	Tons	Income	Tons	Income	Tons	Income	Tons	Income
1906	3,203	£348,235	2,130	£244,309	7,006	£757,079	2,316	£320,741	4,367	£515,567
1907	1,639	£235,144	76	£9,086					2	£124
1908	2,241	£282,457	2,470	£259,923	2,968	£311,244	2,525	£252,610		
1909	4,882	£556,431	3,091	£322,373	3,465	£363,534	3,172	£334,966	3,637	£442,050
1910	8,780	£907,087	8,376	£1,027,592	6,204	£634,479	6,716	£638,212	8,870	£883,454
1911	3,498	£339,932			6,364	£605,534	5,965	£632,399	1,285	£153,674
1912	3,401	£391,292	4,107	£409,136	694	£69,249	199	£20,773	3,116	£316,852
1913	1,630	£142,650	215	£23,605	3,848	£384,328	3,456	£342,930	3,506	£722,129
1914	1,607	£232,197	2,758	£256,607	58	£22,752	1,951	£188,822	6,461	£664,422
1915	76	£9,892			10	£889	51	£5,181	167	£16,294
1916	23	£3,115								
Total	30,980	£348,431	23,223	£2,552,631	30,617	£3,149,089	26,352	£2,736,635	31,410	£3,714,566
					88,379 tons at a cost of £9,600,290					

The British Armour Plate Pool ledger shows that for the Dreadnought fleet, the split of the orders between the five armour makers is relatively equal, although of course the complete armour for one ship has to be added to the Vickers total and for two ships to the Armstrong total.

	% of production
Armstrong	21.7%
Beardmore	16.3%
J Brown	21.5%
Cammell	18.5%
Vickers	22.0%

The percentage of armour plate for the Dreadnought battleships and battlecruisers of the Grand Fleet made by each company. 62% of the armour for these ships was made in Sheffield.

The River Don Engine at Cammell Laird's Grimesthorpe Works in about 1915

THE RIVER DON ENGINE AND THE BATTLE OF JUTLAND

The River Don Engine, which powered the rolling mills at Cammell Laird's armour plate mills in Sheffield, was installed in 1904 and was operational for the whole of this period. The engine is probably the last working piece of the huge armour plate industry which built the Grand Fleet. We know that all the heavy armour plate that Cammell Laird produced would have passed through the rollers powered by this engine, which made the following contribution to British fleet at Jutland:

- The River Don Engine rolled 26,352 tons of the armour of the British Dreadnoughts at the Battle of Jutland.

- A total of twenty-five of the ships, or 69% of the British battlefleet, had armour rolled by the engine.

WHAT WAS ACHIEVED?

Around 105,000 sailors served in the two fleets during the Battle of Jutland and both sides suffered heavy casualties:

	Killed	Wounded	Made prisoner
British	6,097	510	177
German	2,551	507	0
Total	8,648	1,017	177

This means that 11.3% of the British sailors serving were either killed or wounded in the battle compared to 6.8% of the German sailors. This compares with the casualty rate at the Battle of Trafalgar of 10.5% of the British sailors and 21.7% of French and Spanish sailors.

The question has to be asked if the cost of building a battlefleet twice as strong as the opposition and the huge cost in lives of the sailors was worthwhile.

From the German point of view there was much rejoicing immediately after the battle. Their relatively new navy

had taken on Britannia, the ruler of the waves. They had sunk more ships than the British, they had inflicted more casualties and their ships and crews had performed well. The Germans proclaimed it 'the Victory of the Skagerrak' and it can be argued that this was a valid claim. They had had no intention of fighting a major fleet battle; their strategy was to erode the strength of the British fleet in small actions, and there is no doubt that by sinking three British battlecruisers they achieved this goal. In the setting of the North Sea their design of a more heavily protected ship with a less heavy armament proved to be more successful, and their ships were able to take significantly more punishment than the British equivalents.

From the British perspective there were few positives to be taken from the battlecruiser action. They had lost a third of their fleet in a dramatic fashion to major internal explosions and without the help of the 5th Battle Squadron of fast battleships might have been in even greater difficulty. They had not exploited their advantage of longer-range gunnery and, unlike the German navy, they had not fitted anti-flash equipment into their turrets after the lessons of the Dogger Bank action,[2] preferring to emphasise rapid firing instead. There can be little argument that Admiral Beatty lost the battlecruiser action – but that was not, of course, the whole of the battle.

Admiral Jellicoe was by nature a more cautious commander than Beatty, and he recognised that he had wider responsibilities beyond winning a battle whatever the cost. Winston Churchill famously said of the Commander-in-Chief of the British Grand Fleet that 'the destruction of the British Battle Fleet would be final. Jellicoe was the only man on either side who could lose the war in a afternoon.'[3] Admiral Scheer also recognised that he could not risk the High Seas Fleet unless the odds were very much in his favour and his actions throughout the battle were guided by this awareness. The size of the fleets, spread across many miles of sea, made the job of understanding and controlling the situation extremely complex, and both admirals were also handicapped by a lack of information about the position. In the British case many of Jellicoe's captains seemed to have forgotten their responsibility to report information back to their commanders. There was also the added complication that some of the technologies available to the fleet were less advanced that others. Enormous strides had been made in ship design, in making ships go faster, in making guns shoot further and of course in armour plate. But communications within the fleet still relied very largely on visual signalling by flag and signal lights. The delay of the 5th Battle Squadron turning to follow Beatty's battlecruisers is only one example of the weaknesses of this system. Signalling by radio was in its early days and the jamming of signals made this an unreliable method of communication. On top of these problems, position-finding still relied on visual observations and in the heat of battle, in the murky North Sea, many ships reported their position inaccurately.

Given the difficulties that he faced, Admiral Jellicoe did well to position the Grand Fleet at the point of maximum advantage, in a line across the front of the advancing High Seas Fleet. He managed to do this twice and on both occasions the British ships subjected the leading ships of Scheer's line to overwhelming fire that forced them to turn away. When Admiral Scheer launched his torpedo attack on the British line, Jellicoe's decision to turn away was the standard procedure but it was a conservative choice and attracted much public criticism from a country which had a tradition of naval victories, and was disappointed with such an indecisive outcome.

The decisions that Jellicoe made during the night were also controversial. In keeping his main fleet on a southerly course, he enabled the German fleet to fight its way through the cordon of smaller ships covering his rear. He decided that information from the Admiralty from an intercepted German signal about the course of the German fleet was not reliable. It is also difficult to understand his attitude to the sights and sounds of fighting to his north as the German fleet fought their way through the British screen. Writing with the benefit of hindsight after reading Jellicoe's book on the Battle, Admiral Scheer commented on his opponent:

> Nor can it be understood how it was that the enemy's light forces, which were engaged with our Main Fleet up to 4.36 a.m. [2.36 a.m. English time] and thus were in touch with us the whole night, could find a way to inform Admiral Jellicoe and Admiral Beatty of our course and navigation. But even apart from that, it must be assumed that the fire from our guns and the enemy's burning cruisers and destroyers would have pointed out the way to the English Main Fleet.[4]

Churchill, who as First Lord had appointed Jellicoe as Commander of the Grand Fleet, understood his need to be cautious but in his view the admiral's decisions on the night of the 31 May to continue steering south was 'contrary to the main weight of the evidence'.[5] If Jellicoe had responded to either the Admiralty signal or the signs of action to his north he would have been in a position to cut off the German fleet and force an engagement the next morning.

Churchill concluded that 'praiseworthy caution had induced a defensive habit of mind and scheme of tactics which hampered the Grand Fleet'.[6] In November 1916 Jellicoe was appointed First Sea Lord and was replaced by the more dashing and popular Admiral David Beatty as commander of the Grand Fleet. However, the initial exhilaration of the German public and the corresponding British disappointment masked the fact that the battle was a resounding strategic victory for Britain. As an article in London's *Globe* newspaper commented, the German navy had not broken the economic blockade and 'there is one test, and only one, of victory. Who held the field of battle at the end of the fight?' In the USA another newspaper commented that 'The German Fleet has assaulted its jailor, but it is still in jail.' At the end of the war the German newspaper *Berliner Tagblatt* wrote that 'Our Fleet losses were, despite the luck that smiled on us, severe, and on 1st June 1916 it was clear to every knowledgeable person that this battle must be, and would be, the only one. Authoritative quarters said so openly.'[7] In his report to the Kaiser, written three days after the battle, Admiral Scheer wrote that if future fleet operations turned out favourably his fleet would be able to inflict serious damage on the Grand Fleet:

> Nevertheless, there can be no doubt that that even the most successful outcome of a fleet action in this war will not force England to make peace. The disadvantages of our geographical position **and the enemy's great material superiority**, cannot be compensated for by our fleet [my emphasis].

Scheer recommended that 'a victorious end to the war within a reasonable time frame can only be achieved through the defeat of British economic life – that is by using U-boats against British trade.' In February 1917, pressed by both the Naval Staff and the Army High Command, Germany began an unrestricted U-boat offensive against Britain 'with the utmost energy'.

THE IMPACT OF JUTLAND ON THE ARMOUR MAKERS

After the Battle of Jutland, the ships of the Grand Fleet returned to Scapa Flow and Rosyth. The armour makers received a small volume of orders to make plates to replace damaged armour, mostly roof plates for turrets. The total volume ordered was 2,242 tons, worth £210,068. John Brown and Vickers, for example, both received orders for replacement side armour plate for the heavily damaged *Warspite* in December 1916.

After the initial repairs there were also some orders for reinforcing plates for a number of ships, presumably to reinforce their armour based on the experience at Jutland. However, there was little work on armour for new ships. HMS *Hood*, being built at John Brown's yard on the Clyde, continued to generate some work for the armour makers but the Armour Plate Pool Ledgers show a sharp decline in orders.

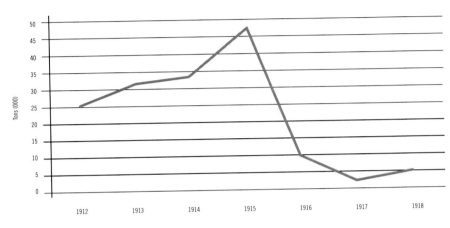

The graph shows the decline in armour orders post-Jutland. The level of demand for armour from 1917 onwards was not sustainable for the armour makers.

Production at this level was not sustainable and after the war the armour plate makers were forced to reorganise the industry to survive. The steel- and armour-making activities of Armstrong Whitworth, William Beardmore, Cammell Laird and Vickers were merged into a new organisation called the English Steel Corporation. The non-steel-making parts of Armstrong Whitworth and Vickers merged into a new company, the giant armaments organisation of Armstrong Vickers. Cammell Laird concentrated on their shipbuilding activities at Birkenhead. The Sheffield companies of John Brown and Thomas Firth, who had had close working relations for many years, merged to form Firth Brown & Co., retaining both their steel and armour works and the shipyard on the Clyde.

Five large armour plate works were no longer needed to meet the level of demand and it was not long before Armstrong's old works at Openshaw in Manchester was demolished and the Cyclops Works of Cammell Laird was mothballed, supported by a government grant, so that it was available should the international situation demand rearmament.

Endnotes

1.   Calculated using: http://www.thisismoney.co.uk/money/bills/article-1633409/Historic-inflation-calculator-value-money-changed-1900.html.
2.   Tarrant, *Jutland: The German Perspective*, p. 33.
3.   Churchill, *The World Crisis 1911–1918*, Vol. 2, p. 1015.
4.   Admiral R. Scheer, *The High Seas Fleet* (Cassell & Co., 1920), Sect. 173.
5.   Churchill, *The World Crisis 1911–1918*, Vol. 2, p. 1069.
6.   Ibid.
7.   Tarrant, *Jutland :The German Perspective*, p. 250.

APPENDICES

APPENDIX A

THE ESTIMATED COST OF MAKING AMERICAN ARMOUR PLATE

The Acting Secretary of the American Navy submitted a report on the costs of armour plate to Congress in November 1906. The report gives a detailed breakdown of the costs of making armour at each stage of the process. A summary of the following table and further discussion of the estimates are found in Chapter 7.

	Tons	Value	Value per ton
Furnace charge:			
Pig	24.30	£90.19	£3.71
Nickel scrap	30.38	£300.67	£9.90
Metallic nickel	1.04	£192.13	£184.74
Ore	1.00	£1.03	£1.03
Additions	2.24	£94.68	£42.27
Flux	6.00	£1.86	£0.31
minus flux	−6.00		
minus Furnace loss (8%)	−4.72		
Sub total – Charge	54.24	£680.56	£12.55
Metal poured:			
Fuel consumed in melting		£13.71	
Material consumed in melting		£1.34	
Repairing and preparing furnaces, preparing charge, charging and pouring:			
– Labour		£18.99	
– Material		£3.35	
Preparing ladles and mould:			
– Labour		£19.90	
– Material		£3.61	
minus Pit scrap (7%) recovered	−3.80	−£29.77	
Sub total – Metal poured	50.44	£711.69	£14.11
Ingot in pit:			
Lifting mould, stripping and chipping ingot		£4.33	
Power (steam, electric, water)		£5.57	
Transportation (proportion)		£16.25	
Superintendance (armour) (proportion)		£1.63	
Superintendance (Open Hearth) (proportion)		£1.39	
Drafting (proportion)		£0.52	
Inspection (proportion)		£0.31	
Laboratory (proportion)		£4.10	
minus Ingots condemned (5%)	−2.52		
Sub total – Ingot at forge	47.92	£745.79	£15.56
Ingots forged:			
minus Ingots forged into condemned plates (5%)	−2.40	−£19.74	
minus Oxidisation and scale (3%)	−1.37		
minus Metal recovered from condemned plates		−£17.81	
Sub total – Ingots entering shipped plates	44.15	£708.24	£16.04
Slab:			
Labour for forging		£20.18	
Material		£3.26	
Fuel and labour		£23.20	
Repairs		£8.25	
Electric power and lights (proportion)		£7.72	
Steam (proportion)		£79.70	

Drafting (proportion)		£0.52	
Inspection (proportion)		£0.31	
Superintendance (proportion)		£4.90	
Laboratory (proportion)		£4.10	
Transportation (proportion)		£10.83	
minus Discard (37%)	−16.34	-£128.02	
Subtotal − Slab	27.81	£743.19	£26.72

Plates for carburising:

minus Oxidation and scale treatment (3%)	−0.83		
Labour		£38.71	
Material		£4.12	
Fuel		£16.24	
Repairs		£9.92	
Steam (proportion)		£1.02	
Electric power and lights (proportion)		£7.72	
Drafting (proportion)		£0.26	
Inspection (proportion)		£0.31	
Superintendance (proportion)		£6.53	
Laboratory (proportion)		£6.15	
Transportation (proportion)		£10.83	
Sub total − Treated Plate	26.98	£850.00	£31.32

Bending and rectifying:

Labour		£9.33	
Material		£5.15	
Repairs		£9.47	
Fuel		£2.47	
minus Machine scrap (26%)	−6.98		
Sub total − Plate rectified	20.00	£871.42	£43.57

Machining and erecting:

minus Metal received from machine scrap		−£66.20	
Labour		£65.69	
Tempering, repairing and renewing tools		£8.25	
Oil, waste and grinding disks		£2.06	
Repairs		£3.94	
Water supply		£1.03	
Steam (proportion)		£10.59	
Electric power and lights (proportion)		£7.72	
Transportation (proportion)		£5.41	
Inspection (proportion)		£0.31	
Drafting (proportion)		£0.77	
Superintendance (proportion)		£2.06	
Laboratory (proportion)		£2.05	
Sub total − Machined plate	20.00	£915.10	£45.76

Shipping:

Labour and material		£2.06	
Sub total − Shipping	20.00	£917.16	£45.86

Company charges per ton:

Interest on working capital		£1.29	
Maintenance of plant		£3.22	
Administration		£0.77	
Miscellaneous expenses		£0.21	
Taxes		£0.32	
Insurance		£0.32	
Depreciation		£9.02	
Sub total − Additions per ton		£15.15	

TOTAL	**20.00**	**£932.31**	**£46.62**

APPENDIX B

PRICES FOR ARMOUR PLATE FOR SHIPS UNDER THE 1912/3 AND 1913/14 PROGRAMMES

This price list was agreed between the Admiralty and the five armour plate makers and the printed list, which was issued to the companies, is from the National Archive ADM116/3456:

Type of Armour	Weight (lbs)	Price	Notes:
	520	£98	
	480	£96	
	440	£96	
	400	£96	
	360	£95	
	320	£94	
Belt Armour	280	£94	
	240	£93	
	200	£93	
	180	£93	
	160	£93	
	120	£85	
	80	£78	
Battery & casement armour 'Iron Duke' type —exclusive of bulkhead type armour.		£105	
Casement backs	80	£82	
	520	£94	
	480	£92	
	440	£92	
	400	£92	
	360	£92	
	320	£92	
Bulkhead Armour	280	£92	
	240	£92	
	200	£92	
	180	£92	
	160	£92	
	120	£84	
	80	£74	

Type of Armour	Weight (lbs)	Price	Notes:
Barbette Armour	520	£99	
	480	£97	
	440	£97	
	400	£97	
	360	£95	
	320	£95	
	280	£94	
	240	£93	
	200	£93	
	180	£92	
	160	£92	Battleship
	160	£93	Cruiser
	120	£92	
	80	£88	
Gun hoist protection	160	£84	
	120	£84	
Conning Tower Armour 'Iron Duke' Type	400	£120	Walls
	400	£120	Walls
	240	£130	Division plates
	160	£98	Door
	200	£112	Roof
	80	£85	Floors and 160 lbs shutters

Prices for bending plates, holes, bolts and other items are not included in this summary of the price schedule.

BIBLIOGRAPHY

Bastable, Marshall J., *Arms and the State: Sir William Armstrong and the Remaking of British Naval Power, 1854–1914*, Ashgate, Aldershot, 2004

Birt, R. A., *British Battleships of World War One*, Seaforth Publishing, Barnsley, 2012

Birt, R. A., *British Battleships 1889–1904*, Seaforth Publishing, Barnsley, 2013

Brassey, T. A., *Papers and Addresses, Naval and Maritime 1872 to 1898*, Vol. I, Longmans, Green & Co, London, 1894

Brassey, T. A., *Naval Annuals* (various, 1890 to 1919), J. Griffin & Co, Portsmouth, 1890–1919

Brown, David K., *The Grand Fleet: Warship Design and Development 1906–1922*, Seaforth Publishing, Barnsley, 2012

Brown, David K., *Warrior to Dreadnought: Warship Design and Development 1860–1905*, Seaforth Publishing, Barnsley, 2014

Churchill, Winston, *The World Crisis 1911–1918*, Vols I and II, Oldhams Press, London, 1938

Churchill, Winston, *The Great War*, Vols I–III, George Newnes Ltd, London, 1933

Colledge, J. J., *Ships of the Royal Navy: The Complete Record of all Fighting Ships of the Royal Navy*, Casement, Newbury, 2010

Dalrymple Hay, Sir John, *Memorandum: Rear Admiral Sir John C. Dalrymple Hay's Compulsory Retirement from the British Navy*, Edward Stanford, London, 1870

Dalton, Stewart, *Sheffield, Armourer to the British Empire*, Warncliffe Books, Barnsley, 2004

Evans, David, *Building the Steam Navy: Dockyard Technology and the Creation of the Victorian Battle Fleet 1830–1906*, Conway Maritime Press, London, 2004

Fawcett, H. W. and Hooper, G. W. W., *The Fighting at Jutland: The Personal Experiences of Sixty Officers and Men of the British Fleet*, Chatham Publishing, London, 2001

Ferguson, Niall, *The Pity of War*, Penguin Books, London, 1999

Gardiner, Robert, *Steam, Steel and Shellfire: The Steam Warship 1815–1905*, Conway Maritime Press, London, 1992

Grant, Sir Allan, *Steel & Ships: The Story of John Brown's*, Michael Joseph, London, 1950

Halsted, Edward Pellow, *Iron Cased Ships: A Series of Lectures*, Royal United Service Institution, London, 1861

Holloway, S. M., *From Trench and Turret: Royal Marines' Letters and Diaries 1914–18*, Constable, London, 2006

Jellicoe, John, *The Grand Fleet 1914–1916: Its Creation, Development and Work*, Cassell & Co, London, 1919

Johnson, I. and Buxton, I., *The Battleship Builders: Constructing and Arming British Capital Ships*, Seaforth Publishing, Barnsley, 2013

Lambert, Nicholas, *Sir John Fisher's Naval Revolution*, University of South Carolina Press, Columbia SC, USA, 2002

Landes, David, *The Unbound Prometheus: Technological Change and Industrial Development in Western Europe from 1750 to the Present*, Cambridge University Press, Cambridge, 2003

Le Fleming, H. M., *Warships of World War I*, Ian Allan Ltd, London, 1967

Macintyre, Donald, *Jutland*, Evans Brothers, London, 1957

Marder, Arthur J., *The Anatomy of British Sea Power: A History of British Naval Policy in the pre-Dreadnought Era, 1880–1905*, Archon Books, Hamden, CT, 1964

Marder, Arthur J., *From Dreadnought to Scapa Flow. Vol. 2 The War Years: To the Eve of Jutland 1914–1916*, Oxford University Press, Oxford, 1965

Marder, Arthur J., *From Dreadnought to Scapa Flow. Vol. 1 The Road to War 1904–1914*, Seaforth Publishing, Barnsley, 2013

McKenna, Stephen, *Reginald McKenna, 1863–1943*, Eyre & Spottiswoode, London, 1948

Menne, Bernhard, *Blood and Steel: The Rise of the House of Krupp*, Lee Furnman Inc., New York, NY, 1938

Napier, James, *The Life of Robert Napier*, W. Blackwood & Sons, Edinburgh, 1904

Novikoff-Priboy, A., *Tsushima: Grave of a Floating City*, Readers' Union, George Allen and Unwin, London, 1937

Oldham, Douglas, *A History of Rolled Heavy Armour Plate Manufacture at the Sheffield Works of Charles Cammell and Vickers*, South Yorkshire Industrial History Society, Sheffield, 2010

Orde Browne, Charles, *Armour and its Attack by Artillery*, Messrs Dulau & Co, London, 1887

Orde Browne, Charles, *Armour and its Attack by Artillery, Supplement 1893–1899*, Messrs Dulau & Co, London, 1889

Padfield, Peter, *Guns at Sea*, Hugh Evelyn, London, 1973

Pears, Randolph, *British Battleships 1892–1957*, Godfrey Cave Associates, London, 1979

Pole, William, *The Life of Sir William Fairburn, Bart*, David & Charles, Newton Abbot, 1970

Preston, Anthony, *Battleships of World War I*, Galahad Books, New York, NY , 1972

Robertson Murray, H., *Krupp's and the International Armaments Ring*, Holden & Hardingham, London, 1925

Russell, A. K., *Liberal Landslide: The General Election of 1906*, David & Charles, Newton Abbot, 1973

Scheer, Reinhard, *Germany's High Seas Fleet in the World War*, Cassell & Co, London, 1920

Scott, J. D., *Vickers: A History*, Weidenfeld and Nicholson, London, 1962

Sondhaus, Lawrence, *Naval Warfare 1815–1914*, Routledge, London, 2001

Sondhaus, Lawrence, *The Great War at Sea: A Naval History of the First World War*, Cambridge University Press, Cambridge, 2014

Steinburg, Jonathon, *Yesterday's Deterrent: Tirpitz and the Birth of the German Battle Fleet*, Gregg Revivals, Aldershot, 1992

Sumida, Jon Tetsuro, *In Defence of Naval Supremacy: Finance, Technology and British Naval Policy, 1889–1914*, Naval Institute Press, Annapolis, MD, 2014

Tarrant, V. E., *Jutland: The German Perspective*, Brockhampton Press, London, 1999

Tarrant, V. E., *Battleship Warspite*, Arms and Armour Press, London, 1990

Taylor, A. J. P, *The First World War: An Illustrated History*, Penguin Books, London, 1966

Taylor, A. J. P, *The Struggle for Mastery in Europe 1848–1914*, Oxford University Press, Oxford, 1987

Tresidder, John Tolmie, *Notes on Armour Plates and their Behaviour under Fire*, Royal Engineers Institute, Chatham, 1894

Very, E. W., *The Development of Armor for Naval Use*, US Naval Institute, Annapolis, MD, 1883

Walton Newbold, J. T., *How Europe Armed for War*, Blackfriars Press, London, 1916

Walton Newbold, J. T., *The War Trust Exposed*, The National Labour Press Ltd, Manchester, 1913

Warren, Kenneth, *Armstrong's of Elswick: Growth in Engineering and Armaments to the Merger with Vickers*, Macmillan, London, 1989

Warren, Kenneth, *Steel, Ships and Men: Cammell Laird, 1824–1993*, Liverpool University Press, Liverpool, 1998

Woodward, E. L., *Great Britain and the German Navy*, Oxford University Press, Oxford, 1935

Wragg, David, *Fisher, The Admiral Who Reinvented the Royal Navy*, The History Press, Stroud, 2009

PICTURE CREDITS

INDEX